NATURALISTIC REASON

VOLUME III

UNIFICATION OF SCIENCE AND PHILOSOPHY

Phillip Scribner

PUBLISHING HISTORY

Paperback Edition 1 / May 2022

ISBN: 978-1-7379884-2-7
Imprint: natReason LLC
Washington, District of Columbia

Library of Congress Control Number: 2022906872

This book is the third of the three volumes in *Naturalistic Reason*.
It is the one enclosed in the box below.

NATURALISTIC REASON

VOLUME III
IS DEDICATED TO

Mary Ellen Kane Scribner (1909-1969),
An Artist

TABLE OF CONTENTS

TABLE OF FIGURES

PREFACE

The three volumes of *Naturalistic Reason* show how the rational pursuit of truth can resolve disagreements of all kinds, including the value disputes that currently divide people into opposing political camps. It is an argument that almost no one believes is even possible, at least not now. But since what it promises is obviously valuable, one would expect that, if it is a good argument, it would be published by a prominent press. So, let me explain why I am self-publishing these volumes (as print-on-demand and e-Books) and promoting the trilogy with videos on the Internet.

I have been working on this argument for over 45 years. It has grown from a hunch about space I had as a teenager, and it is defended here as a discovery about the natural world. Teaching philosophy in a small department, I was able to arrange my course schedule to learn what I needed to know at the time as my students learned what I had already figured out, and since retiring, I have had the time to address more esoteric mathematical issues in physics. This argument and its parts have taken various shapes in a number of unpublished manuscripts, and I have tried to publish many of them. But the argument was not complete in the way that I knew from the beginning was possible, and since its publication did not seem urgent, I did not try more than once or twice for each of many manuscripts before I was taking the next step on this journey. Now that it is finished, I have an original argument to offer that solves puzzles not only in philosophy but also in physics and in every other branch of science, and it is a trilogy.

However, in this era of multiculturalism and relativism, there is so little tolerance for the claim to solve problems that everyone knows cannot be solved that these arguments are seen as a kind of heresy that comes only from cranks and can be dismissed without a second thought. I have learned from 45 years of trying to publish my discoveries that professional associations have editors posted at publishing houses as sentries to recognize such heresies and, if they must, know readers who will find passages that show that their manuscripts are unfit to publish. But intractable problems cannot be solved without defending heresies, and though publishers once saw themselves as facilitating intellectual revolutions, they currently have a reliable income from celebrity authors and processing predicable offerings of academics whose students and colleagues guarantee a sufficiently wide readership. Since the argument is now complete, its coherence may be obvious enough for some editor to be willing to see it through to publication. But there are three volumes, and that is a daunting publishing project because their scope would require favorable reviews from an army of well-trained professionals. And since I am 82 years old, I can't afford to waste time making it public.

To be sure, I have little to gain personally from publishing what I have discovered. At my age, there is no career for me to make. And as my energy fades, it becomes more tempting to stop writing and relax. But I have had the great fortune to live my life in a most meaningful way during this golden age of America. Beings like us cannot help wondering about the nature of what exists—and why there are parts of existence like us that are able to wonder about it. Those questions show what is unique about human nature, and attempts to answer them go back to ancient Greece. Learning from the great philosophers and scientists who have taken up this project over the past two-and-a-half millennia, I have had the joy of discovering a new answer to them. *Naturalistic Reason* offers a solution to all the puzzles that currently stymie physicists and other scientists, and it answers all the questions that have accumulated in the dumping ground of unanswered questions called *philosophy*. Eventually, others will describe what I have discovered more clearly and beautifully. But this is what I am able to offer now. And since I owe the resources and leisure needed to spend my life on this project to my society—my *spiritual organism*—I have a duty to make it available to others.

Fortunately, in this digital age, it is possible to bypass the gatekeepers of prevailing orthodoxy. I have finished an acceptable version of the entire argument, and with little time left, I am publishing it as this trilogy. I have also recorded a series of videos that introduce the argument. For those who want only a more detailed overview, an executive summary of this trilogy is being published as a book called *Sapere Aude*. Links to both the books and videos along with additional information about *Naturalistic Reason*, can be found at <u>natReason.com</u>. And I want to acknowledge that I have had the help of a one-time student, a longtime friend, and, now, the manager of this publishing project, Gary Sisto. I have also had the comfort of a lifelong companion, Philip McClain. And I have learned many lessons from an extraordinarily knowledgeable friend who prefers to remain anonymous.

I know from reflecting on my own motivation that there are others out there who believe in the rational pursuit of truth. I know that this argument solves puzzles posed by intellectuals I admire who have established reputations in relevant fields, and I hope that some of them are willing to consider an argument as unlikely as one that claims to show how Reason can know Reality behind Appearance. I dream of discussing these issues with them and others. But from the outside, as someone who has been marginalized in academia, I have worked pretty much alone. Disillusionment about reason is replacing the last vestiges of Enlightenment, and with endarkenment setting in, I worry that I may be wrong about its reception. I am old enough to be astonished at how fast Western discourse has deteriorated into name-calling and attempts to silence opponents, and enforcement of political correctness may keep my argument from getting a hearing at all. But publishing it in this way, I can provide resources that will make it available after I die, when future generations may be interested in resurrecting Enlightenment values. But those who care enough about the rational pursuit of truth to read the text and take the argument it presents seriously will find themselves in agreement with one another because they will all understand in their faculties of naturalistic imagination how their beliefs and values correspond to Reality.

ROAD MAP FOR READERS

This trilogy is written for two kinds of readers, general readers who want a high-altitude presentation of this argument and technical readers who want to address problematic details along the way. The arguments of all three volumes are laid out along two pathways.

The path for general readers is shorter than the path for technical readers. It is like a highway through mountains with bridges over valleys where technical issues are discussed. The path for technical readers is longer. Instead of taking the next bridge, it leads down into the valley and answers questions that will occur to those familiar with those issues before coming back up and rejoining the highway.

These paths are distinguished in the text by the fonts used. The path for general readers has a Serif font like this, while the path for technical readers has a non-Serif font like this. The headings of sections for technical readers include a double-gear icon like this ✿, and where the two paths divide, there are instructions telling general readers which section they should read next.

The approximate length of the abbreviated pathway for general readers in *Volume III* is 380 pages (150K words), while the approximate length of the complete pathway in *Volume III* for technical readers is 405 pages (165K words).

Introduction:
The Reduction of Philosophy to Ontology

Naturalistic Reason predicts that a scientific revolution will soon resolve all the basic disagreements that divide us. It is a trilogy that begins with a discovery about the nature of space that reduces physics to ontology, namely, the discovery that space is a substance that interacts with matter. *Volume I* predicts that it will unify modern physics by solving all the intractable puzzles of physics and revealing that matter has a *holistic power* that is expressed as a kind of efficient cause not recognized by physics. They are called *geometrical causes*, and *Volume II* predicts that they will make it possible to solve all the intractable puzzles of specialized sciences, unifying science. Geometrical action is the effect of geometrical efficient causes constraining what happens by physical efficient causes, and assuming that matter has a phenomenal way of existing in itself, *Volume III* predicts that science based on ontology will solve the problem of mind-body dualism. It will explain how consciousness is part of the natural world, and given its explanation of the geometrical action of the mammalian brain, it will explain consciousness as what it is like to be a mammal. *Ontological causes* are the foundation of this explanation, and since they imply that only two kinds of *efficient causes* are at work in the natural world, *Volume III* shows how consciousness is a *pseudo-efficient cause*. This is a complete explanation of causation, and it will cut the Gordian Knot of philosophical problems. Since *the Unification of Science and Philosophy* is the final volume of this trilogy, it begins with an overview.

1 The Trilogy

This trilogy is an argument that predicts that science will become naturalistic Reason. *Volume III* is about philosophy, and Figure 1 represents how it depends on the arguments of the other two volumes.

Figure 1 – Naturalistic Reason

As *Volume I* explains, the founding assumption of ontology is that substances enduring through time constitute everything that exists, and ontology is naturalistic because it assumes that what exists is the natural world. Ontology is empirical since it infers the kinds of substances constituting the natural world as the best explanation of what is found in it. Laws of physics describe the most basic regularities that have been found in the natural world, and kinds of substances are inferred as the best ontological explanation of those regularities. Ever since Newton, laws of physics have been formulated mathematically, and the extraordinary success of physics in discovering them is due to what the physicist Eugene Wigner (1960) described as the "unreasonable effectiveness" of mathematics in discovering basic laws of nature. Ontology infers the basic kinds of substances constituting the natural world as the best explanation of the "appropriateness of mathematics" as a language for formulating laws of physics. It discovers that space is a substance in the same sense as matter. But space is not merely a container in which material substances move and interact with one another. The assumption that space is a substance that interacts with matter enables ontology to infer that the natural world is constituted by both substances as the best explanation of the appropriateness of mathematics as a language for formulating laws of physics. Given their essential natures, the only kinds of regularities that interactions of space and matter can generate are quantitative, and using that to explain the "unreasonable effectiveness" of mathematics in discovering laws of physics, ontology is able to solve the intractable puzzles of physics empirically. We have a faculty of naturalistic imagination that enables us to understand the geometrical structure of space, and since that enables us to understand how interactions of space and matter generate regularities, empirical ontology can discover powers that enable space and matter to interact in ways that explain all the laws of physics. That is the reduction of physics to an ontological theory, called *spatio-materialism*, and this way of solving the puzzles of modern physics is the *Unification of Physics*, represented by the triangle in Figure 1.

The unification of physics reveals a regularity about change in the natural world whose consequences reach far beyond physics. It reveals that space has a power, based on its intrinsic geometrical structure, by which its interactions with matter give matter a *holistic power*. This power of matter is expressed as a kind of efficient cause, called *geometrical causes*, and *Volume II: The Unification of Science* shows how the recognition of geometrical causes fills all the gaps in the current physicalist explanation of regularities found in the study of nature, including an explanation of how the mammalian brain works.

Geometrical action is the effect of geometrical causes constraining the collective effects of physical causes, and since the mammalian brain is the geometrical cause guiding behavior, the holistic power of matter has a further expression in how matter helps constitute its geometrical action. As *Volume III: The Unification of Science and Philosophy* shows, a science based on ontology can infer that matter has a phenomenal way of existing in itself as the best explanation of how consciousness is part of the natural world. This phenomenal intrinsic property does not cause any event in the natural world that cannot already be explained by efficient causes, but since it is an ontologically necessary part of the cause of a stage of evolution, consciousness turns out to be a *pseudo-efficient cause.* That shows how the mind is identical to the brain, and since this discovery solves the mind-body problem that vanquished modern philosophy, it turns ontological science into naturalistic Reason.

The discovery of the holistic power of matter solves the puzzles of specialized sciences in a way that unifies them. It is expressed as a kind of efficient cause that physics does not recognize. The basic laws of quantum physics describe regularities about how particles move and interact, and since physics uses them to explain what happens, they are *physical causes*. Physical regularities can be called expressions of *atomistic powers* of matter, by contrast to its holistic power, because physical regularities are about how particles that move independently of one another, called *free particles*, move and interact with one another. But there are also *bound particles*, and they determine what happens in another way. *Groups* of bound particles can also move around independently. But they have geometrical structures that do not change as they move and interact with particles and one another, and since they impose geometrical constraints on what happens as a result of physical causes, they are efficient causes of a different kind, called *geometrical efficient causes*. They are composite bodies, from nuclei and atoms up through all the bodies whose structures depend on how atoms are bonded to one another, and we can understand in naturalistic imagination how their geometrical structures impose regularities on change. Examples are a box containing a gas, a key opening a lock, and a vacuum produced by a motor removing dirt from the floor. These regularities depend on forces that bound particles exert on one another. But contrary to what is assumed in physics, composite bodies are not reducible to physical causes. Since they express the holistic power of matter, geometrical efficient causes are just as basic as physical efficient causes. Both depend on regularities generated by the *inertial system*, the ontological mechanism that explains the basic laws of quantum physics. But while physical causes express atomistic powers of matter (because they depend on regularities about how *free* particles move and interact), geometrical causes express holistic powers of matter (because they depend on how groups of *bound* particles move and interact *as a whole*). In the spatio-material world, ontological causes explain efficient causes, and since the inertial system is the ontological mechanism that constitutes both geometrical and physical efficient causes, the differences between them depend on the initial and boundary conditions under which interactions of space and matter take place in the inertial system.

Since physical and geometrical causes determine what happens in different ways, they can work together in generating regularities about change, and *Volume II* shows how their combination explains the laws of thermo-dynamics. Ontology explains increases in entropy as collective effects of physical causes, and when geometrical causes constrain the motion and interaction of many particles, geometrical causes can do thermodynamic work. It is also called *geometrical action* to remind us that this work expresses the holistic power of matter. The solutions to all the intractable puzzles that specialized sciences have encountered involve showing how they are kinds of geometrical action, and since interactions of space and matter can be understood in naturalistic imagination, this unifies science. The *Unification of Science* is depicted in Figure 1 by the arrow from the triangle labeled *Ontology* to the circle labeled *Science*. Since specialized sciences are reduced to ontology, rather than physics, physical science becomes *ontological science*.

The original goal of science was a complete explanation of the natural order, and that is almost accomplished by ontological science. It explains the origin and nature of life and shows that there is a series of inevitable stages of evolution that lead to the existence of reflective subjects. Furthermore, since goodness is part of the essential nature of life, ontological science reveals what is good for living organisms, including beings like us. But not everything found in the natural world is explained by the reduction of sciences studying fewer general regularities found in nature to spatio-materialism.

Explaining everything in the natural world was the original goal of science, and if this prediction of the unification of science is correct, there will clearly be something in the natural world that has not been explained. All the puzzles of physics and science will have been solved, and since the original goal of science will be fulfilled, that is something that will have to be explained. The puzzles will be solved by basing science on ontology rather than physics, and so ontological science will have to explain itself in order to explain everything in the natural world. Since physics was, along with liberal political institutions and capitalism, an offspring of the Enlightenment, its existence points to the puzzle posed by the rise and globalization of the West. The extraordinary success of physics was due to the "unreasonable effectiveness" of mathematics in discovering basic laws of nature, and this novel and highly successful way of using the empirical method, called *empirical lawism*, derives from a distinctive part of Western culture. In practice, physicists assume that mathematically formulated laws of nature are the deepest possible empirical knowledge about the nature of what exists, and they have taken it for granted that mathematics is known *a priori* because that is how it was explained in Western philosophy. Without empirical lawism, there would have been no science studying nature and, thus, no scientific puzzles to solve, much less a science based on ontology that solves them.

Western civilization is already something that needs explaining, and the explanation of the overall course of evolution in *Volume II* leaves it as an unsolved historical puzzle. History is mostly about the rise and fall of civilizations, and though ontological science explains the repeated rise of civilizations, historians have attributed their falls to various causes, such as the depletion of resources, subjugation by other civilizations, and internal corruption. But the rise of Western civilization is different because it may well be invulnerable to a fall caused in such ways. It has acquired unprecedented power over nature, and its power continues to increase. Indeed, its culture and institutions are being globalized. Almost everyone accepts science as a reliable kind of knowledge, if only because of the technology it spawns. In many civilizations on Earth, a class structure and autocratic government are yielding to political institutions that claim, at least, to respect the moral autonomy of individuals. Though liberal political institutions have yet to spread everywhere, most nations go through the motion of holding elections. And where democracy is most firmly established, corruption is relatively limited, if not eliminated. Almost all civilizations on Earth are being penetrated by free markets that allow capitalists to compete with one another. Their relentless exploitation of technology to produce useful commodities less expensively has led to increasing efficiency. World poverty has fallen to historic lows. History has never seen so many innovations spread everywhere around the globe so rapidly. And all of this began at a high point in the history of Western culture called the *Enlightenment*.

This trilogy predicts that ontological science will explain its own existence and the unprecedented powers that Western civilization will have acquired by completing its explanation of the overall course of evolution. Western civilization will turn out to be a stage of spiritual evolution that follows the stage represented by other civilizations on Earth. *Philosophy* is not just what passes for wisdom in any culture. In Western culture, philosophy is the history of disputes about *metaphysics*. Its defenders argue that beings like us have a cognitive power, called *Reason* by which we can know Reality behind Appearance. (Core terms are capitalized to distinguish metaphysics from other ways of using language.) Ontological science explains evolution by the reproductive mechanism, which implies that a new stage of evolution occurs whenever a higher level of organization in evolving geometrical causes is both possible and functional. *Volume III* shows that arguments about metaphysics have a higher level of linguistic organization than psychological sentences, and since they are both possible and functional, a metaphysical stage of spiritual evolution is inevitable. Since it evolves from the second minor stage of spiritual evolution in the course of the evolution of life, it is the third minor stage, and since the psychological stage is represented by other civilizations on Earth, this solves two puzzles. It explains not only the unprecedented rise and globalization of Western civilization but also the existence of ontological science.

Ontological science is represented by the circle labeled *Science* in Figure 1. It completes the *Study of Nature*, and the arrow from *Science* to *Philosophy* represents the contribution that ontological science makes to the explanation of Western civilization as the beginning of the metaphysical stage. But the third minor stage of spiritual evolution is unlike previous inevitable stages of evolution, which bring reflective subjects into existence. Since what evolves is geometrical action, explanations of stages of evolution depend on recognizing that there are geometrical as well as physical efficient causes. But the metaphysical stage is unlike all the others because its explanation depends on recognizing that a pseudo-efficient cause is at work in nature. It is another way that space and matter constitute what is found in the natural world. The implication of ontology that enables ontological science to explain how consciousness is part of the natural world is represented by the arrow from *Ontology* to *Philosophy* in Figure 1. Philosophy is the *Study of Appearance* in that figure, and combined with the ontological explanation of the evolution of reflective subjects, the ontological cause of consciousness reveals an illusion inherent in consciousness that helps cause the Study of Appearance. That is what the two arrows pointing to the circle labeled *Philosophy* in Figure 1 represent. Ontological science explains everything in the natural world, including science itself, and when it discovers that it is Reason knowing Reality behind Appearance, ontological science becomes naturalistic Reason.

2 Biography of Reason

Since Western civilization is the metaphysical stage of spiritual evolution, its history can be told as a story about how Reason grows up and discovers its real nature, that is, as a *biography of Reason*. Reason was born in ancient Greece from a bold confidence that beings like us are capable of a perfect kind of knowledge about the world. It began when pre-Socratic philosophers set out to discover the first cause of everything found in the natural world. Using the empirical method, they discovered that the substances constitute the natural world are the first cause. But metaphysicians had another way of acquiring perfect knowledge. They assumed that we have a cognitive power called *Reason* that enables us to know Reality behind Appearance, and metaphysics played the leading role in the cultural evolution recorded in the history of Western philosophy. As we shall see, Reason grew up thinking of its cognitive power as having a nature that depends on consciousness. But in its adolescence, it realized that its metaphysical family was bound to fail in its attempt to know Reality behind Appearance, and so it rebelled. It rejected metaphysics, accepted naturalism, and in its new guise as science, it was announced to the world as the Newtonian revolution. Reason assumed that the natural world exists, and in the guise of physics, it used the empirical method to learn about the natural world. It was astonishingly successful for centuries in discovering basic laws of nature. But since physics still depended in a way on its family heritage, it was just Reason suffering an identity crisis. This would become obvious when science recognized that it had abandoned its goal of discovering the Good as well as the True. Reason had become science by rebelling against its metaphysical family, and though it was clear about its commitment to naturalism, it was confused about its identity because its success depended on a family treasure that it had taken with it. Physics assumed that mathematics is known *a priori,* and reliance on this crutch turned the issue of its identity into a crisis when it posed puzzles in modern physics that could not be solved. Since physicists found themselves defending theories about what really exists in the natural world that could not be understood in naturalistic imagination, Reason had to doubt that it was a perfect way of knowing the nature of what exists most basically.

The first step in resolving Reason's identity crisis will be its rejection of empirical lawism in favor of empirical ontology, as described in *Volume I.* The discovery that space is a substance that interacts with matter will solve the intractable puzzles of modern physics, and as described in *Volume II,* ontological science will explain everything found in the study of nature. It will even explain the nature of the Good, an ambition that its adolescent rebellion against its metaphysical family had forced it to abandon. But without an explanation of the existence of ontological science, Reason will still not explain everything found in the natural world. The problem is that it will still lack a full understanding of its own nature, and as described in this volume, *Volume III,* that problem will be solved when ontological science discovers that it is what evolves during the metaphysical stage of spiritual evolution. That is the second and final step in resolving its identity crisis.

The metaphysical stage in the evolution of life was not explained in *Volume II* because it is caused by exchanging metaphysical arguments and an essential part of that cause is consciousness. Reflective subjects are conscious, and since ontological scientists are reflective subjects, consciousness is something that they will find in the natural world. Indeed, it will be part of their understanding of metaphysical arguments. But with an ontological theory that explains how consciousness is part of the natural world, they will be able to use their evolutionary explanation of the origin of reflective subjects to explain how metaphysical arguments cause a third stage of spiritual evolution. Their explanation of how consciousness is part of that cause will reveal that consciousness is a pseudo-efficient cause. By tracing the unprecedented rise and globalization of the Western spiritual organism to powers acquired from arguing about whether Reason can know Reality behind Appearance, they will discover that ontological science is the culmination of the metaphysical stage of spiritual evolution. Since ontological scientists are conscious, they will *find themselves* knowing Reality behind Appearance, and thus, they will recognize that they have Reason. But since they are naturalists who use the empirical method to know Reality behind Appearance, they will insist that they have *naturalistic* Reason. Science becoming Reason in this way is represented in Figure 1 by the label *natReason* at the center of the three geometrical figures. And when ontological scientists realize that science has become the perfect cognitive power that was first imagined in ancient Greece, Reason will have the self-understanding that resolves its identity crisis.

3 Volume III

The Unification of Science and Philosophy defends the prediction that ontological science will explain Western civilization as a stage of spiritual evolution caused by the exchange of metaphysical arguments and recognize itself as naturalistic Reason. To be sure, philosophy seems too academic to cause a stage of evolution. After all, the evolution of the naturalistic and psychological levels of linguistic organization both depend on the evolution of a higher level of neural organization caused by genetic changes in the mammalian brain. But the evolution of the third level of linguistic organization does not depend on genetic changes. As *Part One* shows, the exchange of metaphysical arguments is itself a higher level of organization in the geometrical action of the brain, and it necessarily involves consciousness. Matter has a property that is not relevant in reducing specialized sciences to interactions of space and matter, and when metaphysicians argue that Reason knows Reality behind Appearance, what they always mean by *Appearance* is consciousness. The ontological explanation of consciousness makes it possible to show that metaphysics is a level of linguistic organization that causes a stage of spiritual evolution after the psychological stage. During the metaphysical stage, there is a regularity about change that distinguishes it from other stages in the evolution of language-using mammals, and that enables ontological science to show that the metaphysical stage of spiritual evolution is represented on Earth by Western civilization.

Chapter 1 shows how spatio-materialism enables ontological science to explain consciousness, where *consciousness* is the phenomenal character of experience. For example, when we perceive objects in the natural world, what is immediately present are simple sensory qualia of various kinds, such as colors, sounds, odors, and various kinds of bodily sensations. Since they are all related to one another coherently in a 3-D space, they are *complex phenomenal properties*. But complex phenomenal properties are also immediately present when we reflect on our psychological states, for example, when we remember events, imagine them, form intentions, have emotions, and the like. Unlike sensory qualia, which are vivid and distinct, qualia in reflective phenomenal appearances are fainter, less distinct, and not so consistently related in 3-D space. Since consciousness is the phenomenal character of experience, it can be explained ontologically by a phenomenal way that substance exists in itself. This way of explaining how consciousness is part of the natural world is called *panpsychism*, and it works especially well in a world constituted by space and matter. Species of matter are defined by the spatiotemporal structures of their ways of coinciding and interacting with space, and those spatiotemporal structures can be complex enough to explain the complex phenomenal properties that characterize consciousness.

This explanation of consciousness holds for mammals generally because they are complex phenomenal properties of a kind that depend on the mammalian faculty of imagination. Some matter helping constitute the mammalian brain is the flow of acceleration fuel by which the mammalian brain, as a geometrical cause, guides animal behavior in the natural world, and that matter has a kind of spatiotemporal structure that is isomorphic with the configurations of qualia in 3-D space that are immediately present in perception. Since this matter is flowing in a way that depends on the firing on neurons, it is *neural* geometrical action, and thus, if all matter has a *proto-phenomenal* way of existing in itself, matter helping constitute the neural geometrical action of the mammalian brain can have kinds of complex phenomenal intrinsic properties that are identical to the complex phenomenal properties that are immediately present to mammals perceiving the world. Thus, *Chapter 1* shows that consciousness can be explained as what it is like to be the mammalian brain.

Given the phenomenal intrinsic nature of matter, this reduction of consciousness to spatio-materialism is straightforward. But it is only the foundation for showing how the exchange of metaphysical arguments is a higher level of linguistic organization than psychological sentences. That is what *Chapter 3* explains.

Consciousness is what it is like to be the mammalian brain, and since the consciousness of reflective subjects is just what it is like to be a mammal behaving verbally, the use of language does not explain how metaphysicians refer to consciousness as *Appearance* or as anything but psychological (brain) states or what they represent. The ontological explanation of the metaphysical stage of spiritual evolution is less straightforward because it depends on recognizing an illusion inherent in consciousness. That illusion is what makes it possible for metaphysicians to refer to consciousness as something different from psychological (brain) states and, eventually, describe what is illusory about it. I call it the *illusion of intuitionism* because what it is like to be a mammalian brain makes it appear that complex phenomenal properties are known by their immediate presence, as it they were *objects of intuition*. That illusion makes it possible for reflective subjects to argue about Reason knowing Reality behind Appearance, and since that puts intuitionistic metaphysics on a higher level of linguistic organization than psychological sentences, it can cause a stage of spiritual evolution that comes after the psychological stage.

This ontological explanation of the exchange of metaphysical arguments entails a definite order of developments during the metaphysical stage of spiritual evolution by which it can be confirmed. They are outlined in *Chapter 3*. The first kind of intuitionistic metaphysics that evolves assumes that the perceptual phenomenal appearance *is* the natural world, and since it holds that Reason knows Reality behind Appearance, it entails a distinction between Appearance and Reality of the kind represented by the difference between visible objects and Forms in the Platonic metaphysics of ancient Greece. Indeed, all intuitionistic philosophers assume that Reason is a faculty of rational intuition. But a second kind of intuitionistic metaphysics evolves when metaphysicians recognize that the perceptual phenomenal appearance is part of the subject. The discovery that there is a world outside consciousness is how reflective subjects discover that they are conscious. Indeed, Descartes' famous argument, *I think, therefore I am*, is a description of the intuitionist illusion. He used it to show the existence and nature of mind as a substance, and since ideas in the mind were supposed to be objects of intuition, mind had a distinctive kind of unity. The *Cogito* was the model for clear and distinct ideas by which Descartes distinguished what is known by Reason, and so the intuitionist illusion made it appear that mathematics is known by a faculty of rational intuition. He used the clear and distinct ideas of geometry to describe the nature of the substance constituting the world external to mind where the body was located, and since it was always divisible into parts, he called it *extension*. Thus, he had to believe that the body was part of a substance with a nature opposite to mind. Assuming that the mind used the body to act in the natural world, Descartes was confronted with an unsolvable problem. Mind and body were both parts of Reality, and he had to explain how they interact. That is the mind-body problem, which doomed modern intuitionistic metaphysics. But ontological science solves the mind-body problem. It explains intuitionism by an illusion inherent in consciousness, and by explaining mind as a phantom Reality, it shows that mind is identical to the brain.

Chapter 2 is a technical digression from the main argument of *Volume III*. It compares the mind-brain identity theories of physical and ontological science and explains why the former cannot solve the mind-body problem while the latter can.

Part Two uses what *Chapter 3* shows is ontologically necessary about the order in which kinds of metaphysical arguments evolve to show that the history of Western philosophy was caused by the exchange of metaphysical arguments. *Chapter 4* shows how the intuitionist illusion explains not only the kinds of metaphysics defended in ancient and medieval philosophy but also the kinds of solutions to its problems that were explored and why they failed. *Chapter 5* explains modern philosophy and its metaphysical problems in a similar way. Though intuitionistic metaphysics caused a stage of spiritual evolution, it was bound to fail because it was based on a false theory about the nature of knowledge. Intuitionistic Reason led to beliefs about the nature of Reality that were indefensible. But the culture of Western civilization was on a higher level of linguistic organization than other civilizations, and since it was based on the belief that Reason can know Reality behind Appearance, culture evolved a new range of functional powers. Belief in Reason became universal, and the feudal class structure of Western civilization was justified by a metaphysical religion. God was an infinite rational being outside the natural world, and since all human beings on Earth were created in God's image, believers conceived of the self as understanding the nature of Reality deeply enough to know why the good is good. They lived lives choosing between good and evil, and believing that Reason gave them a free will, they saw themselves as responsible for doing what is good. *Chapter 6* describes how confidence in Reason led to the Enlightenment and its offspring: a science based on the empirical method, a liberal political order, and a capitalist economic system.

Chapter 7 describes how Enlightenment confidence in Reason eventually turned into *disillusionment* with it in science. Science began as Reason splitting from philosophy, taking the existence of the natural world for granted, and using the empirical method to learn about it. Inspired by the Newtonian revolution, science made undeniable progress. But since the success of physics came from the treasure that Reason had taken with it when it rebelled against its intuitionistic family, it led to problems that could not be solved. The method of physics depended on mathematics being known by rational intuition, and though that was a powerful mathoscope for discovering laws of physics, it blinded physics to certain kinds of regularities about change in the natural world. Physics did not provide a foundation on which science could attain its initial goal of explaining everything in the natural world. This became apparent with the arrival of the *four horsemen of disillusionment.* Darwin, Marx, Freud, and Einstein made advances in science that mounted a frontal attack on Reason. They defended theories of human nature that replaced Reason with animal instincts whose goals were rationalized by culture and deformed by ideology, and to top it off, the Newtonian absolute space and time of the natural world were replaced by an entity called *spacetime* that cannot be understood in naturalistic imagination.

The fall of Western culture from the Enlightenment did not end with disillusionment with Reason. When Reason took sides with science, it left philosophy behind, and the rest of Western culture continued on its own path. Imperfections of the Enlightenment and its offspring led romantics to replace Reason with profound feelings or acts of will as a way of having a direct relation to Reality behind Appearance. In political activists, romanticism led to worse excesses, such as the reign of terror during the French revolution. But as *Chapter 8* describes, Enlightenment confidence in progress abated, and even philosophers eventually abandoned Reason. Instead of seeking to show how Reason knows what is true, philosophers came to believe that there is no such thing as the True, with a capital *T*. Ever since, the belief that basic disputes cannot be solved by argument has been spreading. *Endarkenment* is replacing Enlightenment.

A science based on physics has no explanation of goodness, and since its scientists insist that science cannot tell us what ought to be, globalization has spread the gospel of value relativism around the world. A couple of decades ago, optimists still expected the spread of Enlightenment values to lead to a peaceful and prosperous planet. But they were challenged by those who predicted a clash of civilizations with religious commitments to basically different values, and recent history seems to confirm the pessimists. Western culture cannot be defended when the good is seen as nothing but gut-level feelings that reflective subjects project onto the world as *values*. When civilizations project basically different values onto an indifferent natural world, might is what makes right. And as relativism about the good becomes conventional wisdom in the West, even its internal political disagreements will be settled by might. Indeed, the rising tide of endarkenment in the West is making it conventional wisdom that there is no such thing as the True, and so it seems foolish to expect arguments to lead to agreement, even about facts. The percentage of graduates of higher education who even know about the Enlightenment continues to shrink, and those who remember the promise of cultural progress without deception, coercion, and violence are nostalgic. But it is a bitter nostalgia. They hanker after a culture in which the rational pursuit of truth brings agreement about what to believe and what to do. But even the possibility of objective knowledge is in doubt, and no one foresees a restoration of the Enlightenment, except by a miraculous collective act of will.[1]

---

[1] Nostalgia inspires some observers of history, such as Steven Pinker (2018), to remind us of the unprecedented progress that the Enlightenment has caused. But the growing relativism and incoherence of Western culture has alarmed other observers, such as Jonah Goldberg (2018), who warns that our

Though intuitionistic metaphysics is doomed and confidence in Reason is petering out, that does not mean that metaphysics is doomed. Intuitionistic metaphysics was the *beginning* of the third minor stage of spiritual evolution on Earth, and *Part Three* predicts that Enlightenment confidence in Reason will be restored. As the forgoing biography suggests, intuitionism was just the childhood of Reason. The 18th-Century Enlightenment was its adolescence, when it abandoned philosophy in favor of naturalism and started using the empirical method to learn about the natural world. Both disillusionment with Reason in science and the rising tide of endarkenment in popular culture are symptoms of its identity crisis. This trilogy predicts that a discovery about the nature of space will cause a revolution in culture in which Reason resolves its identity crisis. When the "unreasonable effectiveness" of mathematics in discovering laws of physics is explained by *ontological causes*, the puzzles of modern physics will be solved, and their reduction to spatio-materialism will reveal a kind of *efficient cause* not recognized by physics that solves the puzzles that currently stymie the specialized sciences. This replacement of physical science by ontological science will reveal yet another kind of cause, a *pseudo-efficient cause*, that enables science to explain Western civilization as a third stage of spiritual evolution caused by metaphysics. As *Part Three* of *Volume III* shows, when ontological scientists use their explanation of how consciousness is part of the natural world to discount the illusion of intuitionism, they will discover how metaphysics causes a stage of evolution, and they will recognize that they know Reality behind Appearance. That is how ontological science becomes Reason, and since ontological scientists are naturalists using the empirical method, they will have *naturalistic* Reason. *Chapter 9* justifies the prediction that this revolution in culture will occur soon enough to stop the rising tide of endarkenment, and *Chapters 10, 11*, and *12* predict that naturalistic Reason will begin a peaceful exchange of arguments that leads everyone to know the *True*, the *Good*, and the *Beautiful*.

---

ingratitude about the Enlightenment may be the suicide of the West. Yet others, such as Ben Shapiro (2019), can only wait for the Enlightenment to be restored by a renewal of the belief that our rational nature comes from being created in the image of God.

PART ONE:
THE PSEUDO-EFFICIENT CAUSE

The ontological explanation of consciousness defended in *Chapter 1* is the foundation that enables science to explain Western civilization as the beginning of a third stage of spiritual evolution. *Consciousness* is the phenomenal character of experience, and it is something found in the natural world. When reflective subjects perceive the natural world, for example, consciousness is the immediate presence of many kinds of sensory qualia of various kinds, such as colors, sound, and bodily sensations. Qualia are simple phenomenal properties, and since they all seem to be related to one another in a 3-D space where they find their bodies, qualia are parts of complex phenomenal properties. The complex phenomenal properties that are immediately present to mammals can be explained ontologically. As the explanation of the course of evolution by the reproductive mechanism shows, the function of the basic structure of the mammalian brain is to serve as a faculty of imagination, and an ontological explanation of how consciousness is part of the natural world shows that consciousness is simply what it is like to be a mammalian brain.[2]

Since the natural world is constituted by space and matter, ontology can infer that matter has a phenomenal way of existing in itself as the best explanation of consciousness. The assumption that matter has a phenomenal intrinsic property is a form of *panpsychism*, which holds that to be a bit of

---

[2] What it is like to be something is a term of art for referring to consciousness that comes from Thomas Nagel (1974) "What is it like to be a bat?" and Nagel (1979).

matter is to have a qualitative property of some kind that is *immediately present*. It is called a *proto-phenomenal intrinsic property* because when matter has a simple way of coinciding with space, the qualitative property must be very simple and presumably faint. Though there is no knower to which it is immediately present, the phenomenal property exists because it is a way that matter exists in itself. In the spatio-material world, species of bits of matter are defined by the spatiotemporal structure of their way of coinciding with space and how they change as they interact with space and other bits of matter. Since their spatiotemporal structures can be very complex and well-organized, their ways of existing in themselves can also be very complex and well-organized, and so intrinsic phenomenal properties of matter can *be* the complex and vivid phenomenal properties that are immediately present to mammals.

The mammalian brain is a *behavior guidance system* (BGS), and using its faculty of imagination to distinguish it from simpler kinds of neural BGSs, ontological science shows that the complex phenomenal properties that are immediately present to mammals are what we call *consciousness*. In a nutshell, panpsychism can explain why mammals are conscious because the mammalian brain is a geometrical efficient cause whose thermodynamic work is guiding behavior to goals that are good, and this geometrical action includes a species of matter, called *magnetic field matter*, that is laid out continuously throughout the space occupied by the brain. This magnetic field matter mediates interactions of its neurons, and since it has a spatiotemporal structure in every small volume that registers neural activity throughout the brain, its phenomenal way of existing in itself can explain the structures of complex phenomenal properties that are immediately present to mammals.

Thus, this explanation of consciousness is an additional far-reaching implication of the discovery that space is a substance that interacts with matter. The mammalian brain is an expression of the holistic power of matter as a geometrical efficient cause, and its neural geometrical action is how it guides behavior. But since all matter has a phenomenal intrinsic nature, the holistic power also has a phenomenal expression: the immediate presence of phenomenal properties is what is like to be the magnetic field matter helping constitute its neural geometrical action.[3]

This ontological explanation of consciousness does not, however, enable ontological science to explain its own existence as an effect of the rise and globalization of the West as the metaphysical stage of spiritual evolution. It shows how consciousness is part of the natural world, but since it is identical to a phenomenal intrinsic property of matter, consciousness is not an efficient cause. It cannot make any difference in what happens in the brain, much less trigger an entire stage of evolution. The brain guides animal behavior, and if consciousness is just a way that its geometrical action exists in itself, it cannot cause any behavior in a mammal that is not caused by the brain as a geometrical efficient cause guiding its behavior. That is, it can have no kind of effect on the behavior of language-using mammals that it does not have on the behavior of all mammals. But if it were not possible for language to refer to the phenomenal intrinsic nature of that matter as something different from the psychological (brain) states it helps constitute, there would be no way that consciousness could help metaphysics cause a stage of spiritual evolution.

There is, however, a use of language that can distinguish between consciousness and psychological states, and so consciousness can make a difference in what happens in the natural world. It can help cause events in the natural world because there is an *illusion inherent in consciousness*. As *Chapter 3* shows, there is a special way of using language that can describe that illusion, and that special way of using language is what causes the metaphysical a stage of evolution. This way of helping cause a stage of evolution is what is meant by calling consciousness a *pseudo*-efficient cause.

Since consciousness is the phenomenal character of experience, what a subjective animal with a faculty of imagination perceives seems to be a world of qualia objects in a 3-D space where its own qualia body seems to be located. Even psychological (brain) states involved in using imagination to guide behavior, such as desiring something about an object, remembering something, and planning how to act, have a phenomenal appearance. Since phenomenal appearances are immediately present, mammals find themselves

---

[3] The *neural geometrical action* is the magnetic field matter generated by the brain as part of the *cellular geometrical action*, or Gibbs bound energy, by which a mammalian triple-action geometrical cause goes through reproductive cycles. See *Volume II, Chapter 6, Section 1.3.*

located in a qualia world. This is an illusion because the natural world is not a qualia world. I call it the *illusion of intuitionism* because what it is like to be a mammal is to assume that the phenomenal appearance of what is experienced *is* what is experienced, and that is, in effect, to treat the phenomenal appearance as the object of a faculty of intuition. Nothing changes when mammals evolve the use of naturalistic sentences for describing states of affairs in the natural world, nor when mammals evolve the use of psychological sentences for describing their own psychological states. Their verbal behavior and the meanings of sentences constructed in faculties of naturalistic and psychological imagination are additional parts of the qualia world in which their bodies are trapped. But there is a special way of using language that enables reflective subjects to talk their way out of this trap. It depends on *articulating* the illusion of intuition as a false belief. Intuitionistic metaphysicians do that when they try to show that Reason knows Reality behind Appearance. What they call *Appearance* is consciousness, or part of it. What they call *Reason* is another part of consciousness. And when they try to show that Reason can know Reality behind Appearance, they treat both of those parts of consciousness as objects of faculties of intuition.

This way of talking makes sense to reflective subjects because of the illusion inherent in consciousness. Metaphysical arguments exchanged in the culture of a spiritual organism evolve over many generations, and as *Chapter 3* shows, metaphysicians eventually discover that they have been trapped inside consciousness. When they discover that perceptual phenomenal appearances are part of the perceiver, they learn that there is an external world, and that is how they discover that they are conscious. But since they are intuitionists, they discover it in the form of a problematic ontological dualism. This crucial step was taken in Western civilization by Descartes. Treating all of consciousness as Appearance, he took phenomenal appearances to be objects of faculties of intuition, called *ideas*, and assuming that phenomenal appearances of a special kind are objects of a faculty of rational intuition, he used Reason to know Reality behind Appearance. But there were two Realities for Reason to know. While perceptual ideas represented a world external to the perceiver, ideas of all kinds represented the perceiver, and so Descartes had to show how Reason knew the Reality behind both. He called the Reality that Reason discovered behind the objects of perceptual intuition *extension* because he used ideas of geometry as objects of rational intuition to define the external world as a substance whose essential nature is to be spread out like space. The Reality that Reason knew behind ideas of all kinds was called *mind*, and it had an opposite essential nature because Descartes used the argument, *I think, therefore I am*, to know it. His famous *Cogito* was a description of the illusion of intuitionism. The ideas were objects of intuition, and since using them to infer what is true and good was thinking, the mind had a unity that was just opposite to the divisibility of extension. Since the objects of intuition were immediately present, modern metaphysics was a way of talking about consciousness that enabled reflective subjects to discover that they are conscious. But the belief in mind saddled them with an ontological dualism that made metaphysics itself incredible in the end. It was obvious that mind and body interact with one another, but since they had opposite essential natures, no one could find a satisfactory explanation of how that was even possible.

Chapter 3 uses the belief that mind is a substance that is different from the natural world to show how intuitionist metaphysics has a higher level of linguistic organization than the use of psychological sentences. By describing phenomenal appearances as objects of intuition, it separates them from the psychological states of which they are part, and since that makes mind appear to be a substance whose essential nature is opposite to that of the natural world, it creates a substance that is inconceivable in a psychological-level culture. And confidence in Reason caused culture to evolve by Rational selection. Indeed, Descartes expected its knowledge of the essential nature of the external world to be the foundation for what was called *natural philosophy*, and knowing that mind had an opposite nature, Reason would justify belief in the immortality of the soul. But the belief that mind and body interact in a world created by a God who transcends space and time was false, and this explanation of that belief shows how metaphysics uses the illusion of intuitionism to enlist the help of consciousness in causing a stage of spiritual evolution. Since consciousness makes no difference in what happens, it is a pseudo-efficient cause, and accordingly, mind is a *phantom Reality*. Thus, this way of explaining the belief in a mental substance solves the problem of mind-body dualism by showing how the mind is identical to the brain. Mind is just what it is like to be an intuitionistic metaphysician who has discovered that perceptual phenomenal appearances are part of the perceiver.

The reduction of physics and specialized sciences to spatio-materialism turns physical science into ontological science, and after *Chapter 1* uses it to explain how consciousness is part of the natural world, *Chapter 3* shows how the exchange of metaphysical arguments enlists consciousness in helping cause a stage of spiritual evolution in which the belief in mind eventually evolves. Since this is inferred as the best explanation of the rise and globalization of Western civilization, the identity of mind and body in ontological science is a scientific discovery like the discovery of the identity of water and H_2O in physical science. But the challenge was to explain the existence of ontological science, and to go from its explanation of how consciousness is part of the natural world all the way back to the origin of mind-body dualism is to skip over the unsuccessful attempt of contemporary physical science to explain consciousness and mind. And as *Chapter 2* shows, ontological science can explain the obstacle that makes the problem of mind insuperably hard for physical science.

This more technical argument will be of interest to those familiar with the philosophy of mind and attempts by neuroscientists to explain consciousness. Philosophers have been trying to explain mind for centuries, and neuro-scientists are beginning to realize that their contempt for philosophy as unscientific is actually a failure to appreciate how profoundly difficult the problem of mind is. The existence of consciousness is called the *hard problem of mind* by both philosophers and neuroscientists, and what makes it so hard is the ontological dualism of mind and body. Physicalists, as naturalists, assume that mind must somehow be identical to the brain, and in the wake of a compelling refutation of an early attempt to defend the identity of mind and brain, they discovered how hard the problem of mind is. The objection to the *physicalist mind-brain identity theory* was that the identity could not be an empirical discovery unless the scientific theory also explained why the initial belief in the contingency in the relation between them was just an appearance. That was a compelling objection to the physicalist mind-brain identity theory, but it does not hold against the *ontological mind-brain identity theory*. The contingency of the relation between mind and brain is explained ontologically as an appearance caused by the intuitionist illusion, and the identity of mind and brain is clearly an empirical discovery because it is entailed by an inference to a metaphysical stage of evolution as the best explanation of Western civilization. Indeed, it is a theoretical identification in ontological science in the same sense that the identity of water and H_2O was a theoretical identification in physical science, along with many other theoretical identifications.

CHAPTER 1:
THE ONTOLOGY OF CONSCIOUSNESS

Even physicalists recognize that the explanation of mind depends on explaining consciousness. They call the explanation of how the brain guides behavior the easy problem of mind because they assume it can be explained by physical causes. But since the laws of physics do not even mention phenomenal properties, they call the existence phenomenal properties the *hard problem of mind*. It is considered an intractable puzzle in neural science as well as contemporary philosophy of mind. But the existence of consciousness is not a hard problem at all for ontological science.

Chapter 1 is the first part of the explanation of how consciousness causes a stage of spiritual evolution. It shows how consciousness can be explained as part of a natural world constituted by space and matter. Since consciousness is the phenomenal character of experience, it depends on the existence of complex phenomenal properties, and the ontological explanation of their existence is straightforward. The mammalian brain has been explained as a geometrical cause guiding behavior, and given the holistic power of matter, ontological science can infer that matter has an intrinsic phenomenal character as the best explanation of the existence of consciousness.

Section 1 lays the foundation for this discovery by defining the *unity of consciousness* rigorously and showing how the kinds of configurations of qualia that are immediately present in perception and reflection correspond to the geometrical structure of a neural behavior guidance system with a faculty of imagination. *Section 2* shows how complex phenomenal properties are identical to intrinsic properties of a species of matter that helps constitute the geometrical action of a mammalian brain, expressing the holistic power of matter. *Section 3* shows how parts of complex phenomenal properties are related to parts of representations in the mammalian brain that help generate behavior, including verbal behavior that describes them. *Section 4* explores the extent of consciousness in the natural world.

1 Unity of Consciousness

Consciousness is the phenomenal character of all our experience, including not only perception of the natural world but also reflection on our own psychological states. All the puzzles about consciousness depend on its unity, and to keep it simple, I use *perceptual* phenomenal appearances to define what is meant by the *unity of consciousness*. Their unity enables us to recognize that they are part of the subjective animal rather than objects that exist independently of them in space. But this unity also holds of phenomenal appearances of the psychological states on which we reflect, since reflection is just the use of psychological sentences to represent brain states as part of the process guiding behavior.

Consider what it is like to perceive, say, a red tulip on a desk at which we are sitting. The tulip seems to be located in front of our body in a remarkably vivid way. For example, the red color of the tulip is a quality that seems to be located on the surface of the flower. It is different from the green color of the leaves and stem. Colors are simple properties, and since we can define them only by *how* they appear, the only way to explain the difference between red and green qualia is to point to instances of them. Simple qualitative properties like these are called *qualia*, and when we look around the tulip, other color qualia seem to be parts of surfaces of the vase, desk, and other objects located at a distance from our body. Indeed, other sensory modalities also have distinctive kinds of qualia. Hearing involves sounds, olfaction odors, and there are various kinds of bodily qualia, such as tastes, tactile sensations, and pain. All these sensory qualia seem to be located in the same 3-D space, either as parts of objects around the body or as parts of the body itself (or qualia involved in kinesthesia). Indeed, the way that sensory qualia of all kinds are related to one another, along with the way they change as our body moves, makes it appear that they are the very objects in space that we perceive by way of our sensory organs. We know that these qualia exist, and if we wanted, we could classify them and describe in detail their relations to one another in a 3-D space.

This is an example of what I mean by the *phenomenal appearance* of the natural world. In perception, the natural world appears to be many qualia of various kinds with locations in a 3-D space in and around our body. But, remarkably, *all* the qualia are immediately present to us. This way of appearing is implicit in calling them *phenomenal*, and it holds of complex as well as simple phenomenal properties. To accept the complex phenomenal appearance of the natural world at face value is to be a *direct realist about perception*. It is called *direct* because perception of the natural world is not mediated. But since this is our default assumption, it is also called *naïve* realism. Whatever it is called, it is *realism about perception* because it takes the perceptual phenomenal appearance of natural world to exist on its own, independently of us—except, of course, for those that seem to be located in our body. But direct realism is not true. Indeed, it is naïve.

Knowing how space and matter constitute the natural world, ontological scientists can know that direct realism is false. The reason is that qualia cannot have all the properties that direct realism assumes. Qualia are supposed to be properties of the objects perceived in space. But simple qualitative properties are *intrinsic properties* of whatever they are properties of. That is, each kind of quality is a way that something *exists in itself*, rather than a way of exiting in relation to other entities (or *extrinsic properties*). But as a simple qualitative property, the redness of the tulip, for example, cannot be defined by its spatial relations to other qualia. It can be defined only by pointing to instances of it, that is, only ostensibly. However, qualia do seem to have spatial relations to one another, and when we perceive other objects in space, qualia seem to exist outside our body. As Ontological scientists, we are scientific realists about perception, and so we believe that the objects that we perceive in space outside our bodies exist independently of us and one another, like the tulip on our desk. As ontological scientists, we believe that objects in the natural world are constituted by matter and the parts of space with which they coincide. Since the bits of matter exist self-subsistently, they have ways of existing in themselves, and it is not impossible that how they exist in themselves is characterized by simple qualities, like qualia. Thus, such simple intrinsic properties could be what it is like to be the bits of matter. But bits of matter have extrinsic properties, including their relations to space, and thus, when they coincide with different parts of space, they are outside one another. Their intrinsic properties are ways that they exist *where* they coincide with space. Since bits of matter could have qualitative ways of existing in themselves, it could be like something to be a bit of matter. But that it is something that each bit of matter would keep to itself. Thus, even if qualia were phenomenal intrinsic properties of bits of matter that help constitute the tulip, they could not be immediately present to us because *what* they are like would be *how* they exist in themselves where they coincide with space, and those parts of space are outside our body.

What falsifies direct realism about perception is a puzzling aspect of the phenomenal character of the subjective appearance of the natural world that defines the *unity of consciousness*. Since many qualia of various kinds are all parts of what is immediately present at once, there is a unity about the phenomenal appearance. That is, phenomenal appearances are complex. Since each quale is an *intrinsic* property of whatever it is a property of, it is how something exists in itself, distinct from its relations to anything else. Since each quale is a *simple* property, kinds of qualia cannot be defined by their parts. Their kinds can be defined only by how they appear to us. We can use their spatial relations to one another to refer to particular qualia since they are located in a 3-D space that seems to be public. That enables direct realists to point to particular qualia and define their kinds by how they exist in themselves. This is to use the extrinsic properties that qualia seem to have to refer to them, and so this way of defining kinds of qualia clearly depends on them being part of a complex phenomenal property. But in order to pick particular qualia out by the spatial relations to one another that they appear to have, *they must all be immediately present to the subject at once*. Thus, even though each quale is the way that something exists in itself, the way that each exists in itself is immediately present to beings like us along with many other qualia of various kinds. That is the unity of a complex phenomenal property, and it is an example of the *unity of consciousness*.

The unity of consciousness shows that direct realism about perception is false. The tulip's red qualia are immediately present to us, and they seem to be located in an object outside our body. But they cannot be located outside our body because, if they were, they would be intrinsic properties of parts of a flower that coincide with another part of space, and so their way of existing in themselves could not be immediately present *to us*. The same goes for bodily qualia. Qualia that seem to be located in our body cannot actually be located in those parts of our body because the self is the neural BGS, and if they were intrinsic properties of the parts of the body where they seem to be located, they could not be immediately present to us in the same way as other qualia. Let us call the kind of 3-D space in which sensory qualia seem to be related to one another *phenomenal space* in order to distinguish it from the space in which objects of the natural world exist, that is, as bits of matter coinciding with different parts of *substantial space*.

Though direct realism is our natural attitude about perception, it is naïve, and we must give it up because the relations of qualia in phenomenal space cannot be constituted by the relations of objects in substantial space. The phenomenal appearance has a kind of unity that is radically different from the unity of the natural world. Since sensory qualia have locations in phenomenal space, they have extrinsic properties as well as intrinsic properties. But as phenomenal properties, they are extrinsic properties of a radically different kind from those of bits of matter. Since qualia are parts of the phenomenal appearance, they have extrinsic properties because of their relations to one another in phenomenal space. But since they are all immediately present to a subject, the unity of complex phenomenal properties is radically different from the spatial relations of objects in the natural world. Objects in space are constituted by interactions of space and matter, and when the objects have different locations in space, their spatial relations are extrinsic properties. The unity of the natural world comes from objects all coinciding with different parts of the same spatial substance, and so how those objects exist in themselves is something they keep to themselves. Their intrinsic properties, whatever they are, cannot be immediately present to the reflective subject perceiving them. Hence, there is a fundamental difference between the *unity of the natural world* and the *unity of complex phenomenal properties*.

When we give up direct realism about perception, we find ourselves accepting *representative realism*. It is *representative* because, when we perceive something, we take its phenomenal appearance to represent what exists in the natural world. Since this is to reject *naïve realism,* our natural attitude is also called *critical realism*. It is *realism* because it posits the existence of the objects represented in the natural world. That is, it holds that perception involves a correspondence between the phenomenal appearance of the natural world and the natural world itself. But representative realism does not explain the unity of the phenomenal appearance. It merely locates the phenomenal appearance in the reflective subject. When beings like us discover that direct realism is false, qualia in phenomenal space are still immediately present, and since perceptual phenomenal appearances represent the natural world, we accept *representative realism* about perception. They represent the natural world as a world of objects in space because the subjective neural behavior guidance system has a faculty of imagination that enables mammals to think about their spatial relations and how they change when objects move.

When mammals evolve the use of psychological sentences, they become reflective subjects, and since the use of psychological sentences enables them to think about their psychological states and their causal roles as part of the process of guiding behavior, they have reflective as well as perceptual phenomenal appearances. Their linguistic ability depends on both a naturalistic and a psychological faculty of imagination, and since naturalistic imagination is located in the nonverbal hemisphere of the cerebrum, let us keep this explanation of the structures of phenomenal appearances simple and consider, first, the faculty of naturalistic imagination in a non-linguistic neural BGS.

From the ontological explanation of the stages of evolution, ontology discovers that imagination is the function of the basic structure of the mammalian brain. Mammals are subjective animals because their faculty of imagination represents their own bodies to them as one object in a world of objects in space that can move and interact with one another. It is a faculty of imagination because mammals can behave not only by moving their bodies in the natural world, that is, *overtly*, but also by moving their bodies *covertly*. Covert behavior calls up images recorded in the neural BGS from experience that represent its consequences, and so mammals can use covert behavior to predict what will happen. They can plan how to behave overtly in ways that are likely to satisfy their desires.

As we have seen, the three subfunctions of the mammalian neural BGS are served by three circuits (all through the thalamus to the neocortex and back to the thalamus via a third structure in the cerebrum): the *sensory input circuit*, the *motor output circuit*, and the *choosing circuit*. The faculty of naturalistic imagination is just an interaction between the motor output circuit and the sensory input circuit, and since the sensory input circuit uses input from various sensory organs to construct a representation of objects in the natural world, perception is basically the construction of a representation of the surroundings, called the *input scene* (assembled in the parietal cortex). Indeed, the motor output circuit can be seen as the subject that uses the input scene to perceive the natural world, since it organizes motor output relative to objects represented in the *input scene* (using not only a projection from the parietal cortex and the rest of the posterior sensory cortex, via the caudate nucleus, to the globus pallidus of the corpus striatum, but also by its association fibers with the frontal cortex and the connections of both regions of cortex with the claustrum in the insular cortex). This interaction between the sensory input circuit and motor output circuit explains the subjective appearance in perception as a representation of the natural world that is constructed in the neural BGS. But it does not explain what representative realists mean by representations of the natural world when they give up direct realism. The subjective appearance is mainly a pattern of firings of neurons in the parietal cortex, and the subject means the *phenomenal appearance* of the natural world in perception. Both are different from the natural world that they represent. But the subjective appearance does not explain the phenomenal appearance. The *structure* of the subjective appearance could explain the *structure* of the phenomenal appearance, since the subjective appearance and the phenomenal appearance both correspond to the natural world. But the subjective appearance does not explain the phenomenal appearance itself because the input scene (and the circuits of which it is part) does not explain the unity of the phenomenal appearance. It is the same puzzle that falsifies direct realism.

Bundles of neurons pass picture-grade signals around the sensory input circuit, and different neurons in the input scene of the sensory input circuit represent different parts of the natural world, for example, the tulip and its stem. But even if those neuron firings somehow had intrinsic properties that are simple qualities, they could not constitute qualia in phenomenal space. The neurons are outside one another in substantial space, and whatever they are in themselves when they fire, they could not all be immediately present to the perceiving subject at the same time. (Furthermore, even if the phenomenal appearance were somehow constituted by the sensory input circuit as a whole, the motor output circuit could not be the subject to which sensory qualia are immediately present because each circuit is a distinct bundle of neurons in the mammalian neural BGS. Whatever intrinsic properties the sensory input circuit might have, its neurons exist outside the neurons in the motor output circuit, and so regardless of what they are in themselves, they cannot be immediately present to the motor output circuit.) The basic problem is that neurons in the bundles whose firings pass picture-grade signals around circuits of the subjective neural BGS are bits of matter that coincide with different parts of space, and since their intrinsic properties are ways of existing in themselves that are outside one another in space, they cannot appear all at once to a single subject.

The perceptual phenomenal appearance is a complex phenomenal property. Many qualia of various kinds are all immediately present to a single subject at the same time, and since that gives consciousness a unity that is radically different from the unity of the natural world, the question is, *How can consciousness be part of the natural world?* That is a question that science can answer once it has discovered that space is a substance that interacts with matter.

2 Ontological Cause of Consciousness

As we have seen, this discovery about space solves the puzzles confronting branches of science studying more limited regularities about change in the natural world. The *inertial system* (which generates all the regularities about how particles move and interact that are described by laws of quantum physics) has two parallel parts, the *mechanical system* (which gives particles a location and enables them to move), and the *electromagnetic system* (by which particles exert the forces by which they change one another's motion). Space interacts with matter in the inertial system in a way that gives the mechanical system a quantum structure, and as we have seen, this is how space gives matter a holistic power. By helping constitute composite bodies, it gives matter unchanging geometrical structures that constrain how physical particles move and interact (and how physical forces generally are exerted). These geometrical efficient causes are not recognized by a science based on physics because it assumes that composite bodies are reducible to physical causes. It assumes that they can be explained by the regularities about how free particles move and interact described by laws of quantum physics (including the Pauli exclusion principle). Those laws justify using physical causes to explain what happens, and physicalists assume that they explain every event in the natural world (except what depends on quantum uncertainty). As we have seen, the discovery that space is a substance that interacts with matter reveals that atoms and bodies composed of them are *geometrical causes* that help determine what happens, and the recognition of geometrical efficient causes enables the specialized branches of science to explain the evolution of life as involving a series of stages that leads inevitably to the existence of reflective subjects.

What happens when geometrical causes constrain the collective effects of physical causes is called *geometrical action*, and at every level of geometrical organization in the natural world, geometrical action expresses the holistic power of matter. *Molecular geometrical action*, the geometrical action of chemical reactions, is relatively simple. But the molecular geometrical action helping constitute the cells of living organisms, called *cellular geometrical action*, is much more complex. And since animals have a BGS in which firings of neurons generate magnetic field matter waves, their geometrical action includes *neural geometrical action*, and since mammals have a faculty of imagination, their *neural geometrical action* has a spatiotemporal structure whose phenomenal intrinsic nature can be the complex phenomenal properties that are immediately present to mammals.

The geometrical action of a mammalian brain is what enables science to explain how consciousness is part of the natural world. Some matter that is part of the geometrical action of the mammalian brain has intrinsic properties that can explain the structural aspects of complex phenomenal properties. Assuming that matter with those intrinsic properties has a phenomenal character, the holistic power of matter explains the unity of consciousness. That is, the best explanation of consciousness is that these intrinsic properties of matter are identical to the complex phenomenal properties that are immediately present in consciousness. This way of explaining consciousness ontologically depends on *panpsychism*.

The assumption that mater in the spatio-material world has intrinsic properties with a phenomenal character is an ontological kind of panpsychism. It holds that phenomenal properties are part of the natural world because it is like something to be a substance, and what it is like to be a bit of matter can explain complex phenomenal properties because how a bit of matter exists in itself depends on the spatiotemporal structure of its coincidence and interaction with a part of space. That spatiotemporal structure can be quite complex, and thus, if simple bits of matter have a *proto-phenomenal intrinsic property*, ontology can explain complex phenomenal properties as what it is like to be bits of matter with a complex spatiotemporal structure. Thus, vivid sensory qualia would exist only as parts of such a spatiotemporal structure.

To explain conscious as what it is like to be the mammalian brain, the matter that has this proto-phenomenal intrinsic property must be *magnetic field matter*, a species of matter in the electromagnetic part of the inertial system. Its flow between charged particles mediates the forces by which they interact with one another. But this is only part of the interaction between space and matter in the inertial system. The parallel part of the inertial system is the mechanical system, and its quantum structure is how space gives matter a holistic power, which is expressed as geometrical efficient causes and their geometrical action.[4] Physics overlooks the quantum structure of the mechanical system because its use of a mathoscope to discover quantitative regularities about change filters out the role of space in helping matter generate physical regularities.[5] As part of the inertial system, the mechanical system is responsible for the location, motion, and velocity of charged

---

[4] Since the quantum structure of the mechanical system explains the entanglement of particles, entanglement holds of particles throughout the universe, and the role of space in causing entanglement explains the puzzling non-locality demonstrated by Bell's inequality. The quantum structure of the mechanical system is what enables space to give matter a holistic power, and so it is also what explains geometrical efficient causes and their further expression as the unity of consciousness.

[5] Even the unification of the two branches of modern physics depends on recognizing the quantum structure of the mechanical system because it plays the central role in explaining the spacetime curvature to which modern physics attributes gravitational acceleration and in explaining the expansion of the universe to which big bang cosmology attributes the Hubble redshift.

particles, and since the electromagnetic system is responsible for the acceleration fueling that enables the mechanical system to change the velocities of particles, the geometrical power that matter acquires from space in the mechanical system is also expressed in the electromagnetic system. That is part of the geometrical action of composite bodies, and that is the location of the magnetic field matter whose proto-phenomenal intrinsic properties are identical to consciousness.

Geometrical action expresses the holistic power of matter because it is the effect of geometrical causes constraining the collective effects of physical causes. The lowest relevant level of geometrical organization is the constitution of atoms and molecules.[6] Electrons are bound to nuclei in atoms by cycles of interactions punctuated by atomic events with precise locations in space and time that depend on the quantum structure of the mechanical system, and similar bonds between atoms enable bodies composed of atoms to interact as a whole with the rest of the world, constituting the geometrical efficient causes that specialized sciences need to explain the regularities they study. (Geometrical causes are a special case of the quantum entanglement of particles.) At the lowest energy levels of motion and interaction, there is evidence of geometrical structures of composite bodies acting as a whole, for example, in the interference phenomena produced by the famous double-slit experiment. At higher energy levels, there is abundant evidence geometrical causes acting as a whole in the rigidity of composite bodies, such as levers, which can serve as tools. Since steam engines are macro-level geometrical causes that constrain the collective effects of molecules, the thermodynamic work they do is geometrical action. Chemical reactions are micro-level geometrical efficient causes that do work on their surroundings by doing work on themselves, and that way of constraining the collective effects of physical causes is the geometrical action that is turned into living organisms by the reproductive mechanism.

What changes in evolution are *double-action geometrical causes* that go

---

[6] At the lowest level, the quantum structure of the mechanical system helps matter constitute the elementary particles described in the Standard Model. The combination of the mechanical and electromagnetic systems explains not only the charged leptons, such as electrons and quarks, but also baryons, such as protons and neutrons. Those triplets of quarks depend on the quantum structure of the mechanical system, and strong nuclear forces mediated by quark-antiquark pairs bind nucleons together as nuclei.

through reproductive cycles in regions with finite flows of acceleration fuel in which they do both essential kinds of work. They gradually acquire powers that enable them to promote conditions under which they can reproduce. Beginning with RNA molecules that are driven through reproductive cycles by the cycle of night and day as parts of colonies of RNA that are driven through reproductive cycles by other external conditions, colonies of RNA eventually acquire a geometrical efficient cause, called a *behavior guidance system* (BGS), which enables them to go through reproductive cycles on their own. Since they are *triple-action geometrical causes*, they are the beginning of life. The reproductive mechanism, operating on two levels at once, shapes the geometrical action of RNA at one level of geometrical organization into prokaryotic cells at a higher level. This is the first form of life, and a similar bi-level embodiment of the reproductive mechanism shapes the geometrical action at one level of organization into a new form of life on a higher level three more times, constructing a four-story edifice of life. Thus, prokaryotes going through reproductive cycles in colonies that are driven through reproductive cycles by external conditions become cells with a nucleus inside serving as a BGS, called *eukaryotic cells*, that go through reproductive cycles on their own as a second form of life. Multicellular organisms evolve on the third floor in a similar way from eukaryotes, except that the behavior guidance system they acquire depends on eukaryotic cells sharing a plan rather than the construction of a cell to enclose them. But its geometrical action is on a higher level than eukaryotes, and for multicellular organisms that acquire acceleration fuel by ingesting energy-rich objects, it constructs an animal body with a neural BGS to guide its behavior through reproductive cycles.

Neurons are energy-consuming cells with axons along which signals are sent as action potentials, generating magnetic field matter waves, and neurons are organized in the body on a series of levels that causes a series of minor stages of animal evolution. At the first level (somatosensory animals), single neurons firing can serve each of the three essential functions of a BGS: *registering sensory input*, *choosing how to behave*, and *generating motor output*. At the second level (telesensory animals), bundles of neurons serve each of the three essential functions, enabling a centralized nervous system to guide animal behavior relative to objects at a distance. And since neurons organized as bundles with a regular 2-D structure can send picture-grade signals from one location in the nervous system to another, there is a third level of neural organization in which interactions of three circuits of bundles of neurons, each serving one of the essential functions of a BGS, gives subjective animals a faculty of imagination. This level of organization of geometrical action is where magnetic field matter waves generated by the firing of energy-consuming neurons has a kind of a spatiotemporal structure in which its proto-phenomenal intrinsic property are complex phenomenal properties that are immediately present to the animal. It is the neural geometrical action helping constitute mammals.

Geometrical action of animals at the subjective level of neural organization is where an intrinsic property of field matter helping constitute the brain has configurations of vivid qualia with distinct locations in a 3-D space. Since sensory input is registered in a faculty of physical imagination, the natural world appears as objects in space around a body where locomotion can change spatial relations. This is physical imagination, and since all mammals are conscious, animals whose brains have higher levels of neural organization differ only by having immediately present configurations of qualia that represent additional aspects of the world. In manipulative animals, such as primates, geometrical imagination enables them to predict the effects of using their limbs to manipulate the geometrical structures of objects in the same 3-D space where locomotion can change the body's spatial relations to surrounding objects. When mammals first acquire the use of language, they have a faculty of naturalistic imagination for understanding the meanings of naturalistic sentences, and so they can think about ways that objects in space are related and use regularities about how they change to understand how they can change. When mammals acquire the use of psychological sentences, they also have a faculty of psychological imagination by which they can reflect on their own psychological states and understand them as reasons for behavior, either in the very process by which they help cause their own behavior or when seeing into the minds of other subjects. Since verbal behavior generated by the language-using mammalian brain is the spiritual BGS, it is another kind of geometrical action helping constitute spiritual organisms along with the cellular and neural geometrical action of their members, and their nature is called *spiritual* because the geometrical cause guiding their behavior is nothing but *linguistic geometrical action*.

The neural geometrical action at these levels of organization in mammalian brains is constituted by a species of matter that is spread out in the part of space with which it coincides, and the best ontological explanation of the perceptual phenomenal appearance is that it is an intrinsic property of magnetic field matter. It might seem that the phenomenal appearance could be an intrinsic property of that part of space rather than the field matter since interacting with that field matter requires space to have a property with the same spatiotemporal structure. But space acts on magnetic field matter in the electromagnetic system merely by carrying bits of magnetic field matter across space at the speed of light, and since space acts on every wavelength (and every phase in every wavelength) in every direction in the same way, ontology would have to postulate an additional intrinsic property of space for a property of space to be identical to the phenomenal appearance. Thanks to the mechanical system, the way that magnetic field matter coincides with space already has the relevant spatiotemporal structure, and so the ontological explanation of consciousness is simpler when the phenomenal appearance is explained as the intrinsic nature of matter rather than space.

Species of matter are defined by the spatiotemporal structures of their coincidence and interaction with parts of space, and since the relevant spatio-temporal structure is how magnetic field matter coincides and interacts with space, it is necessarily how the magnetic field matter exists in itself as it coincides with space.[7] Thus, ontology explains how complex phenomenal properties are part of the natural world more simply when it holds that it is identical to magnetic field matter because, instead of postulating a previously unrecognized property, it merely discovers that an intrinsic property it already recognizes also has a phenomenal character. Thus, assuming that an intrinsic

---

[7] All matter must have a proto-phenomenal intrinsic property, since it is another way that matter exists in itself independently of space, along with having an intrinsic quantity. Thus, mechanical matter must also have it. But the parts of space with which bits of mechanical matter interact are so small and discontinuous that what it is like to be them cannot be immediately present to a mammal. However, the behavior of electric field matter is so continuous with that of magnetic field matter that physics does not even distinguish them, and so an intrinsic property of electric field matter must also be proto-phenomenal in a way that is immediately present to a mammal, though we can't know what it is like to be a solitary bit of electric field matter.

property of every bit of magnetic field matter has a *proto-phenomenal character,* ontology uses the spatiotemporal structure of its coincidence with space to explain the complex phenomenal properties that are immediately present in consciousness. Thus, the structures of qualia in phenomenal space are what it is like to be magnetic field matter when it has the relevant spatiotemporal structure. But for this identity theory to be adequate, magnetic field matter must have spatiotemporal structures of a kind that is able to explain the structures of sensory qualia that mammals have when they perceive the natural world.

We are conscious mammals, and when we reflect on our perception of the natural world, there are many qualia of various kinds in phenomenal space. Since qualia are intrinsic properties of whatever they are properties of, the challenge is to show how a way that magnetic field matter exists in itself could be all the qualia that are immediately present to us at the same time. The neural BGS is the geometrical cause that is responsible for its behavior, and the collective effect of physical causes is the flow of acceleration fuel that it uses to do the thermodynamic work of guiding animal behavior.

The faculty of imagination is built into the basic structure of the mammalian brain (as the three circuits from the thalamus through the neocortex back to the thalamus via a third part of the cerebrum), and so its geometrical action includes all the brain processes by which imagination helps guide behavior. They involve the firings of neurons throughout the mammalian brain, and since action potentials of neurons generate waves of magnetic field matter, the magnetic field matter helping constitute the functioning of the mammalian brain expresses the holistic power of matter. From the ontological explanation of the evolution of the mammalian brain, we know that the *subjective appearance* is constructed from sensory input in a faculty of imagination, and since magnetic field matter helps mediate interactions of neurons, an intrinsic property that matter has because of its spatiotemporal structure is the best ontological explanation of the unity of consciousness in the spatio-material world.

The unchanging geometrical structure of the mammalian brain is the geometrical cause that the animal BGS constructs in the mammalian body to guide its behavior, and its geometrical action includes neuron firings. When they fire, their action potentials are flows of charged particles in and out of their axons that propagate along them, and the acceleration fuel whose flow between particles changes their motion is magnetic field matter. This neural geometrical action is part of the flow of acceleration fuel from the Sun through Earth's surface that becomes Gibbs bound energy in evolving geometrical causes, and in cells of the body, it flows from mitochondria (which produce ATP molecules in cells) and is used in the firing of neurons. Some of the acceleration fuel that accelerates charged particles is carried away as magnetic field matter waves by the inertial system at the speed of light,[8] and some of it escapes the brain as so-called *electromagnetic waves*. This is still Gibbs bound energy because it is part of the thermodynamic work that chemical reactions must do on themselves to have the Gibbs free energy of chemical reactions that occur spontaneously. But as waves of magnetic field matter flow through the mammalian brain, they affect the acceleration of charged particles along their pathways, and this interaction between neural and cellular geometrical action is part of Gibbs bound energy helping constitute the mammalian brain. The acceleration of charged particles at one location in the subjective neural BGS affects the acceleration of charged particles elsewhere at the speed of light, and the combined effect of all the neuron firings is that the geometrical action of the entire subjective neural BGS is registered as waves of magnetic field matter everywhere in the brain. Though magnetic field matter is only part of the geometrical action of the mammalian brain, it is the species of matter whose spatiotemporal structure can explain configurations of qualia in phenomena space. And since it is Gibbs bound energy helping constitute the mammalian brain, the consciousness of mammals is explained by what it is like to be the part of Gibbs bound energy called *neural geometrical action*.

Let me describe these electromagnetic interactions in the brain in more

---

[8] Recalling how the basic electromagnetic regularities were explained in *Volume I*, electric field matter coincides with the charge fields of particles at rest, and it can fuel the acceleration of other charged particles coinciding with it (even when they are at rest). But when charged particles *move*, magnetic field matter as well as electric field matter coincides with their charge fields, and the motion of magnetic field matter across space can fuel the acceleration of charged particles when they are moving through it. This magnetic field matter is a form of bound matter that mediates local interactions of particles, along with electric field matter. But when charged particles are *accelerated*, some bound magnetic field matter is freed as waves that are carried across space by the inherent motion, and some of the magnetic field matter in these waves can be absorbed by charged particles lying along their paths in the brain before they escape the neural BGS entirely.

detail. When a neuron fires, ions (atoms carrying a net charge) accelerate across its plasma membrane into its axon, a cylindrical part of the neuron that can be quite long. This action potential propagates along its entire length, and since the acceleration of ions at each point triggers a similar acceleration at the next point, a signal is carried along the axon (which is much faster when the axon is surrounded by a myelin sheath). As we have seen, the firing of neurons in bundles of neurons with unchanging 2-D arrays sends picture-grade signals around the three circuits of the subjective neural BGS, each with multiple junctions. They include massive projections between the thalamus and neocortex, and since mechanisms in the thalamus synchronize the firing of such neurons throughout the neural BGS (as brainwaves that are detectable by electroencephalograms), fibers connecting the thalamus and neocortex generate magnetic field matter waves simultaneously. The firings of neurons generate magnetic field matter waves, and since the firings of neurons in one part of the mammalian brain affect the firings at every other location, the magnetic field matter waves have a complex spatiotemporal structure.[9]

In short, the functioning of the neural BGS involves the firing of many neurons at once, and the field matter available to fuel the acceleration of ions used by a neuron depends not only on their own motion but also on two other factors: the magnetic field matter coinciding with other nearby moving charge fields and the (wavelengths and phases of) the magnetic field matter waves passing through their location from every direction at the speed of light.[10]

---

[9] Though bits of electric field matter have a simple radial field, bits of magnetic field matter coinciding with moving charge fields have a more complex structure. Magnetic field matter is bound to a charged particle when it moves, and it has a two-dimensional intrinsic orientation (one in the radial direction of its charge field and the other in the direction of its motion). It can accelerate only moving charges. But waves of magnetic field matter generated by the *acceleration* of charged particles have an even more complex intrinsic structure (because the inertial system carries magnetic field matter across space in the direction of its intrinsic radial orientation). And since magnetic field matter waves are carried across space at the speed of light, the flow of field matter at any location is affected by the acceleration of charged particles elsewhere.

[10] The flows of acceleration fuel in the electromagnetic system are constrained by the mechanical system, where the motion of charged particles is constituted by bits of motor matter shifting bits of movable matter from one linear half-unit to the next. As we have seen, their ship-pilot couples are all related by its quantum structure, expressing a non-local power of space. Hence, the ions flowing in and out of axons of neurons are moved across space by ship-pilot couples of doubled actions, and since endpoints of linear half-units are atomic events with precise relations in space and time, the quantum structure of the mechanical system constrains all the flows of acceleration fuel by which the subjective neural BGS does the thermodynamic work of generating the synchronized firings of neurons throughout the cortex.

With flows of acceleration fuel in small volumes everywhere in the neural BGS registering its geometrical action everywhere, magnetic field matter throughout the subjective neural BGS has a kind of spatiotemporal structure that is able, in principle, to explain the structure of the phenomenal appearance ontologically.[11]

To be sure, the spatiotemporal structures of flows of acceleration fuel in small volumes in different regions of the neural BGS are not exactly alike. They have different locations, and since the directions from which magnetic field matter waves arrive at any neuron depend on its location relative to other firing neurons, flows of acceleration fuel vary systematically with their locations. But their spatiotemporal structures are all isomorphic with the configuration of qualia in phenomenal space, and since field matter is spread out in space, spatiotemporal structures at different locations are all connected continuously. All the small volumes fit together seamlessly in 3-D space, and since they are all part of the neural geometrical action of the brain built into the mammalian body, it is not possible for any local flow of acceleration fuel in the electromagnetic system to exist without all the others. Thus, consciousness can be explained as what is like to be the magnetic field matter that helps constitute the neural geometrical action of the mammalian brain.[12]

---

[11] The acceleration fuel available to an ion depends on a superposition (vectorial addition) of the magnetic field matter due the motion of nearby ions and the magnetic field matter waves generated by the acceleration of all the other ions elsewhere. The waves have amplitudes that vary in a direction transverse to the direction of their propagation, like waves in water, and the strengths and orientations of all the waves arriving in every direction are combined with the bound field matter at any location. Since magnetic field matter has a two-dimensional intrinsic orientation, this superposition is very complex. But a Fourier analysis of the waves is a mathematical tool that might be used to picture the spatiotemporal structure of acceleration fuel *at each location*. It would reveal that there are many different frequencies and phases of waves both ways in every direction, and a combination of such patterns for every direction in 3-D space would be a structure that could register the thermodynamic work done throughout the electromagnetic system. But the causal relevance of magnetic field matter waves in brain functioning is evident in magneto-induction therapy.

[12] The unity of consciousness expresses the holistic power of matter in two ways. First, since the holistic power of matter is expressed as geometrical efficient causes, it is expressed as the neural BGS with a faculty of imagination that gives magnetic field matter its distinctive spatiotemporal structure. Second, since the magnetic field matter is the effect of a geometrical cause constraining the collective effects of physical causes throughout the mammalian brain, the holistic power of matter is expressed as the *unity* of consciousness, specifically, the way that many qualia of various kinds are all immediately present to the mammal at once. (If the same motion and acceleration of ions happened to occur in a plasma of ions, that is, independently moving charged particles, what is was like to be that plasma would not be a complex phenomenal property. At most it would be many simple phenomenal properties.) But given the unity of complex phenomenal properties, the illusion inherent in consciousness depends on the first expression of

In summation, the phenomenal character of the intrinsic property that magnetic field matter has because of the role that its spatiotemporal structure plays in helping guide behavior can explain what it is like to be a mammalian brain of which it is part. Consciousness is the phenomenal intrinsic nature of mammalian neural geometrical action, but since magnetic field matter is the flow of acceleration fuel in the electromagnetic system, it is only part of the geometrical action of the mammalian brain. The electromagnetic system is only one of two parallel parts of the inertial system, and the mechanical system is responsible for the geometrical cause that channels the flows of acceleration fuel. It imposes geometrical constraints on collective effects of physical causes at every level of geometrical organization all the way down to atoms and how they are bound together in the molecules helping constitute the mammalian brain. Like all composite bodies, the power of its geometrical structure to constrain what happens depends, at the bottom, on the quantum structure of the mechanical system. Thus, the ontological explanation of the unity of consciousness, like everything else, depends on how space is a substance that interacts matter: the discovery about space that empirical ontology makes by reducing physics to spatio-materialism.

3   Efficacy of Phenomenal Appearances

For representative realists, perceptual phenomenal appearances are just one kind of phenomenal appearance among others that occurs as they reflect on their psychological states. Reflection is the use of psychological states to represent psychological states as part of the thermodynamic work that the mammalian brain does in guiding behavior, and like all psychological states,

---

the holistic power of matter, neural BGS as a geometrical cause, because the faculty of imagination is what makes it appear that qualia are configured in a phenomenal space where the qualia body is located. That way of perceiving and understanding the natural world is why mammals are called *subjective animals*, and since it is like something to be the magnetic field matter that helps constitute the geometrical action of the mammalian brain, conscious subjects naturally assume that the immediate presence of phenomenal properties is how they known. (If neurons firing in a similarly synchronized way as part of a comparable complex composite body with a different geometrical structure, there would be complex phenomenal properties. But there would be no intuitionist illusion because there would be no subject to which they seemed to be immediately present.) In other words, there are two aspects to the unity of consciousness. One is the unity on which complex phenomenal properties depend, and the other is the structure of complex phenomenal properties that characterizes the consciousness of mammals and is the illusion of intuitionism inherent in it.

this verbal behavior has a phenomenal character. But the phenomenal character of experience has no effect on behavior. What causes behavior are psychological (brain) states, and their phenomenal appearances are simply what it is like to be the mammalian brain guiding behavior. Since phenomenal appearances are intrinsic properties of magnetic field matter helping constitute geometrical action, ontology can trace qualia, their relations in a 3-D space, and other aspects of what it is like to be the parts of the mammalian brain that mediate its effects on behavior. The parts of phenomenal properties and the firings of neurons are both parts of the geometrical action of the brain.

Consciousness is plausibly attributed to the neural geometrical action of the mammalian brain because the work done by the human brain consumes about 20% of the energy consumed by the body, even though it is only about 5% of body weight. Perception is a basic operation of neural BGSs with a faculty of imagination, and the qualia objects in phenomenal space that represent the natural world can be traced to parts of a neural BGS with a faculty of imagination by which they help guide behavior. Imagination is just an interaction between the motor output circuit and the sensory input circuit in which covert behavior calls up images of its consequences. Including the choosing circuit, there are three circuits in the subjective BGS, and in all three, there are at least three links of multiple-fiber bundles of neurons. By considering how the faculty of imagination constructs the subjective appearance of the natural world in perception, we can see how the efficacy of the sensory qualia that seem to have locations in a 3-D space depends on the sensory input circuit. (The parts of the mammalian brain mentioned here are explained in more detail in *Chapter 7* of *Volume II*.)

The flow of acceleration fuel depends mainly on firings of neurons in the bundles that carry picture-grade signals in both circuits from the thalamus to the cortex and back to the thalamus by way of other forebrain structures in both circuits. Their firings must be synchronized to carry picture-grade signals, and since longer axons are roughly parallel, they generate waves whose orientations and complex picture-like signals register their neuronal activity in the superposition of magnetic field matter waves throughout the brain.[13]

In the sensory input circuit, picture-grade signals from the retina in the eye are projected along the optic nerve to the (lateral geniculate nucleus of the) thalamus, and six (retinotopically aligned) lamina relay color-coded picture-grade visual signals to the occipital cortex in the posterior cerebrum. Thus, for example, the red qualia that seem to be located on the surface of the tulip can be attributed to the rapid synchronized firing of a pattern of neurons in a certain lamina of the lateral geniculate nucleus.[14] This is how the sensory input circuit receives visual input, and since neuron firings in other bundles of neurons projecting both ways between other regions of the occipital cortex and the thalamus analyze the patterns represented in this picture-grade sensory input, this processing of visual input can explain our ability to perceive and describe aspects of a visual phenomenal appearance, such as the tulip's shape, its location on the desk, and the difference between red and green qualia. Synchronized firings of neurons in similar bundles register input from the ears and olfactory bulb, and since signals received from all the bundles of neurons are combined in the sensory input circuit, their firings can explain the vivid qualia involved in all sensory discrimination. The thalamus synchronizes the

---

[13] Crick and Koch (1990) defend the hypothesis that the 40-75 hertz synchronization of the firing of thalamic neurons to the cortex is the *neural correlate* of consciousness. The flows of acceleration fuel in the electromagnetic system that help constitute the synchronized firing would explain their hypothesis ontologically in the spatio-material world. They focus on the difference between consciousness and unconsciousness, and it can be explained ontologically by the difference between the mammalian brain doing thermodynamic work on the world in guiding behavior and doing thermodynamic work on itself, for example, in dreams, as a way of forming more permanent memories and reconciling conflicting desires attached to familiar objects. But only intrinsic properties of substances helping constitute the brain can explain the phenomenal character of experience.

[14] Evidence that projections from the lateral geniculate nucleus (LGN) of the thalamus to the occipital cortex are essential to visual qualia is *blindsight*. a condition in which patients are blind in regions of the visual field because of lesions in the occipital cortex. They deny consciousness of visual images corresponding to them, but they can direct behavior relative to objects represented in blind areas better than chance. Blindsight can be explained by a projection from the optic nerve by way of the optic tectum (or superior colliculus) of the midbrain to regions of the forebrain generating motor commands. On the other hand, energy-consuming projections from the LGN to the occipital cortex carry hundreds of action potentials per second, making their firings stand out in the spatiotemporal structure of the magnetic field matter coinciding with space, as one would expect of vivid visual sensory qualia. But they are probably also responsible for the vivid qualia in reflective phenomenal appearances, such as dreams and eidetic images. There are about ten times as many fibers projecting from more central processing areas of the mammalian neural BGS to the LGN as there are fibers from the LGN to the occipital cortex, suggesting that they play a crucial role not only in analyzing visual input, but also in generating phenomenal appearances. The qualia of phenomenal appearances caused by imagination may usually be fainter, but as hallucinations show, they can be as vivid as visual sensory input.

firings of neurons in bundles projecting between the thalamus and the posterior cortex, and since bundles of neurons passing picture-grade signals from one major junction to the next enable the sensory input circuit to integrate input from all sensory modalities as parts of the *input scene* (located in the parietal cortex), the sensory input circuit can explain all the sensory qualia that appear to be located in space around the body when a subject perceives the world.

The motor output circuit does not cause sensory qualia because its function is to generate the motor commands that direct behavior relative to objects in the input scene. But there are qualia representing the body in the sensory input circuit. Somatosensory input registered in a nucleus of the thalamus is relayed to a strip of posterior cortex located across the central sulcus from the motor cortex (the strip of the frontal cortex that sends motor commands directly to all parts of the body), and fibers connecting neurons across this sulcus enable the motor output circuit to contribute to the phenomenal appearance, even though it does not receive sensory input. Furthermore, since the firing of neurons in all the bundles projecting picture-grade signals between the thalamus and the cortex in the motor output circuit can contribute to the spatiotemporal structure of flows of magnetic field matter throughout the neural BGS, the motor output circuit can explain less vivid aspects of the phenomenal appearance than sensory qualia.

For example, a subject who perceives the red tulip on the desk sees it *as* an object with a location in space, and as we have seen, the concept of an object in space depends on how the motor output circuit interacts with the sensory input circuit. The tulip is represented in the input scene constructed by the sensory input circuit, and this representation is presented to the motor output circuit. (The input scene, located in the parietal cortex, projects mainly by way of the caudate nucleus to the globus pallidus of the corpus striatum, where this representation is combined with the picture-grade signals passed around the motor output circuit in order to set up motor commands for behavior relative to objects in the input scene.[15]) The concept of an object in

---

[15] Stereopsis, the perceptual phenomenal appearance of the third dimension as depth in the visual system, is probably mainly due to what is it like to be the caudate nucleus carrying picture-grade signals from the parietal cortex to the globus pallidus. It also includes a few highly unusual fibers from the motor

space depends on how the motor output circuit uses the input scene to set up motor commands for the body to manipulate the object. The subject can anticipate the effects of, say, reaching out and pushing the tulip around in its vase because covert behavior set up by the motor output circuit calls up images of what would happen in the input scene (mainly by way of fibers from the frontal cortex to the anterior cingulate gyrus and its projection to the posterior cingulate, which is connected to the posterior cortex). The subject *sees* the tulip as an object in space because that is what it is like to be both circuits of the faculty of imagination as their interaction enables the subject to *think* of the tulip as an object in space that can be manipulated or tracked as it moves. (The ability to distinguish the parts of the input scene representing the hands and body controlled by the motor output circuit from the parts of the input scene representing the objects acted can be attributed to the claustrum, in the insula, a large region of neocortex located deep beneath the surface of the cerebrum, since fibers connect parts of it with all parts of the neocortex in both the sensory input and motor output circuits.)

Language-using mammalian brains can describe what they perceive, and since a complex phenomenal property is immediately present, they naturally assume that they are describing qualia objects in phenomenal space. Critical realists about perception know that they are describing representations constructed in the input scene of the sensory input circuit. But putting this mistake aside, naïve realists are not mistaken about what they are describing because qualia objects are identical to parts of the intrinsic property that magnetic field matter has as part of the geometrical action of the brain. For example, when we refer to the qualia tulip that we perceive in our desk, we are referring to a part of the input scene that represents the tulip in our sensory input circuit because that part is responsible for the relevant part of the spatiotemporal structure of the magnetic field matter whose intrinsic phenomenal property *is* the qualia. Indeed, when we use the red qualia to which we are pointing to define what we mean by *red*, we are defining the

---

output circuit that would explain how stereopsis can guide the hand in touching objects. And gestalt shifts, such as the Necker cube, can be explained as switches between different possible projections from the input scene in the parietal cortex to the caudate nucleus. (Keep in mind that the parietal cortex is part of the sensory input circuit, which has many projections carrying signals downward to the LGN and other regions where sensory input is registered.)

kind not only by its phenomenal appearance but also by the kind of part of the input scene that represents red objects. Both are the part of the geometrical action by which the brain distinguishes colors and generates the verbal behavior that names their kinds. Furthermore, when language-using mammalian brains describe relations among qualia objects in phenomenal space, they assume that they are describing structural aspects of the perceptual phenomenal appearance, and that is also correct because, according to the ontological explanation of consciousness, the phenomenal appearance of space is identical to an intrinsic property of the magnetic field matter helping generate the verbal behavior. They are describing both the spatial relations among qualia in phenomenal space and the spatial relations among the parts of the mammalian brain that are responsible for those parts of the phenomenal appearance.[16]

Imagination and memory also have a phenomenal appearance, and it also depends on the operation of the faculty of imagination. When the subject imagines reaching out to the tulip, for example, covert behavior calls up a representation of the hand moving toward the tulip, and besides anticipating consequences that would hold for any object, it may also call up, for example, memory images of clumsily knocking a vase over. In any case, firings of the neurons in the input scene are called up from memory, and since they do not depend on the rapid firing of neurons that registers sensory input in the sensory input circuit, brain activity has a less pronounced effect on the spatiotemporal structure of acceleration fuel flow. Hence, such phenomenal appearances involve fainter and less distinct qualia, and their locations in 3-D space may appear less consistent.[17]

The structure of the faculty of imagination also explains the phenomenal

---

[16] Since there is a correspondence between the relations of qualia objects in phenomenal space and the relations of the parts of the mammalian brain responsible for the qualia objects, they must have an orientation relative to one another in substantial space. The subject for which the input scene is the subjective appearance is presumably the motor output circuit to which it projects, and since phenomenal space is what it is like to be the mammalian brain, the forward direction in phenomenal space, where the qualia objects seem to be located, will probably turn out to be pointing toward the posterior of the cerebrum, just opposite to what we naturally assume.

[17] In dreams and hallucinations, centrally generated picture-grade signals cause more vivid structures of visual qualia. There are interactions between the occipital cortex and the lateral geniculate nucleus of the thalamus whose waking function is to provide feedback that refines visual input to the thalamus. But in dreaming, higher-level processing caused by even random stimulations can have effects on the lateral geniculate body that are vivid like sensory qualia.

property that we have when we reflect on our perception of the tulip. As we have seen, we reflect by using psychological sentences to represent our own psychological states. Their meanings are constructed in psychological imagination, not just naturalistic imagination. Thus, what is immediately present includes not only the psychological state but also the verbal behavior involved in saying (or preparing to say) something like, *I see a red tulip on the desk* (accompanied by a vague feeling that it is true, which is caused as the BGS somehow detects that the meaning of the naturalistic sentence embedded in the psychological sentence is already contained in the input scene constructed from sensory input, as indicated by the verb of propositional attitude).[18] Work done by the motor output circuit does not itself cause qualia that appear to be located in space. But verbal behavior (or the geometrical action setting it up) can be part of what it is like to reflect on the perceptual phenomenal appearance because verbal behavior, like all covert behavior, calls up images of its consequences in the sensory input circuit. These consequences include not only the somatosensory input that would be involved in generating the verbal behavior overtly but also (by way of mirror neurons) the sensory input by which the same kind of verbal behavior would be recognized in others. And since our neural BGS can somehow detect whether the meaning of the embedded sentence is imposed on the input scene by our choice or is imposed by remembering a particular event, the faculty of psychological imagination can also explain what it is like to reflect on *imagining* pushing the tulip to the opposite side of the vase and what it is like to reflect on *remembering* knocking a vase over in the past.

This is a rough sketch of what is involved in reflection on our own psychological states, and since brains are very complex organs, there are many varieties of each kind of psychological state. Daydreaming is not the same kind of imaging as trying to solve a problem. But let me mention how the use of language explains abstract objects since it will be relevant.

Naturalistic sentences are kinds of verbal behavior generated in the verbal

---

[18] Verbal behavior may be able to refer to the tulip as part of the input scene because fibers from the frontal eye field to the inferior parietal area mark fixations of the eyes on objects in input scene and because, in the primate brain, there is a new and highly unusual projection from area 9 of the prefrontal cortex, just anterior to the frontal eye fields, to the caudate nucleus, which otherwise contains only signals from the sensory input circuit, including the input scene.

hemisphere, and when Broca's area combines words grammatically, it causes their meanings to be constructed in the faculty of imagination based in the nonverbal hemisphere. (Wernicke's area mediates this effect since it associates words in the posterior verbal hemisphere with representations in the posterior nonverbal hemisphere that correspond to objects and kinds of objects in the natural world.) Objects can be classified in many ways, including properties, such as colors, which correspond to kinds of qualia. But the properties can be much more general, including geometrical structures, such as spheres and triangles, and physical properties, such as mass and motion. We can understand the meanings of such general words because they are associated with representations in nonverbal imagination that correspond to a much wider range of objects than non-linguistic animals need, and we use their meanings to identify the perceived object to which they correspond. And since meanings of words determine neuron firings in the input scene, abstract objects have a phenomenal appearance. This explains what reflective subjects mean by *abstract objects*, and so there is nothing puzzling about how they exist in the spatio-material world. Nor about how they correspond to objects in space.

Subjects with the use of psychological sentences can also reflect on their reflection, and the phenomenal appearances that occur in reflection can also be explained as what it is like to be the faculty of psychological imagination. We use *I* to refer to the subject that has the psychological state, and when we use psychological sentences to describe our use of psychological sentences to describe our own psychological states, what we are referring to is the *self*, that is, the reflective subject that can tell a story about its identity over time. The self is the neural BGS generating this verbal behavior, which is responsible for choosing goals that are good and pursuing them. Since the motor output circuit does not cause vivid qualia like the sensory input circuit, the meaningful verbal behavior involved in telling the story is the structure of the phenomenal appearances that are caused by our neural BGS as we think about who we are.

To be sure, when beings like us reflect on our own psychological states, what is immediately present often includes feelings and emotions, such as hunger, anger, and pleasure. They occur when certain desires are aroused or are being satisfied. These feelings are effects of the choosing circuit on the motor output circuit that trigger dispositions to set up behavior of relevant kinds. The qualia they involve can all be attributed to the sensory input circuit, since they are either faint images called up in imagination by the kind of covert behavior that desires motivate or they are bodily qualia caused by the body preparing to behave overtly, such as the tenseness and alertness that occurs when we are afraid or angry.[19] In a similar way, bodily qualia caused when a neural BGS is functioning well can explain other subtle feelings, such as the confidence we feel when we are not confused and understand what is going on and the *Ah Ha!* experience that accompanies the dawning of a new insight.

There are also abstract objects that depend on psychological imagination. The use of psychological sentences to impose their meanings on the entire neural BGS explains our capacity to understand general words denoting subjects, such as *person* and *woman*, and kinds of subjects, from personality traits, such agreeable and conscientious, to character traits and moral virtues, such as trustworthiness and civility—not to mention roles in institutions and other parts of the spiritual world. The phenomenal appearances of abstract objects that depend on the concept of the subject are what it is like to be a neural BGS with psychological imagination.

This illustrates how complex phenomenal properties can be explained as intrinsic phenomenal properties of the magnetic field matter that helps constitute the geometrical action of language-using mammalian brains. But this explanation of neural geometrical action is only the first step in a research project that ontologists expect to show in detail how every aspect of the phenomenal character of experience can be traced to flows of acceleration fuel constrained by the basic structure of the mammalian brain, the additional geometrical efficient causes built into it by more powerful faculties of imagination, and the structures formed from experience during development. There are waves of magnetic field matter sweeping through each point from every direction at the speed of light that register the activity of the neural BGS everywhere at that point, and further study will reveal which combinations of synchronized magnetic field matter waves are responsible for vivid sensory qualia and how they jointly constitute the phenomenal space in which they are

---

[19] That is why these qualia are called *somatic markers* by Antonio Damasio (1994, 2010).

located. But since reflective subjects are just one kind of animal, it makes sense to ask what it implies about other objects in the natural world.

4   Extent of Consciousness

Since ontology discovers that magnetic field matter has a proto-phenomenal intrinsic property, it is a form of *panpsychism*, the theory that every substance of some kind helping constitute the natural world shares in the nature of consciousness. Consciousness is the phenomenal character of our experience, and since the phenomenal properties that are immediately present to us are complex, consciousness has a unity that is radically different from the unity of the natural world. In perception, as we have seen, many qualia of various kinds seem to have locations in phenomenal space in and around our bodies. Such structures are explained ontologically by the spatiotemporal structure of the magnetic field matter that helps constitute the geometrical action of our language-using mammalian brains, that is, by the flows of acceleration fuel by which such neural BGSs do thermodynamic work. This shows what to look for as evidence of consciousness in other kinds of organisms, non-living composite bodies, and even bits of magnetic field matter by which charged particles fuel one another's acceleration. Starting with the complex phenomenal properties in reflective mammalian brains, there must be a decrease in the complexity of phenomenal properties as we consider the less complex geometrical action in simpler nervous systems, and here is what the proposed research project into consciousness is likely to find.

For reflective subjects, perceptual phenomenal appearances are configurations of sensory qualia in phenomenal space, and since they depend on the geometrical action of a neural BGS with a faculty of imagination, consciousness does not extend very far down levels of neural organization. Since all mammals have a faculty of imagination, they are subjects for which the natural world has such a phenomenal appearance. All mammals must assume that the perceptual phenomenal appearance *is* the natural world since that is what it is like to be a subjective neural BGS. Hence, they are direct realists about perception, though, without the use of language, they can't know that they are. They are trapped inside consciousness.

The detail of the perceptual phenomenal appearance presumably depends on the complexity of the mammalian brain, and other kinds of mammals may have different kinds of qualia. But we can expect to discover empirically what it is like for them as more is learned about how neuron firings in the mammalian brain give magnetic field matter a spatiotemporal structure. We could imagine what it is like, for example, if it turned out that other mammals had color qualia with fewer kinds or if the spectrum of their color qualia were spectrally shifted or inverted.

Kinds of qualia are not the only challenge in understanding what it is like to be mammals of other kinds. Why qualia of various kinds all appear to be located in a 3-D phenomenal space will be understood more completely when neural science explains how the input scene is constructed (by the sensory input circuit) and how it is used (by the motor output circuit) to guide behavior. I have used the ontological explanation of the faculties of physical and geometrical imagination to show how the spatiotemporal structure of the magnetic field matter waves that they generate give phenomenal properties their structures. When any mammal perceives an object, it conceives of it as located in space because it can anticipate consequences of locomotion relative to it and the motion of other objects. And when great apes perceive an object in space, they must also think of it as an object with a shape because they can anticipate how manipulative behavior will change the shapes against the background of locomotor space or change the shapes. Since elephants are mammals that act in similar ways on the structures of objects in space, they must have a geometrical faculty of imagination of some kind.

What we already know about complex phenomenal properties enables us to imagine what it is like to be a bat or other species with echolocation, such as dolphins, whales, and other cetaceans. Since echolocation is a modality of sensory input that the motor output circuit uses along with input from other senses to direct behavior relative to objects in space, sensory qualia that depend on receiving echoes of sounds generated in certain directions must have locations in the same phenomenal space as other sensory qualia. In effect, it is the use of sound signals to touch objects at a distance in a range of directions, and though we cannot define the kinds of qualia involved by pointing to them, as we do our own qualia, further research into echolocation could determine the range of differences among qualia, how many kinds there are, and whether they can discriminate among shapes. A more direct way of learning what it is like to be a bat would be to alter genetic instructions for constructing neural BGSs so that beings like us have echolocation.

When telesensory animals perceive objects, however, qualia objects cannot be located in phenomenal space because they lack imagination. At their level of neural organization, bundles of neurons carry picture-grade signals from sensory organs to the center of their nervous system and somatotopic motor output to the body. But since the bundles are not lined up alongside one another, connecting several junctions in three different circuits through the thalamus with the cortex in the centralized nervous system, their firings cannot be synchronized in a way that makes qualia appear to be located in phenomenal space. In the telesensory BGS, the most intense neuron firings occur in bundles in and around the optic tectum of the midbrain, where sensory input is used in a robot-like way to direct behavior relative to objects in space. Since it does thermodynamic work that gives magnetic field matter a spatiotemporal structure, telesensory animals probably have complex phenomenal properties of some kind. But without a motor output circuit in which covert behavior can call up images of consequences in an input scene provided by a sensory input circuit, they lack the concept of an object in space, and they can't think about their own bodies as one object among others in space. The firings of olfactory neurons or other forebrain neurons choose goals that are good, and this thermodynamic work may constitute phenomenal properties that resemble odors. But the objects detected cannot seem desirable or dangerous since telesensory animals have no concept of an object to which desires may be attached. And since their motor output does not involve a representation of their own body in the input scene of a sensory input circuit, they cannot feel emotions like subjective animals. Indeed, since the use of sensory input to choose goals is work done by the forebrain, while the use of sensory input to direct behavior relative to objects in space is work done in the midbrain, magnetic field matter waves generated by the firing of neurons are so unconnected that telesensory animals probably have no phenomenal property that includes both.

Corvids, such as crows and jays, may be somewhere between mammals and other telesensory animals. They have instinctive manipulative behavior, and if their covert behavior calls up representations of what happens in their representation of sensory input (the *Wulst*), they may have a kind of manipulative imagination. Magnetic field matter helping constitute the geometrical action of their brains may have an intrinsic spatiotemporal property that is identical to a phenomenal intrinsic property in which qualia appear to be located in an object outside the body. Octopuses also have manipulative behavior, and with large, centralized brains, they may have a kind of manipulative imagination. But most of the neurons generating manipulative behavior are distributed along their tentacles, and thus, if they do have a perceptual phenomenal appearance, it probably does not depend on intrinsic properties of magnetic field matter waves caused by their firings.

What it is like to be a somatosensory animal does not involve having phenomenal properties at all. It may be like something to be a single neuron firing, but it is probably nothing like the sensory qualia that beings like us have, at least, in somatosensory animals where no bundles of neurons carry picture-grade signals from one location to another. And since brainless chordates, such as lancelets, have little more than a spinal cord, there are probably no more conscious than other somatosensory animals.

Plants and simple living organisms are not conscious since they lack the energy-consuming neurons that generate magnetic field matter waves. To be sure, waves of magnetic field matter are generated wherever charged particles are accelerated, and they must have proto-phenomenal intrinsic properties of some kind. But magnetic field matter waves without a spatiotemporal structure like those generated by the mammalian brain are merely a previously unsuspected aspect of their intrinsic properties.

Consciousness is a trait of animals on the third floor of the edifice of life. It is lacking in organisms at lower levels of biological organization. But since each new form of life evolves from a previous form, organisms on the fourth floor must be conscious. But the behavior of spiritual organisms is guided by a geometrical cause that depends on their members using language and having a spiritual desire to pursue goals that are determined by its culture, and since their only body is all the animal bodies of their members, they cannot be consciousness as a whole.[20] The spiritual level of biological organization is conscious only by virtue of the consciousness of its animal members, and so the spiritual level is evident in consciousness only because the neural geometrical action helping constitute the members is part of the linguistic geometrical action by which the spiritual BGS guides behavior to goals that are good spiritual organisms. Their consciousness includes the effects of the levels of neuro-linguistic organization of the imagination required for members to use naturalistic sentences and psychological sentences. But linguistic geometrical action is necessarily consciousness since it depends on neural geometrical action by language-using mammalian brains, and so members of spiritual organisms participate in a spiritual life that may be immortal and is always embodied in consciousness reflective subjects.

Since computers are just linguistic robots, they are not conscious. Computers can be very complex, and they can generate the behavior of bodily robots. But this explanation of what it is like to be a composite body shows that they lack consciousness. They can be programmed to generate sentences, including sentences that represent their internal states, and such sentences might be programmed to help determine their output as a simulation of reflection. But it will be radically different from our way of using psychological sentences to reflect on our psychological states because it will lack a faculty of naturalistic imagination. And even when computers can guide a robot's behavior in a world of objects in space as well as a mammalian brain, it will be just a simulation of the cognitive powers of a mammalian faculty of imagination, and so they will not be conscious like us. To be sure, magnetic field matter helps constitute the motion and interaction of electrons in silicon chips, and magnetic field matter waves are generated when electric currents are started and stopped. But the gating of electron flows in silicon chips involves much less energy than neuron firings in the mammalian brain, and their geometrical action is at the micro-level relative to neurons and spread out on a silicon chip. Even if robots did use enough acceleration fuel to generate magnetic field matter waves as energetic as those of reflective neural BGSs, interactions of charged particles in digital machinery cannot be aligned

---

[20] This is the premise of Searle's (1980) *Chinese room* argument against the functionalist explanation of the understanding of conscious reflective subjects.

with one another in a way that gives magnetic field matter the kind of spatiotemporal structure that accounts for the complex phenomenal properties whose unity makes consciousness puzzling.

This lack of consciousness in robots settles some popular disputes about computer-based intelligence. For example, there are digital tycoons who hope to become immortal by transferring the information embodied in their brains to supercomputers. But they will be disappointed, albeit without feeling it. Such digital computers are just linguistic robots, that is, machines that process linguistic representations that we take to be meaningful. And hyperbolic apprehension about advances in artificial intelligence making robots a danger to beings like us is unfounded. If robots have a faculty of naturalistic imagination and can use psychological sentences to reflect on their internal states, they will have the analog of a spiritual desire, and a motive to be moral can be built into them. But since they will not be conscious, they will not be members of spiritual organisms like us, and so they will not have the moral rights that reflective subjects have in psychological-level spiritual organisms.

By the same token, when it becomes possible to use neurons and other wetware to construct reflective BGSs like ours in the laboratory, they will be conscious. Though they will not be forms of life that evolve by the reproductive mechanism, they could be full members of spiritual organisms with rights protected by moral rules.

All mammals are conscious, but the use of language, by itself, does not enable us to refer to consciousness as something different from the complex spatiotemporal structure of the magnetic field matter helping constitute the geometrical action guiding our behavior. It is possible, but it is a special way of using language that depends on an illusion inherent in consciousness. *Chapter 3* shows how metaphysics is a way of referring to complex phenomenal properties makes it appear that consciousness is a *mind*. Since that entity has a nature opposite to the nature of the body and other composite bodies, it leads to an ontological problem called *mind-body dualism* that metaphysicians cannot solve. But it is solved when ontological science traces its own origin to the volume of culture by Rational selection in Western civilization.

But the problem of mind is a live issue in contemporary philosophy of mind, and more recently, neural scientists have recognized that they cannot explain how the brain works without solving it. Its solution is the ontological mind-brain identity theory entailed by the explanation that traces the origin of ontological science to the exchange of metaphysical arguments in Western civilization. But since its solution involves technical philosophical issues that are not essential to this explanation of how ontological science becomes naturalistic Reason, they are discussed in *Chapter 2*, the next chapter. It is meant for those who are familiar with this more technical discussion of consciousness. Readers who want a more direct path from the ontological explanation of consciousness to naturalistic metaphysics can skip from here to *Chapter 3: Metaphysics* and see how the illusion inherent in consciousness makes metaphysics possible.

CHAPTER 2:
ONTOLOGICAL MIND-BRAIN IDENTITY THEORY ✤

The ontological explanation of consciousness is itself something that needs to be explained because ontological science evolves from physical science, and physicalists cannot explain it. Physicalists call it the *hard problem of mind* because they distinguish two problems: one easy and the other hard.[21] The easy problem of mind is explaining how the brain works, that is, how it uses sensory input to generate bodily behavior. That explanation is not yet complete. But neural scientists are hard at it, and physicalists expect physical causes to explain it. The *hard problem of mind* is explaining consciousness. Consciousness is the phenomenal character of experience, including everything from simple phenomenal properties, such as sensory qualia, to the complex phenomenal properties of which they are parts that mammals have in both perception and reflection. This problem is hard for physicalists because phenomenal properties are not even mentioned by the laws of physics. Basic laws of quantum physics describe the motion and interaction of particles, and the properties predicated of them are *physical*. Since the physicalist ontology postulates nothing but particles, the *hard problem of mind* is explaining how phenomenal properties are part of such a world. Since sensory qualia pose the hard problem in its simplest form, and qualia have been the main focus of philosophers of mind who are worried about how phenomenal properties are part of the physical world. But there is a *harder problem of mind* because qualia are just parts of complex phenomenal properties. Even if physicalists could explain qualia, they would still have to explain why many qualia of various kinds are all immediately present at once. This is one form of what is called the *binding problem*, and by putting it aside until after explaining simple phenomenal properties, it will be easier to explain what makes the hard problem of mind so hard for physicalists.

In the end, ontological science solves the problem of mind by showing that the mind is identical to the brain. It is called the *ontological mind-brain identity theory*, and its foundation is the *ontological explanation of consciousness*, which holds that consciousness is the intrinsic nature of neural geometrical action helping constitute mammals. Ontological science discovers that the mind is identical to the brain when it traces its own existence to philosophy and shows that Western civilization is the beginning of the metaphysical stage of spiritual evolution. To see the difference in the foundations that physical and ontological science provide for solving the problem of

---

[21] This is largely the consequence of work done by David Chalmers (1996).

mind, let us contrast their versions of the so-called *identity theory.*[22]

1   Physicalist Mind-Brain Identity Theory ⚹

Since naturalists believe that the natural world is what really exists, an identity theory is the obvious way for them to solve the problem of mind, and it began the physicalist discussion of the problem of mind in the 20th century. The body is part of the natural world, and since the brain is the organ that uses sensory input to guide its behavior, the mind would fit neatly into the natural world if it were identical to the brain. Assuming that a constant conjunction between reports of phenomenal properties and brain states has been confirmed, it claims to solve the problem of mind by holding that they are referring to the same thing. But the bare assertion of their identity is not a solution to the problem of mind. For science to solve it, the identity of mind and body must be a discovery of science.[23] The inability to show how the physicalist identity theory could be an empirical discovery of science is the reason that it was almost universally rejected around the middle of the 20th century.

The example used to defend the physicalist identity theory was the identity of feelings of pain and the firing of C-fibers in the brain. Neural science would discover this identity as the best explanation of the regularity with which feelings of pain are accompanied by certain events in the subject's brain. That is, it would be a *theoretical identification*, like the discovery that lightning is identical to electricity and that water is identical to H_2O. Such an explanation would be acceptable to physicalists because it would not amend the physicalist ontology. Only particles would exist, and explanations by physical causes would be complete. Hence, the physicalist identity theory would be just another discovery about the physical world, not unlike the discovery of the mass of a basic physical particle or a new kind of force that particles exert.

The identity theory fell out of favor after Saul Kripke's (1980) objection to it.[24] It

---

[22] I use *identity theory* to refer to the belief that the mind is identical to the brain. Since that would explain the existence of complex phenomenal properties, it would solve the so-called *hard problem of mind.* But in the philosophy of mind, that term is still commonly used to refer only to the explanation of psychological states by brain states, or the easy problem of mind, and that problem is solved in *Volume II* as part of the reduction of specialized sciences to ontology. The ontologically necessary structure of the mammalian brain is entailed by the explanation of how animals evolve at the subjective minor stage of evolution on the third floor of the edifice of life. Mammals with the use of psychological sentences can describe their psychological states, and since they are described as causes of behavior in the process of guiding behavior, they are necessarily causally relevant brain states.

[23] For some of the first proponents, see Place (1956), Feigl (1958), and Smart (1959).

24 Kripke's (1980) objection was based on an analysis of a posteriori identity claims in which they were required to be metaphysically necessary in the sense of holding on every possible world like ours. Thus, if pain is identical to C-fibers firing, there must be no possible world in which feelings of pain occur without C-fibers firing and no possible world in C-fibers fire without any feeling of pain. That holds for the identity of water and H2O. If water is H2O in our world, it must be identical to H2O in every possible world like ours, because if we were to find stuff on some distant planet, called twin Earth, with all the observable properties of water on Earth, and it turned out to be made up of XYZ, we would not classify it as water. It would be the discovery of something that appeared to be water, but wasn't. A

depends on an analysis of *metaphysical necessity*, and it has been reformulated in various ways since then, depending on how the nature of the identities discovered in science are analyzed. For our purposes, there is a simpler way to convey the brunt of Kripke's objection to the identity theory. Ontological science assumes that the solution is ontological, and the bare claim that the mind is identical to the brain does not have the ontological necessity of identities discovered by science. Using classical examples, the relation between feelings of pain and firings of C-fibers does not have the ontological necessity of the theoretical identification of water and H_2O.

Water was discovered to be identical to H_2O because all the properties by which we ordinarily recognize water, such as fluidity at normal temperatures, transparency, dissolving salt, and the like, could be explained by its molecular structure or regularities about the motion and interaction of the H_2O molecules of which it is composed. There is no room for doubt about the necessity of the identity of water and H_2O because ontologists can show how there are two different ways of knowing about the same stuff. The ordinary way to recognize water is by its interactions with sensory organs of our bodies at the macro-level, while the molecular explanation is known by confirming a theory about the constitution of water on the micro-level. Since the identity of water and H_2O is part of a reductive explanation of everything in the natural world, there is no possible physical world in which it does not hold, and since we cannot conceive of the relation as not holding, it is necessary.

No such necessary relation holds between pain and C-fibers firing because we can conceive of reflective subjects feeling pain when no C-fibers are firing—or even when they have no brain at all. That possibility is understood by anyone who understands Descartes' argument about mind, and that is, after all, why the problem of consciousness is called the hard problem of *mind*. And physicalists can imagine C-fibers firing without any feelings of pain. That is how neural science explains pain. Indeed, neural scientists could explain how the firing of C-fibers causes reports of feeling pain in language-using animals that have no feelings at all. That is entailed by the completeness of physical causes. Moreover, even assuming that reports of pains are true, the evidence for the relation between such reports and the firing of C-fibers is a mere correlation, and that does not show how firings of C-fibers and feelings of pain are identical. To justify the claim that they are identical in a way that is analogous to the justification of the identity of H_2O and water, identity theorists would have to show that the way that reflective subjects know about the feelings of pain that they report and the way that neural scientists know about their C-fibers firing are two ways of knowing about the same events. That is not necessarily true, as the difference between mind and brain described by Descartes shows. And if it is contingently true, the identity of feelings of pain and C-fiber firings must be justified as an empirical discovery of science, and that depends on an explanation of how we have two ways of knowing about the same events as part of a reductive explanation of everything in the natural

---

similar argument based on the assumption that phenomenal properties supervene on physical properties is presented by Chalmers (1996, with a comparison to Kripke on pp. 146-152).

world, as in the case of water and H_2O.

Such an explanation of the identity of mind and brain is what ontological science discovers in the end. But it is not even a possible explanation in physical science, and as a first step in explaining why, let us recall how ontological science solves the problem of explaining why phenomenal properties are known in a different way from physical properties that is not possible for physicalism.

2 Panpsychism ♂

As we have seen, the ontological explanation of consciousness depends not only on recognizing that space interacts with matter but also on *panpsychism*. Species of matter are defined by the spatiotemporal structures of their ways of coinciding and interacting with space, and thus, assuming that all matter has a primitive phenomenal way of existing in itself, properties of matter can explain the complex phenomenal properties that are immediately present to mammals as what it is like to be a mammalian brain. As we have seen, there is such a species of matter helping constitute the geometrical action of the mammalian brain. Neural geometrical action is magnetic field matter, and it has a kind of spatiotemporal structure that can explain the structures of complex phenomenal properties. But to explain their phenomenal character, ontology must assume that matter has a phenomenal intrinsic property as part of its essential nature. That is, *being* a bit of matter must be like something, in the sense that a qualitative property of some kind is immediately present to it. When the way that matter coincides with space is simple, it would presumably be a primitive and simple phenomenal property, or *proto-phenomenal intrinsic property*. But when the coincidence of matter and space has a more complex spatiotemporal structure, complex phenomenal properties would be immediately present to it. That explains how complex phenomenal properties are part of a natural world constituted by space and matter. Being such matter explains the immediate presence of complex phenomenal properties, while their configurations of qualia are explained by the faculty of imagination that evolves in the mammalian brain at a minor stage of animal evolution. The contribution of panpsychism to the ontological mind-brain identity theory is represented in Figure 1 by the arrow from *Ontology* to *Philosophy*, while the contribution of the reduction of the mammalian brain to spatio-materialism is represented by the arrow from *Science* to *Philosophy*.

However, panpsychism does not enable physicalists to explain how consciousness is part of the natural world.[25] They assume that physical causes are responsible for every event in the natural world (except for what is covered by Heisenberg uncertainty), including all the events that occur in the constitution of atoms and bodies composed of them, and so they are committed to an ontology that posits nothing but the particles mentioned by the basic laws of quantum physics. If physical particles had a proto-phenomenal way of existing in themselves, it would be like

---

[25] For a defense of panpsychism by a physicalist, see Strawson (2006).

something to be a physical particle. But since basic physical particles are very simple, what it is like to be a physical particle must be simple. Thus, even if what it was like for a particle were the immediate presence of a vivid sensory quale or a feeling of pain, that would not explain how consciousness is part of the natural world because it would not explain why that simple quale is immediately present to a mammal, much less why many qualia of various kinds are all immediately present at once, as in perception.

The holistic power of matter is what enables consciousness to be explained ontologically. The discovery that space is a substance that interacts with matter enables ontology to explain the laws of quantum physics (and solve the puzzle about their probabilistic character). But what is more, it reveals that space has a power, based on its geometrical structure, by which it gives matter a holistic power. Its holistic power is expressed by *geometrical causes* and their effects. Those causes are composite bodies whose shapes do not change as they move and interact with particles and other composite bodies, and they are efficient causes because they constrain what happens. Since the constraint they impose is geometrical, they are called *geometrical* (efficient) causes. What they constrain are physical causes, that is, what happens as physical forces are exerted. And when they constrain the collective effects of particles moving freely, they do thermodynamic work, so their effects are called *geometrical action*. Thus, the holistic power of matter is expressed as geometrical action, where that is the effect of the unchanging geometrical structure of the mammalian brain on neuron firings throughout the brain as it guides behavior. If, as physicalists believe, the functioning brain were just the interaction of particles, particles would not have the coherent spatiotemporal structure that enables magnetic field matter helping constitute the geometrical action of the mammalian brain to explain consciousness. Its coherence depends on how matter interacts with space because of the quantum structure of the mechanical system, and physical particles with atomistic powers would not interact in that way, not even if space were a substance containing them. Since this expression of the holistic power of matter in a brain with a faculty of imagination is what explains the unity of consciousness, blindness to the holistic power of matter is the underlying problem that keeps physicalists from solving to the problem of mind.[26]

---

[26] Physical scientists may insist that they can embrace a form of panpsychism similar to ontological science. The basic entities to which laws of quantum physics correspond can be described as infinite quantum fields, rather than particles, and if they had phenomenal intrinsic properties, physicalists could explain the unity of consciousness as part of the natural world in a similar way. Each particle is a wavelike excitation in the quantum field for particles of its kind, and the superposition of different kinds of infinite quantum fields allows energy to flow between them. Since photons are all particles of the same kind, they are all excitations in a single infinite quantum field, and interactions of charged particles in the brain can be explained by flows of energy between the superposed quantum fields of photons and charged particles. Thus, the electromagnetic quantum field could have a phenomenal intrinsic nature like magnetic field matter, and physicalists could also use its spatiotemporal structure to explain complex phenomenal properties in the same way as ontologists. But as Schrödinger would point out, this explanation of quantum fields as infinite substances is not a plausible explanation of what he meant his equation to describe. His wavefunction was just the probability of finding a particle at each location. And even if it

3   Property Dualism ✤

The immediate presence of complex phenomenal properties is the harder problem of mind, and the inability of physicalists to defend a kind of panpsychism that explains the unity of consciousness forces them to posit complex phenomenal properties in addition to physical properties to solve it. That is, to explain how consciousness is part of the natural world, physicalists must accept *property dualism*.[27] Physical science can discover regularities about the relation between brain states and reports of reflective subjects about their complex phenomenal properties, and it can infer a law of nature that describes them, called a *psychophysical law*, as the best explanation of consciousness. This law is acceptable to physicalists, even though they assume that physical causes explain every event that can be explained, because it describes a one-way causal relation from brain states to phenomenal properties. Though complex phenomenal properties are effects of brain states, they have no effect on what happens in the natural world. Such properties are called *epiphenomenal*, and this simple kind of property dualism is called *epiphenomenalism*.

To describe the regularity about the relation between physical and phenomenal properties as a law of nature is to hold that it is basic, like the relation between force and acceleration in Newtonian physics, and like laws of physics, the psychophysical law is assumed to hold universally. But there is scant evidence of its holding universally. Indeed, since the behavior of reflective subjects is fully explained by physical causes, it is possible that there are reflective subjects in the physical world who behave in all the same ways as conscious reflective subjects, but who have no phenomenal properties. They are called *zombies*. The only reason not to doubt that other reflective subjects are zombies is the assumption that psychophysical laws are universal, and that is just an assumption, which science cannot confirm.

Indeed, the only evidence for this law is the correlation between reports of phenomenal properties and certain kinds of brain states that holds for each conscious individual separately. But that does not show that other reflective subjects who report having complex phenomenal properties actually have them. Physicalists who try to solve the mind-body problem assume that each of us knows of one instance in which it is true. But that does not provide evidence of the universality of the psychophysical law because it is available only to each reflective subject separately, and for all they know, everyone else may be a zombie. Indeed, if we think of physical science as just an abstract practice in which laws of nature are confirmed by regularities about change in the natural world that are known by what bodies can perceive, it is possible that

---

were plausible, physical science would still not explain the unity of consciousness in the same way. Ontological science can attribute the unity of the phenomenal aspect of the neural geometrical action of mammalian brain to the entanglement of particles because it explains their entanglement by the quantum structure of the mechanical part of the inertial system, whereas in modern physics, entanglement is just a puzzling quantum regularity that seems to contradict Einstein's special theory of relativity.

[27] See Chalmers (1996, esp. p. 125ff) for more about property dualism as the hard problem of mind for physicalists.

everyone is a zombie. The only evidence of consciousness would be what reflective subjects say about it.

The problem of zombies points to a deeper problem about mind. Physicalists who try to solve the mind-body problem assume that they can know that they are conscious, but they have no way to explain how they know that they are conscious. To hold that they know that they have phenomenal properties because they are immediately present is to assume that phenomenal properties do have effects on what happens in the brain, and that contradicts physicalism. To defend epiphenomenalism, therefore, physicalists must, first, explain how they know that they are conscious.

To be sure, physicalists who defend panpsychism can abandon the belief in a psychophysical law in favor of an identity theory of mind and holds, instead, that phenomenal properties are identical to brain (psychological) states with a phenomenal intrinsic property. That is, they can hold that the phenomenal properties that cause their reports about consciousness are identical to brain states by which neural scientists would explain their verbal behavior. But that does not quite solve the problem of mind. Even to assert the identity of mind and brain, they must refer to consciousness, and so they must explain how they know that they are referring to something different from brain states when they say that their phenomenal properties are identical to them. The causes of reports about phenomenal properties must be different in some way from reports about brain (psychological) states, or the identity theory is meaningless. This is the problem faced by physicalists who would defend the identity theory of mind that Kripke was getting at.

The problem of explaining how reflective subjects know that they are conscious is so hard for naturalists who assume that physics is the basic branch of science that they have little choice but to find ways of avoiding it. The simplest way to avoid it is to deny that there is any such thing as consciousness to explain. The denial of the existence of the phenomenal aspect of experience is called *eliminative materialism*.[28]

Naturalists who believe that they know that they have phenomenal properties are forced to amend physicalism. There are other puzzles confronting physicalism, and the problem of explaining how consciousness is part of the natural world can be hidden by equating it with one of them. Physicalists who permit the use of supervenient properties can explain consciousness as a property that *supervenes* on the brain. But that way of defending reductionism has lost favor with the recognition that what is missing from physical science is something more like *information*, and consciousness can also be

---

[28] *Eliminativism* takes various forms depending on how physical causes are supposed to explain the brain. Functionalists assume that functional states supervene on physical states of functional systems, and so by reducing psychological states to functional properties, they deny the existence of phenomenal properties. For example, see Dennett (1978, 1998, and 2017). But as physicalists who do not accept functionalism, P. M Churchland (1988) and P. S. Churchland (1994) would eliminate all references to qualia as well as ordinary psychological states in favor of materialism. Other defenders of eliminativism can be found in Chalmers (1996, p. 166).

conflated with it.[29] But the challenge of explaining how consciousness is part of the natural world is so daunting that some naturalists even change what counts as science to include emergentism, while others redefine its goal as finding ways of describing the world that we happen to find interesting.[30] Those who admit defeat defend science by insisting that it is not possible for science to explain how consciousness is part of the natural world.[31]

This explanation of what makes the problem of mind so hard for physical science has taken the ontological explanation of how consciousness is part of the natural world for granted, and since the best defense is offense, physicalists will be inclined to argue that the same problems confront ontological science.

4   Knowledge of Consciousness ✄

The problem of mind arises for physical science because it explains how phenomenal properties are part of the natural world by postulating a psychophysical law, and physicalists can defend their attempts to solve the problem of mind by arguing

---

[29] The currently popular *integrated information theory* takes the structural aspects of consciousness as basic and reduces complex phenomenal properties to them. Though it assumes that physical causes are responsible for everything that happens, it postulates information as part of the physical world, and as we have seen, what corresponds to *information* in the spatio-material world is linguistic geometrical action, that is, the part of the geometrical action of spiritual organisms that guides their behavior to goals that are good. Integrated information theory assumes that whenever information processing in the physical world is sufficiently complex and integrated, it has an intrinsic property that is identical to complex phenomenal properties. That is to hold that configurations of qualia in phenomenal space are immediately present to information processing machines, and in the spatio-material world, that would mean that spiritual organisms are conscious as a whole and that the linguistic geometrical action embodied in each member has an intrinsic phenomenal nature. For the defense of such a theory, see Tononi (2004). Its claim to being a scientific explanation is mathematical. It depends on analyzing the integration of information in a way that determines a quantity. That quantity is seen as a measure of consciousness, and since integrated information processing of any kind has such a measure, complex phenomenal properties do not necessarily exist only in brains. It exists in all forms of life, including spiritual organisms, and even computers using microprocessors. For an account of attempts to find neural correlates of the consciousness explained in this way, see Koch (2012, 2019).

[30] Emergentists reject reduction by explaining consciousness as something that simply emerges during evolution by natural selection because it serves some function. The traditional goal of science is to explain everything by the same causes, like the efficient causes discovered by physics, and that goal is rejected by emergentists because they hold that the regularities studied by specialized sciences can be explained by simply describing them. calling them laws of nature, and assuming that they are necessary and universal in the same way as basic laws of physics. Another way of making science trivially easy is to abandon the goal of science is by denying its objectivity. For example, instead of taking physics to be a description of the basic nature of what exists, it can be embraced as a just one useful way of describing the world among others. The *manifest world* of commonsense is also useful, since that is where our arguments start, and since specialized sciences, functional explanations, explanations that postulate information, references to consciousness, and the like are also useful ways of describing the world, this way of this way of determining what counts as science insists that they are all on a par with physics. See, for example, Searle (1992), Nagel (2012), Carrol (2016), or Humphrey (1992, 2011).

[31] For example, McGinn (2004). As a pluralist about basic categories, he denies that there is a reductionistic explanation of everything in the natural world that includes consciousness.

that ontologists can do no better.

Consider the problem of zombies. Physical scientists recognize the possibility that reflective subjects are zombies because they must hold that phenomenal properties have no effect of what happens in the natural world. But ontological scientists are in a similar position. They explain how phenomenal properties are part of the natural world by assuming that matter has a proto-phenomenal intrinsic property, and since it has no effect on what happens in the natural world, it is also possible for reflective subjects to exist in a spatio-material world without having any phenomenal properties. In both cases, what makes zombies possible is that every event already has an efficient cause.

In its usual form, this argument from the possibility of zombies does not work against ontological science. It is usually posed as a problem faced by reflective subjects who know that they are conscious: *they* have no way to know that *other* reflective subjects are not zombies. But this is a problem only when phenomenal properties are explained by a psychophysical law. They are just effects of brain states that have no effect on what happens in the brain as if God *tacked them on* after creating the physical world,[32] and there is no way to know whether the psychophysical law is universal. But if phenomenal properties are an intrinsic property of matter, reflective subjects who know they are consciousness do know that other reflective subjects are also conscious because reflective subjects are all constituted by substances of the same kinds. The proto-phenomenal intrinsic property of matter is not just a puzzling effect of what happens in the natural world. It is, rather, an intrinsic property that matter has independently of space, like its intrinsic quantitative property, and since it is part of the first cause of everything, it is ontologically impossible for some reflective subjects to be conscious and others not.

In its more general form, however, the possibility of zombies does pose a challenge to naturalistic Reason because it seems to imply that the reduction of physics to ontology is not an adequate foundation. In the physical world, zombies are possible because everything that happens can be explained by physical causes. Similarly, in the spatio-material world, zombies are possible because everything that happens can be explained by a combination of geometrical and physical causes. Thus, physicalists and ontologists must both hold that zombies would behave in the same way as reflective subjects do in natural world, and that is puzzling for both since their behavior includes reports of being conscious and all the verbal behavior by which reflective subjects describe their phenomenal properties. But it seems to be show-stopper for ontological science because it means that the exchange of metaphysical arguments would cause a third stage of spiritual evolution even in a spatio-material world where reflective subjects were not conscious.

Though this argument points to an important issue, it does not imply that there can be a zombie spatio-material world. It implies that, for all we know, there could be spatio-material worlds where *consciousness* has a different meaning. What reflective subjects

---

[32] This famous metaphor is from Saul Kripke (1980).

mean by consciousness is whatever is immediately present when they describe the difference between the unity of consciousness and the unity of the natural world, and it may well be possible for complex phenomenal property to be configurations of different kinds of qualia. For example, it seems that there could be a spectrum inversion of color qualia. But there are probably limits on the range of what is possible to be discovered by the research project, proposed earlier, into the relation between the spatiotemporal structures of the magnetic field matter helping constitute the neural geometrical action of the mammalian brain and configurations of qualia in phenomenal space. And what it is like to be magnetic field matter will depend in some way on the kind of intrinsic property that matter has, that is, on what it is like to be even the simplest bits of matter. But even if matter did not have the same phenomenal way of existing in itself as it does in our spatio-material world, matter would have some way of existing in itself because substances must have intrinsic properties to have the powers that they express by how they interact with one another. Thus, magnetic field matter helping constitute mammalian neural geometrical action would have an intrinsic property made up of parts that are configured in three dimensions in the same way as qualia in our spatio-material world, and reflective subjects would be able to describe the difference between the unity of that complex intrinsic properties and the unity of the natural world. Even if their visual sensory qualia were not vivid colors like ours, reflective subjects would be conscious in the sense required by this explanation of Western civilization as the metaphysical stage because it is what it is like to be geometrical action expressing the holistic power of matter in mammalian brains. What is immediately present would have the same spatial structure as complex phenomenal properties, and since its parts would all be immediately present at once, its unity would still be different from the unity of a world constituted by substances that exist outside one another in space. But since the parts might not be sensory qualia like ours, what they mean by *consciousness* would be different.

How different what they mean has yet to be determined. But keep in mind that this is speculation about possible spatio-material worlds, not speculation about possible reflective subjects in our natural world. Reflective subjects in our spatio-material world are all constituted by the same kinds of substances in the same way, and so we can know from what it is like for us what others mean by consciousness.

Though the ontological explanation of consciousness will enable scientists to answer the challenge posed by the possibility of zombies, there is still the challenge of explaining how reflective subjects know that they are conscious. What happens depends on efficient causes, and thus, in the spatio-material world, where geometrical and physical causes determine completely what happens, consciousness cannot cause anything that is not caused by them. But if consciousness has no effect on what happens in the spatio-material world, how can reflective subjects know that they are conscious? Indeed, how can consciousness cause a stage of evolution?

Chapter 1 showed how ontological scientists know that they are consciousness. They are reflective subjects who know that the natural world is constituted by space and matter, and naturalistic imagination enables them to describe the unity of the natural world as one in which material substances exist outside one another in space. At the same time, psychological imagination enables them to reflect on their psychological (brain) states, and as we have seen, they describe all the parts of representations of the natural world in their faculties of imagination as immediately present to them at once. Hence, when they perceive the natural world, they can contrast the unity of their complex phenomenal properties with the unity of the natural world (and with the unity of the brain representations that register sensory input and determine their structures). And since they know how their mammalian brains work, they can explain the difference between them by the difference between the complex phenomenal intrinsic property of the magnetic field matter helping constitute their mammalian brains and states of the faculty of naturalistic imagination that register sensory input. (This is the difference between *knowing and being* the psychological state, like the reflective subject who has the state, and merely *knowing* them, like the neural scientists, which explains why there are two ways of knowing about the same thing, as a theoretical identification in science requires.)

Since most reflective subjects will not learn how ontological causes explain all the regularities found in the study of nature until physics is reduced to ontology, there is still a problem about how they know that they are conscious. But that is also something that ontological science can explain. Since consciousness is what it is like to be a mammalian brain, mammals are trapped inside consciousness. Their faculty of imagination enables them to perceive their bodies as objects along with other objects in space, and since they are conscious, they naturally assume that the phenomenal properties that are immediately present are the natural world. In a similar way, they take their reflective phenomenal appearances to be their psychological states. Nor does that condition change when mammals acquire the use of language since verbal behavior, like all behavior, is inside consciousness. Thus, since everything that they believe exists seems to be a phenomenal property of one kind or another, there is a problem about how reflective subjects who are not ontological scientists know that they are conscious.

As we shall see, ontological scientists explain how reflective subjects know that they are conscious by showing how they discover that there is a world external to consciousness. Indeed, this is how ontological science solves the hard problem of mind, and it even explains why the problem of mind is so hard for physical scientists. Physicalists approach the problem of mind from the opposite direction because they take it for granted that they are in a world constituted by particles that exist outside one another in space, and since they assume that everyone already knows the nature of the natural world, the problem they face is explaining how reflective subjects know that they are conscious. And physicalists cannot solve the problem of mind because even to pose the problem, they must explain their knowledge of phenomenal properties by their immediate presence, and that contradicts physicalism because they must assume that their verbal behavior has a non-physical cause. However, since ontological scientists start by recognizing that mammals are inside consciousness, the problem of mind that they confront can be solved.

Though language-using mammals are, indeed, trapped inside consciousness, there is a special way of using language that enables them to talk their way out of it. Reflective subjects can know that they are conscious because there is an illusion that is inherent in consciousness, and when it is articulated in the right way, it leads to false beliefs that make a difference in what happens in the world. That is what caused the problem of mind-body dualism in Western civilization, and as explained in *Chapter 3,* that is historically how reflective subjects discovered that they are conscious.

This illusion is inherent in the unity of consciousness in mammals. Consciousness is the immediate presence of complex phenomenal properties, and when structures of complex phenomenal properties depend on how the mammalian brain uses a faculty of imagination to guide behavior, the configurations of sensory qualia in phenomenal space that occur in perception make it seem to mammals that they have a qualia body in a world of qualia objects. That is, since perceptual appearances are immediately present, they seem to *be* the natural world. Though reflective appearances are configurations of less distinct and fainter qualia, they likewise seem to *be* the psychological (brain) states on which subjects reflect. Thus, mammals implicitly assume that the immediate presence of complex phenomenal properties is how they know about their phenomenal properties and what they represent. This is false because, as the ontological explanation of consciousness implies, everything that mammals know and say about their phenomenal properties is caused by the brain as the geometrical cause guiding their behavior. However, all mammals naturally assume that phenomenal properties are known as objects of a faculty of intuition, and so this assumption is called the *illusion of intuitionism.* Falling for the intuitionist illusion is simply what it is like to be a mammalian brain—at least, as long as mammals are direct realists about perception.

Though consciousness cannot have any effect on the behavior of language-using mammals that it would not have on all other mammals, the illusion of intuitionism can give consciousness a necessary role in causing what happens in the natural world because there is a special way of using language that articulates the illusion. As *Chapter 3* shows, the intuitionist illusion enables metaphysics to enlist the help of consciousness in causing a stage of evolution. Intuitionistic arguments about how Reason knows Reality behind Appearance are a way of talking about knowledge that presupposes *intuitionism.* What metaphysicians mean by Appearance is consciousness (or part of it), and they treat it as an object known by a faculty of perceptual intuition because they assume that their knowledge of Appearance is an effect of its immediate presence. To them, therefore, it is plausible that they also have a parallel faculty of rational intuition that enables them to know Reality behind Appearance. The use of language in making metaphysical arguments is meaningful because, by assuming that the immediate presence of complex phenomenal properties is how they are known, they distinguish the phenomenal intrinsic properties of magnetic field matter from the psychological (brain) states helping guide behavior of which that matter is part. That way of referring to consciousness puts metaphysical arguments on a higher level of linguistic organization than the use of sentences that describe only psychological states, and so metaphysics is on a third level of linguistic organization. Since metaphysics is not only possible but also functional, it causes, according to the reproductive mechanism, a third minor stage of spiritual evolution. When metaphysical arguments are exchanged over centuries, culture evolves by Rational selection, and eventually, metaphysicians discover that direct realism about perception is false. That is how reflective subjects talk their way out of the trap of consciousness. Intuitionistic metaphysicians discover that there is a world outside consciousness, and since they can describe the difference between the unity of the natural world and the unity of consciousness, they know that being conscious is different from just being part of the natural world. They discover that they are conscious, and they realize that they have been conscious all along.[33]

This is how Descartes discovered what he called *mind*. In the spatio-material world, the belief in mind comes from references that separate phenomenal intrinsic properties of matter helping constitute neural (and linguistic) geometrical action from the psychological (brain) states that determine their spatiotemporal structures, and *Chapter 3* says more about how it is discovered as part of the metaphysical stage of spiritual evolution. But in this context, it is more relevant to notice how the difference between physical science and ontological science makes the hard problem of mind so impossibly hard for physicalists. As the biography of Reason suggests, ontological scientists will trace the origin of ontological science to the beginning of Western philosophy, and since physical science is part of its history, Reason can look back and explain why physicalists were unable to solve the hard problem of mind.

Reason became physical science by rebelling against its metaphysical family, accepting naturalism, and abandoning the assumption that perceptual knowledge about the natural world depends on a faculty of perceptual intuition. Though physical science becomes ontological science by reducing physics to spatio-materialism, ontological and physical science are both forms of naturalism committed to *scientific realism* about perception (and about theoretical entities discovered by science). Ontologists and physicalists both inherit the concept of mind from philosophy. But they have radically different assumptions on which to base their attempts to explain it. Ontologists use the assumption that matter has a phenomenal way of existing in itself to explain how consciousness is part of the natural world, and that explains why phenomenal properties are immediately present to mammals. Thus, ontologists are

---

[33] The discovery of consciousness does not occur in psychological-level spiritual organisms because it is not possible to give up direct realism about perception in favor representative realism without referring to consciousness as an object of intuition. Religious practices in psychological-level cultures focus on altered states of consciousness, such as those produced in whirling dervishes, by Zen meditation, and by psychedelic drugs, as a way of exploring our spiritual nature. But differences in states of consciousness do not show the difference between the unity of consciousness and the unity of the natural world.

conscious, and they can explain not only how they know they are conscious, but also, historically, how reflective subjects learn they are conscious. Physicalists are also conscious and since they are reflective subjects who have inherited the discoveries of Western civilization, they also know that they are conscious. But since they take the naturalism of physical science for granted, they start with the assumption that what exists are particles that exist outside one another in space, and when they are asked to explain how they know that they are conscious, they succumb to the illusion of intuitionism and accept the Cartesian belief about the nature of mind. They explain how they know that phenomenal properties exist on the assumption that reflective subjects know about them because they are immediately present, and without the ontological explanation of how consciousness is part of the natural world, they cannot reconcile their intuitionism about configurations of qualia with their assumption that every event in the natural world is determined by physical efficient causes. The problem of mind is not merely hard for physicalists. It is intractable.

5 Mind-Body Dualism ☙

In our spatio-material world, reflective subjects are conscious and know that they are conscious because they are members of a spiritual organism in which intuitionists have exchanged metaphysical arguments for centuries. As *Chapter 3* shows, metaphysicians eventually become representative realists, who discover that there is a world outside consciousness, and since they assume that they have a faculty of rational intuition that enables them to know the essential nature of Reality behind Appearance, they realize that the natural world has a nature just opposite to mind. Since they discover representative realism about perception by correcting the mistake of direct realism, they cannot deny that the mind depends on the body for its perception of the natural world and that the mind uses the body to act in the natural world. Thus, when intuitionistic metaphysicians discover that mind and body have opposite natures, they find themselves unable to explain how mind and body interact, and so they encounter the problem of mind-body dualism.

Mind-body dualism was a fatal problem for intuitionistic metaphysics, as *Part Two* shows. But the problem of mind-body dualism is only an episode in the biography of Reason. Its intuitionistic parents believed in mind before Reason rebelled against them, accepted naturalism, and used the empirical method of physics to learn more about the natural world. However, Reason would not have been successful as science if it had not kept a treasure from its intuitionistic heritage.

What made physics successful and inspired the study of nature was the belief that mathematics is known *a priori*, and since it came from intuitionistic metaphysics, physics was committed to what might be called *intuitionistic naturalism*. Mind was supposed to have a faculty of rational intuition in which mathematical arguments were self-evident, as if mathematical truth were known because of the immediate presence of certain kinds of complex phenomenal properties. Thus, when physicists used the empirical method to learn about the natural world, they took it for granted that mathematics is known independently of perception. As we have seen, the use of equations that depend on coordinate systems for their references to the natural world is a *mathoscope* that can focus on quantitative regularities about change generated by the interaction of space and matter, and physics was so successful using it to discover mathematically formulated laws of nature that others were inspired to use the empirical method to learn about regularities of all kinds in the natural world. When empirical ontologists infer spatio-materialism as the best explanation of the "unreasonable effectiveness" of mathematics in discovering laws of physics, those ontological causes will enable them to explain all the regularities found in the study of nature, and when they trace the origin of ontological science to a civilization with a culture at the metaphysical stage of evolution, they will understand how mathematical truths that seemed to be known independently of perception made physics so successful.

Empirical lawism assumes that mathematics is known *a priori*, and thus, from its birth, physics accepted at least part of the belief in mind. But instead of depending on the self-evidence of mathematics, empirical ontology relies on the faculty of naturalistic imagination built in the brains of reflective mammals, and that enables science to discover the role of space in helping matter generate the regularities described by laws of physics. This reveals that matter has a holistic power, and after reducing the specialized sciences to spatio-materialism, ontological science uses it to explain how consciousness is part of the natural world. Thus, it discovers how the illusion of intuitionism makes it possible for the exchange of metaphysical arguments to begin a third stage of spiritual evolution. As *Chapter 3* shows, when intuitionistic metaphysicians become representative realists about perception, they discover the difference between the unity of consciousness and the unity of the natural world, and so they find themselves believing in mind. But since their description of the nature of mind is a description of the illusion inherent in consciousness, their belief in mind is false. Consciousness is a *pseudo-efficient cause*, and thus, when metaphysicians treat it as a cause of knowledge, they create a *phantom Reality* behind Appearance. Since ontological scientists trace this phantom Reality to consciousness by way of a special way of using language, they discount the intuitionist illusion, and so they are able to identify what intuitionistic metaphysicians refer to as *mind* as something in the natural world. It is what reflective subjects believe exists when they fall for the illusion of intuitionism and assume that they know about their phenomenal properties because they are immediately present. That is, when Descartes discovered the mind, what he was referring to as a substance was the mammalian brain, and when he described the unity that makes the essential nature of mind just opposite to the essential nature of the external world, what he was referring to was the intrinsic phenomenal property of the magnetic field matter that helps constitute the geometrical action of that brain. That is how ontological science shows that mind is identical to the brain.

The obvious way for naturalists to explain the relation between mind and the body is by the identity of mind and brain. But at the beginning of the contemporary discussion of the problem of mind over a half-century ago, physicalists who tried to defend mind-brain identity theory were defeated by their inability to show how the identity of mind and brain could be a discovery of science. And now, we can see how ontological scientists are able to defend mind-brain identity as a theoretical identification of science.

Recalling the standard example, physicalists held that science could discover that feelings of pain are identical to the firing of C-fibers, and Kripke challenged them to defend their claim that it is a discovery of science like the relation between water and collections of H_2O. A theoretical identification is the theory that two things that seem to be different turn out to be identical, and since things that are identical are necessarily identical, science must be able to explain why they once seemed to be different, or else it could not be an empirical discovery. This was easy in the case of water and H_2O because their identity involves a part-whole relation. Physical science could explain why the stuff that we ordinarily describe as water appeared to be different from what physical chemists describe as collections of H_2O molecules because they are the same object in the natural world, but on the macro-level, it seems to be water, while on the micro-level, it seems to be H_2O. Science discovered that water is made up of many small parts moving and interacting with one another. Nor was there any doubt about their identity. The macro-level physical properties were all explained by the motion and interaction of H_2O in vast collections on the micro-level in a way that is intelligible in naturalistic imagination.

Physicalists could not defend their mind-brain identity theory in that way. Neural science describes C-fiber firings as physical properties, while reflective subjects describe feelings of pain as objects of intuition. Without any way to show that there is an illusion inherent in consciousness, physicalists could not discount the intuitionist illusion and show how the illusion causes metaphysicians to believe in the mind, and so they were stuck with the assumption that feelings of pain are known by the immediate presence of vivid pain qualia. That contradicted the physicalist assumption that physical causes explain every event (that can be explained), and thus, even though C-fiber firings and feelings of pain were correlated, the relation between them necessarily appeared contingent. Since physicalists could not show that the contingency of the relation between them is just an appearance, they could not answer Kripke's challenge. They lacked an explanation of how the same thing could be known in two different ways.

That is what ontological science provides when it uses its ontological explanation of consciousness to trace its own origin back to a belief in mind that necessarily evolves during the metaphysical stage of evolution. This solves the problem of mind-body dualism because when ontological scientists discount the illusion of intuitionism, they discover that the mind is identical to the brain of a mammal arguing about metaphysics. This is an empirical discovery because the mind-brain identity is entailed by an inference to the best explanation of the origin of ontological science as a product of the metaphysical stage of spiritual evolution.

Indeed, the ontological mind-brain identity theory is a theoretical identification in the same way as all the other identities established by the reduction of objects studied by specialized sciences to spatio-materialism. They are identities that involve part-whole relations, and they are like the identity of water and H_2O, except that the part-whole relations hold between geometrical causes that evolve at different stages as products of the reproductive mechanism. (See Figure 3.) Molecules are the parts of prokaryotes; prokaryote-like geometrical structures (and other molecules) are the parts of eukaryotes; eukaryotic cells are the parts of animals; and animals are the parts of spiritual organisms. (See *Volume II, Chapter 6*.) And in the neural BGSs that the animal BGS builds into animal bodies, the three essential subfunctions of a BGS are served by a series of seven levels of part-whole complexity in the organization of neurons. The first six neurological levels are single neurons, bundles of neurons, circuits of bundles of neurons, multiple circuits of bundles of neurons in circuits of bundles of neurons, interactions of verbal and nonverbal hemispheres of the brain containing them, and verbal behavior in the left hemisphere that represents entire states of the neural BGS. (See *Volume II, Chapter 7*.)

The seventh level of part-whole relations in the nervous system explains the identity of brain and mind. It does not seem to be a part-whole relation because mind is not a new geometrical structure that depends on genetic changes in the brain, like all the previous levels of geometrical organization in neural BGS. The metaphysical level of linguistic and neural organization is constituted by reflective subjects using metaphysical sentences to refer to phenomenal properties as something different from their psychological (brain) states. When metaphysicians fall for the intuitionist illusion, they mistakenly assume that phenomenal properties are objects known by a faculty of intuition, and since what they mean by ideas in the mind is something with a different nature from psychological (brain) states, they separate phenomenal properties from the psychological states of which they are parts. At the psychological level of linguistic organization, reflective subjects use psychological sentences to describe their psychological (brain) states as causes of their behavior as part of the process of guiding behavior. At the metaphysical level, reflective subjects use metaphysical sentences to refer to phenomenal properties as something different from psychological (brain) states, but since they describe these objects of intuition as representations of the natural world and their own psychological states, they assume that the self is a subject who uses objects of intuition to judge what is true and choose what is good. That is the belief in mind. Its parts include not only psychological (brain) states of all kinds but also all the intrinsic phenomenal properties that are parts of them, and as shown in *Chapter 3*, they work together as a faculty of metaphysical imagination that enables reflective subjects to understand metaphysical arguments. But since the distinction between phenomenal properties and psychological (brain) states depends on falling for the illusion of intuitionism, the belief in mind is false. Treating the pseudo-efficient cause as a real efficient cause creates a phantom Reality called mind. Thus, by exposing the illusion inherent in consciousness, ontological science shows that mind is just a phantom. That is how it discovers the ontological mind-brain identity theory. Minds are reflective subjects who believe that their knowledge of phenomenal properties is an effect of their immediate presence. That illusion turns the unity of consciousness into the unity of mind and, since it is just opposite to the unity of the natural world, it causes the ontological problem of mind-body dualism. Thus, ontological science solves the mind-body problem. And since the problem is solved by starting with mind and explaining the body, it explains why physicalists, who start with body and try to explain mind, are confronted by a problem that is not just hard, but downright unsolvable.

This conclusion about mind as part of an ontological explanation of the natural order that comes to exist in the course of evolution. What is known is often different from how it is discovered, and since the metaphysical stage depends on an illusion inherent in consciousness, it can be discovered only by ontological scientists who are conscious. To explain intuitionistic metaphysical arguments, ontological scientists must discount the illusion inherent in their own consciousness. Since they already know that the world is constituted by space and matter, they find themselves knowing Reality behind Appearance, and thus, they recognize that ontological science is Reason. But they know Reality by using the empirical method in the natural world, and since that is how Reason resolves its identity crisis, they insist on calling the perfect way of knowing they have *naturalistic* Reason.

Chapter 3:
Metaphysics

Ontological science explains consciousness as what it is like to be a mammalian brain. It is like something because magnetic field matter helping constitute the geometrical action of the mammalian brain has a phenomenal way of existing in itself. Intrinsic phenomenal properties of magnetic field matter that help constitute the geometrical action of the mammalian brain are identical to the complex phenomenal properties that are immediately present to the mammal, and since they are phenomenal intrinsic properties of matter, they play no role in causing behavior. This holds for all mammals, including mammals with the use of language. Though verbal behavior has a phenomenal appearance to the speaker, it is just part of consciousness, and since speaking is inside consciousness, this ontological explanation of consciousness makes it seem that reflective subjects cannot describe themselves as conscious. But there is a way of using language that can describe consciousness because there is an illusion inherent in the consciousness of mammals, and since being taken in by the illusion can lead to false beliefs, consciousness has an effect on what happens.

Indeed, it has a profoundly significant effect on what happens. This illusion is a necessary part of the cause of a stage of spiritual evolution that follows the psychological stage. It is called the *metaphysical stage* since the cause is the exchange of metaphysical arguments, and *Part Two* shows that this stage is represented on Earth by Western civilization. To show that it is, this chapter describes what is ontologically necessary about the metaphysical stage of evolution. It is a hypothesis suggested by the ontological explanation of consciousness, and its predictions about how the metaphysical stage of spiritual evolution unfolds are used to confirm that Western civilization is a spiritual organism at the beginning of the metaphysical stage of spiritual evolution.

There is an illusion inherent in consciousness. Its unity, combined with the way that qualia are configured in phenomenal space, makes it appear that the immediate presence of complex phenomenal properties is what causes our knowledge of them. It is an *illusion* because it is false. As we have seen, complex phenomenal properties are identical to intrinsic properties of magnetic field matter that help constitute psychological states in mammalian brains. Those psychological states have roles as representations in helping guide behavior that give qualia configurations that seem to represent the natural world and psychological states, and those configurations are immediately present. But what enables us to know about them and describe them is not their immediate presence. Consciousness itself makes no difference in how the mammalian brain generates behavior. The assumption that the immediate presence of complex phenomenal properties causes what we know and say about them is called the *illusion of intuitionism* because, when the illusion is articulated, it is expressed as the belief that they are objects of a faculty of intuition. It falsely attributes a causal role is attributed to them. But even after the evolution of language, being taken in by that illusion is what it is like to be a mammalian brain. Only when language is used to exchange metaphysical arguments does the assumption implicit in consciousness become explicit. Metaphysics is the third level of linguistic organization, and since it is both possible and functional, it causes as third stage of spiritual evolution. That is the beginning of a way of knowing about consciousness that, in effect, escapes from being trapped inside consciousness into the natural world. .

Consciousness is explained ontologically as what it is like to be a mammalian brain, and since all of experience has a phenomenal appearance, mammals are trapped inside consciousness. They assume that complex phenomenal properties are known by their immediate presence because that is what it is like to be a mammalian brain, and so they are taken in by the intuitionist illusion. When mammals acquire the use of naturalistic sentences, they can describe states of affairs in the natural world, and when they acquire the use of psychological sentences, they can describe their own psychological states as parts of the process by which those states help guide behavior. But consciousness still makes no difference in the behavior generated by the brain.

It is merely what it is like to be a mammal using language.

But consciousness can affect what happens in the natural world because there is a way that mammals with the use of language can *talk themselves out of being trapped inside consciousness*. It happens in a spiritual organism whose culture evolves by the exchange of metaphysical arguments. It makes reflective subjects aware of being conscious, enables them to describe consciousness, and leads to an understanding of how consciousness is part of the natural world when science is reduced to ontology.

1 The Metaphysical Stage of Spiritual Evolution

Reflective subjects are mammals with the use of psychological sentences, and they are trapped inside consciousness, like all mammals, because they do not know that they are conscious. But metaphysics is a way of arguing their way out. The escape is not easy because intuitionists must make more than one kind of metaphysical argument. They must explore the puzzling implications of one kind of metaphysical argument before coming up with the second, and then, its puzzling implications must be explored. This involves such a fundamental change in how reflective subjects understand themselves and their world that the escape takes many generations. The exchange of metaphysical arguments causes the culture of a civilization to evolve, and since each new kind depends on the last, these developments have a necessary order. That enables ontologists to distinguish the metaphysical stage from earlier stages of spiritual evolution.

The first kind of metaphysics is based on *direct realism* about perception. Though it does not enable metaphysicians to escape from the trap of consciousness, the second kind does. It is based on *representative realism*, and since metaphysicians learn that there is a world outside consciousness, they discover that they are conscious. But they are inside consciousness looking out, and only when science evolves and naturalism is taken for granted do they escape from consciousness. As scientific realists about perception, physical scientists try to explain consciousness from outside, but scientists cannot succeed until physics is reduced to ontology.[34] That is the foundation

---

[34] Though Hilary Putnam (1981) was right about brains in a vat being "scientific realists", who know a world outside the vat, he was taken in by the illusion of intuitionism, and as an intuitionistic naturalist,

for the *naturalistic metaphysics* defended in this volume.

What motivates reflective subjects to argue about metaphysics is acquiring the kind of knowledge that it promises. It is wisdom, the perfect knowledge from which philosophy acquires its name, *love of wisdom*. Wisdom is perfect knowledge of everything that matters to reflective subjects. Knowledge of Reality is complete because it is about the natures of the substances constituting everything. Substances explain what exists, and Since substances constitute everything that exists, substances explain everything that exists. Knowledge about the natures of the substances constituting the world is complete knowledge of Reality because it explains everything. Thus, if reflective subjects discover such an explanation, they know whether beliefs correspond to Reality, and that is to know the True, with a capital *T*. (Terms essential to metaphysics are capitalized to distinguish metaphysical arguments from psychological sentences.) Since Reality explains everything, it explains the nature of the good, that is, the property that identifies the goals that reflective subjects ought to pursue, and so the Good is part of the True. Indeed, assuming that the beautiful is how means to ends are good, the Beautiful is part of the Good. The knowledge of Reality that metaphysics promises is complete because the True, the Good, and the Beautiful include everything that matters to reflective subjects.

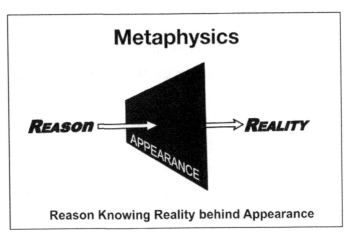

Reason Knowing Reality behind Appearance

Figure 2 – Structure of Metaphysical Arguments

---

he wrongly denied the possibility of "metaphysical realism." Brains in a vat using a science based on ontology would discount the intuitionist illusion, and as ontological naturalists, they would be "metaphysical realists," using Reason to know Reality behind Appearance.

Metaphysics is the belief that beings like us have a cognitive faculty that enables us to know Reality behind Appearance. (See Figure 2.) That cognitive power is called *Reason*, and so belief in Reason is what distinguishes civilizations in which metaphysical arguments are exchanged from civilizations evolving at the psychological stage. Ontological science recognizes philosophy by the distinctive kind of argument that it calls *metaphysics*. But metaphysics is only part of philosophy. Many philosophers doubt that Reason can know Reality behind Appearance, and so, *philosophers* refers to those who defend skepticism about metaphysics as well as those who defend it.

Metaphysics is a stage in the evolution of life that could not be explained as part of its reduction of science based on physics to spatio-materialism. As we have seen, a science based on ontology explains the existence of reflective subjects as the product of a series of inevitable stages of gradual evolution. But this volume of *Naturalistic Reason* predicts that ontological science will discover that there is also a metaphysical stage of evolution. According to the reproductive mechanism, what makes a new stage inevitable is a higher level of organization in evolving geometrical causes that is both possible and functional—*possible* in the sense that it can be tried out as a random variation on geometrical causes that are evolving during a stage of gradual evolution, and *functional* in the sense that it enables the gradual evolution of an entire order of functional powers that were previously out of reach. Evolution is progressive, and since the metaphysical stage is the final stage discovered by ontological science, let us recall the series of stages leading up to it.

There are two kinds of stages of evolution, major and minor. A major stage is a higher biological level, during which a two-part major stage of evolution brings a new kind of BGS into existence. The reproductive mechanism eventually constructs a four-story edifice of life. Minor stages are stages that occur during a major stage. They are caused by a higher level of organization in a BGS. Animals are a form of life that evolves on the third floor of the edifice of life, and since multicellular animals have a plan-sharing BGS that constructs an animal body, it must build an organ in the body to guide the animal's behavior in the natural world, called a *neural BGS*. A centralized neural BGS is called a *brain*, and a series of levels of neural organization causes a series of minor stages of animal evolution. (See Figure 3.)

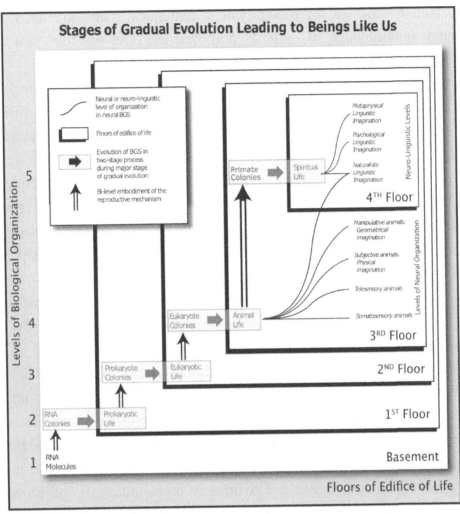

Figure 3 – Stages of Evolution

Spiritual organisms are the form of life that evolves on the level of biological organization higher than animals, and since they have a plan-sharing BGS based on the use of language, there are minor stages of spiritual evolution caused by levels of level of linguistic organization. Though the first two levels of linguistic organization depend on a higher level of neural organization, the third stage does not. The first minor stage of spiritual evolution is the naturalistic stage, which is characterized by the use of naturalistic sentences (with a simple substance-predicate grammar). The second minor stage is the psychological stage, characterized by the use of psychological sentences (which predicate psychological states, such as beliefs and desires, of subjects). The third minor stage is the metaphysical stage, characterized by the use of metaphysical sentences. They are used in the exchange of metaphysical arguments, and their use does not require a higher level of neural organization than psychological sentences.

Spiritual organisms at the naturalistic and psychological stages are defined by their levels of linguistic organization, and they can be identified by the genetically determined levels of neural organization in their members' brains. But there is no such indication of the metaphysical linguistic level in the brains of members of spiritual organisms evolving at the metaphysical stage. What distinguishes the third level from the psychological level of linguistic organization is the use of sentences to refer to consciousness as something different from psychological and naturalistic states. Metaphysical arguments are made using sentences that contain the terms *Reason*, *Appearance*, or *Reality*, and all three can be used to refer to consciousness (or parts of it) as a cause of knowledge. Since ontological science explains the nature of consciousness, it can identify the metaphysical stage of spiritual evolution by its culture's use of sentences that refer to consciousness.

A stage of spiritual evolution after the psychological stage is inevitable on planets where life evolves because the use of metaphysical sentences is both possible and functional. The metaphysical linguistic level is possible because there is an illusion inherent in consciousness that makes the use of metaphysical sentences plausible. The unity of consciousness, combined with the way that sensory qualia are configured in phenomenal space, makes it seem that their immediate presence is what causes knowledge of them.

The first kind of metaphysical argument is based on direct realism about perception, and since all three key terms refer to parts of consciousness as playing a causal role in knowledge, these metaphysicians are trapped inside consciousness. *Appearance* refers to perceptual phenomenal appearances. Assuming that they are objects of a faculty of intuition, certain reflective phenomenal appearances can be seen as the *Reality* behind Appearance that is known. Since they can be explained as objects of a faculty of intuition, metaphysicians can refer to *Reason* and explain it as a cognitive power that knows Reality behind Appearance.

The second kind of metaphysical argument is based on representative realism. Since those metaphysicians know that the natural world is outside consciousness, Reality is not inside consciousness, and only two essential terms refer to consciousness. *Appearance* refers to perceptual phenomenal appearances as objects of a faculty of perceptual intuition, and *Reason* refers to certain reflective phenomenal appearance as objects of a faculty of rational intuition.

The first two kinds of metaphysical arguments are intuitionistic because they depend on the false belief that we know about phenomenal appearances because of their immediate presence. But there is a third kind of metaphysical argument. Its foundation is ontological science, and since that is a kind of naturalism, it accepts scientific realism about perception. Naturalists believe that they have animal bodies with sensory organs that are located in a world along with other objects in space that exist independently of them, and they use the empirical method to know about the natural world. When science is reduced to ontology, ontological science explains its own existence as part of the metaphysical stage of evolution, and that is how it becomes Reason knowing Reality behind Appearance. When it discovers the substances constituting the natural world and uses those ontological causes to explain everything studied by science, it knows Reality. Only Appearance still refers to consciousness, and it refers to all of consciousness. Since ontological science explains consciousness as complex phenomenal properties that are identical to intrinsic properties of magnetic field matter helping constitute the geometrical action of mammalian brains, it is not misled by the illusion of intuitionism. Ontological scientists are conscious reflective subjects, and knowing that Appearance is not an object of intuition, they discount the intuitionist illusion. Hence, they find themselves knowing Reality behind Appearance. That is how ontological science becomes naturalistic Reason. Its explanation of the natural world is *naturalistic metaphysics*.

2 Possibility of Intuitionistic Metaphysics

Metaphysical arguments begin in the commonsense world, where reflective subjects argue about what to believe about the situation and which goals to choose in it. As we have seen, the commonsense world includes both the natural world in which reflective subjects have bodies alongside other objects in space and a spiritual world in which each is a self that interacts with other subjects who can see into one another's minds. Reflective subjects perceive the natural world because it is represented in their neural BGSs by the input scene constructed from sensory input by the sensory input circuit, and the spiritual world is thermodynamic work done by the spiritual BGS of which they are part. The commonsense world is where pre-Socratic philosophers discovered that the first cause is all the substances constituting the world. But as explained in the previous chapter, reflective subjects are conscious, and there is an illusion inherent in consciousness. They reflect on perception by using psychological sentences to describe the self as using the input scene to represent the natural world, and since the natural world has a phenomenal appearance, qualia in phenomenal space appear to *be* the natural world. Configurations of sensory qualia are immediately present, and when reflective subjects perceive the natural world, they naturally assume that their immediate presence is the efficient cause of (or reason for) their beliefs about the natural world, including the qualitative properties of objects and their relations to one another in space. That belief is what it is like for reflective subjects to perceive the natural world, and as we have seen, it is false. And since perceivers who have internalized a metaphysical-level culture distinguish Appearance from Reality, they articulate the false belief and describe phenomenal appearances as objects of intuition.

There are two illusions involved in perception. One illusion is *direct realism*, or the assumption that the perceptual phenomenal appearance *is* the natural world. This is the world that perceivers ordinarily believe they share. But when perceivers recognize that the perceptual phenomenal appearance is part of themselves, they give up direct realism in favor of *representative realism. Chapter 1* showed that direct realism is mistaken by contrasting the unity of the perceptual phenomenal appearance with the unity of the natural world. But its illusory nature can also be detected without making this distinction. For example, when one hand has been submerged in hot water and it is put into a bucket of lukewarm water, the water can feel cool, even though it feels lukewarm to the other hand, which is accustomed to it. Optical illusions, dreams, hallucinations, and some kinds of meditation also help dispel the first illusion involved in perception. There are many other kinds of evidence that the natural world that direct realists believe they share is just an appearance of the natural world in the subject. But there is a second illusion involved in perception, and it is more difficult to discount. It is the assumption that the subject knows about qualia in phenomenal space because of their immediate presence. It is so compelling that reflective subjects still believe it when they give up direct realism. Though they recognize that perceptual phenomenal appearances are part of the subject, they continue to assume that their immediate presence is what causes their knowledge about qualia in phenomenal space, and so they are *representative realists*. Their assumption is implicit in what it is like to reflect on psychological states. But it is mistaken, and since the assumption is that the object of knowledge causes beliefs about it, this more basic mistake is aptly called *intuitionism*. Direct realists and representative realists both believe that perception depends on a *faculty of perceptual intuition*, despite having different views about its nature.[35]

Intuitionism is implicit in what it is like to be a subjective neural BGS, and since it makes metaphysics plausible, it helps cause a third stage of spiritual evolution. This stage begins with the belief that perception depends on a faculty of intuition. But since intuitionism is incompatible with phenomenal appearances being identical to intrinsic properties of magnetic field matter helping constitute the geometrical action of the mammalian brain, it is false. In the spatio-material world, what enables reflective subjects to know about the natural world is their neural BGS, a geometrical efficient cause that uses sensory input to construct a representation of the natural world in the input scene of the sensory input circuit. The motor output circuit uses the subjective appearance to guide behavior relative to objects in space, and the phenomenal appearance of the natural world is just what it is like to be a brain that uses that faculty of imagination to guide behavior, including verbal behavior. As we have seen, flows of acceleration fuel in small volumes located throughout the subjective neural BGS have spatiotemporal structures that give

---

[35] Since the ancient atomists believed that what exists in the natural world are atoms defined by their sizes and shapes, they recognized that sensory qualia are part of the subject. But they apparently weren't representative realists, because they didn't try to explain how phenomenal space is part of the subject.

matter an intrinsic property with a structure that explains the configurations of qualia in phenomenal space that are immediately present. Thus, when we describe the tulip as red, the motor output circuit generates the meaning of a naturalistic sentence that refers to the tulip as an object in space and predicates a color property of it. The fact that we have a phenomenal appearance in which red qualia seem to be located on the surface of a tulip flower is not causally relevant. Qualia merely help constitute the meaning of the verbal behavior describing them. What happens when we describe what we perceive is completely determined by geometrical and physical causes. To be sure, in a metaphysical-level culture, qualia eventually cause reflective subjects to say that their beliefs about them are caused by their immediate presence. But that is a false belief, and it has an effect in the natural world only because it is part of the metaphysical arguments that lead to the discovery that beings like us are conscious. The belief that knowledge depends on intuition is what makes it seem that mind is not identical to the brain, and it is corrected when science discovers that the intuitionist illusion is a phenomenal expression of the holistic power of the magnetic field matter helping constitute the geometrical action of the mammalian brain whose geometrical expression causes descriptions of its causal role.

What it is like to be a reflective mammalian brain is to assume that the immediate presence of spatial relations of qualia enables one to refer to the tulip by its location and that the immediate presence of its red qualia enables one to classify it as red. This is an implicit assumption of mammals at the psychological stage and earlier. But it becomes explicit when metaphysical sentences are used because they refer to sensory qualia in phenomenal space as objects of a faculty of perceptual intuition. Metaphysicians call the phenomenal appearance that occurs in perception *Appearance*, and by treating the phenomenal appearances of certain other psychological states as objects of a *faculty of rational intuition,* intuitionists argue that Reason knows Reality behind Appearance. Ontological science explains this verbal behavior as part of the geometrical action of the neural BGS. When subjects reflect on their psychological states, they use psychological sentences to describe the self as having propositional attitudes toward the meanings of sentences embedded in psychological predicates, and these reflective psychological states also have phenomenal appearances. Because of what it is like to reflect on psychological states, they take it for granted that the cause of what they say about perceptual appearances is that they are immediately present, and some psychological states have phenomenal appearances that can plausibly be interpreted as objects of a faculty of rational intuition with the power to reveal Reality behind Appearance. Since Reality is what really exists, it must be something constituting the world that is self-subsistent, and how it exists must cause all the kinds of things found in the world. In the end, as we shall see, even Appearance must be explained in this way, and that is the Achilles heel of intuitionistic metaphysics. But to explain how reflective subjects know Reality behind Appearance, intuitionists assume that Reason is a faculty of rational intuition. This belief is false in the same way as the belief that perception is a faculty of perceptual intuition. Both are expressions of the *intuitionist illusion*, that is, the second and more basic illusion in our naïve assumption about perception: the belief that the immediate presence of qualia in phenomenal space is what causes the verbal behavior by which we describe them. But since they are just intrinsic properties of matter helping constitute the geometrical action by which the brain speaks, this belief is false.

A metaphysical theory holds that beings like us have a cognitive power, called *Reason*, by which we can know Reality behind Appearance, and consciousness makes intuitionistic metaphysics possible because what it is like to reflect on our psychological states makes it seem that knowledge depends on intuition. The illusion of intuitionism makes a third stage of spiritual evolution possible because when metaphysical arguments describe knowledge as depending on a faculty of intuitionism, they refer to consciousness as something different from the psychological states they help constitute. That makes consciousness part of a third level of linguistic organization. Without a way of referring to consciousness, it would not be possible for metaphysicians to discover that we are conscious, nor could ontological scientists explain how it is part of the natural world. But consciousness itself in not an efficient cause. Its only role is helping constitute the metaphysical arguments that cause the metaphysical stage. That is an essential role, and since it seems to be a cause of knowledge, consciousness is called a *pseudo-efficient cause*. But consciousness as something different from the psychological states it helps constitute is not an efficient cause of anything, not even the possibility of metaphysics. Its possibility depends on the illusion of intuitionism, and that since is just the unity of consciousness together with the subjective configuration of qualia due to the mammalian faculty of imagination, it depends on the holistic power of matter.

Though consciousness is just a pseudo-efficient cause, it is part of the third level of linguistic organization, and so it is essential to the cause of a stage of evolution. The metaphysical level is not a level of grammatical organization like the naturalistic and psychological levels of linguistic organization because it does not depend on a change in the genetic plan by which the animal BGS constructs a neural BGS. It begins as just a random variation in cultural evolution during the psychological stage in which metaphysical sentences are used to make an argument. They use the intuitionist illusion to refer to consciousness as a cause of knowledge, and since language-using mammals understand sentences by constructing their meanings in a faculty of imagination, there is a faculty of metaphysical imagination.

As we have seen, the use of naturalistic sentences depends on the power to construct their meanings in a faculty of naturalistic imagination. Likewise, the use of psychological sentences depends on the power to construct their meanings in a faculty of psychological imagination, of which naturalistic imagination is a part.[36] The use of metaphysical sentences also depends on the power to construct their meanings in a faculty of imagination. The *faculty of metaphysical imagination* depends on both naturalistic and psychological imagination being parts. When intuitionists use metaphysical sentences, they use psychological sentences to describe phenomenal appearances of psychological states as objects of intuition, and that reference makes consciousness part of their faculty of metaphysical imagination. When intuitionists explain how they perceive the natural world, they refer to phenomenal appearances of representations constructed from sensory input in naturalistic imagination as objects of a faculty of intuition. And when they explain how they know Reality behind Appearance, they refer to phenomenal

---

[36] Naturalistic imagination is basically an interaction between the verbal and nonverbal hemispheres of the cerebrum. Psychological imagination is a power of the motor output circuit in the verbal hemisphere to impose the meanings of sentences on the mammalian brain temporarily to understand their consequences.

appearances of representations in both naturalistic and psychological imagination as objects of a faculty of intuition. All these objects of intuition are inside consciousness. The references to consciousness as objects of intuition put metaphysics on a third level of linguistic organization.[37] And the faculty of metaphysical imagination in which the meanings of metaphysical sentences are constructed does not depend on any genetically determined change in the neural BGS.

Since consciousness makes intuitionistic metaphysics possible, it can be tried out as a random variation on cultural evolution during the psychological stage, and since it is a higher level of linguistic organization than psychological sentences, it makes a metaphysical stage of spiritual evolution *possible*. But for this stage to be inevitable in the overall course of the evolution of beings like us, the higher level must also be *functional,* and the functionality of these false beliefs about the nature of knowledge is explained in *Section 6*, paving the way for *Part Two* to explain in detail how intuitionistic metaphysics enabled Western civilization to evolve an unprecedented order of functional powers. But, first, I will describe what ontology reveals about the structure of intuitionistic metaphysical arguments. As we have seen, the ontological explanation of evolution reveals the essential nature of reflective subjects, and since the ontological explanation of consciousness entails the identity of complex phenomenal properties and intrinsic properties of magnetic field matter helping constitute the geometrical action of the brain, ontology discovers the essential nature of intuitionistic metaphysics. That is

---

[37] Though this third level of linguistic organization is constituted by the use of metaphysical sentences in making an argument, rather than by a higher-level grammatical structure in sentences, it is on a higher level of linguistic organization than psychological sentences in much the same way that the grammatical structure of psychological sentences is on a higher level of linguistic organization than naturalistic sentences. Recall that psychological predicates are verbs of propositional attitude followed by a sentence that identifies the proposition about which the attitude is taken. As we have seen, the truth of a psychological sentence is not necessarily preserved when words in the embedded sentence are replaced by other words that refer to the same objects because the propositional attitude is about the *meaning* of the embedded sentence, not the *state of affairs* to which it corresponds. (The truth of psychological sentences about others depends on coordinating *meanings* constructed in faculties of imagination in different neural BGSs.) The places for words in such sentence are called *opaque* (or *intensional*) *contexts*. References to objects of intuition are opaque contexts in a similar way. The truth of the metaphysical theory is not preserved by replacing references to phenomenal properties as objects of intuition by references to the psychological states (or the states of the neural BGS to which they are identical) because metaphysical arguments are about psychological states as phenomenal appearances, not psychological states as part of the geometrical action of the brain.

the ontologically necessary framework used to explain the history of Western philosophy.

3   The Phenomenal Subject

Beliefs that are implicit in what it is like for subjective animals to reflect on their psychological states are made explicit by metaphysics. These beliefs assume that knowledge of phenomenal appearances is caused by their immediate presence, and that is false because phenomenal appearances are intrinsic properties of matter that is part of the geometrical action by which the neural BGS guides behavior. Thus, ontology reveals mistakes that intuitionism causes. One is a conception of the self. It is the assumption that the self *is* the subject to which phenomenal appearances are objects of intuition, though intuitionists do not necessarily state it or even acknowledge it.

Philosophy is the study of Appearance because metaphysicians explain knowledge in relation to Appearance. They hold that Reason knows Reality behind Appearance. What they call *Appearance* is the phenomenal appearances that reflective subjects have when they perceive the natural world. They are vivid sensory qualia that seem to have locations in and around a body in phenomenal space. Ontology explains them as the phenomenal appearance of the representation constructed from sensory input in the input scene of the sensory input circuit. But phenomenal appearances seem to be immediately present to a subject, and believing that their immediate presence is what causes the subject to know that qualia exist, what kinds they are, and how they are related, intuitionists interpret them as objects of a faculty of intuition that makes them aware of the natural world. Hence, they assume that there is a subject to which they are immediately present. I call it the *phenomenal subject*. It is not only a knower but also an agent. The phenomenal subject seems to use objects of perceptual intuition to direct the behavior of its animal body relative to other objects in space.

The black region in the diagram represents consciousness, the condition in which reflective subjects find themselves, and intuitionistic metaphysicians assume that there is a phenomenal subject with a faculty of rational intuition as well as a faculty of perceptual intuition. (See Figure 4, below.) This is plausible because, besides the vivid and changing spatially structured qualia that enable behavior to be directed relative to objects in space, there are less vivid phenomenal appearances of unchanging objects. They are the phenomenal appearance of representations that are constructed in the input scene by the faculties of imagination on which the use of language depends, and they seem to be objects of a faculty of rational intuition, distinct from perception. Thus, the intuitionist illusion makes it plausible that the phenomenal subject has Reason, that is, a cognitive power by which it can judge the truth of beliefs that are part of Appearance by their correspondence to Reality.

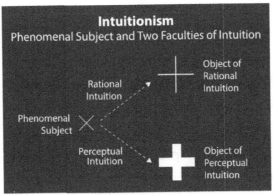

Figure 4 – Knowledge from Objects of Intuition

There is, however, no phenomenal subject. In the spatio-material world, the subject who judges truth and guides behavior is the self, and as we have seen, that is the reflective neural BGS. It uses the input scene constructed from sensory input by its sensory input circuit as a representation of the natural world to generate motor output that directs bodily behavior relative to objects represented in the input scene. Intuitionists interpret phenomenal appearances of such representations of the natural world as objects of perceptual intuition. When they reflect on perception, therefore, they expect to find a phenomenal appearance that can be interpreted as the phenomenal subject. But all they find is a phenomenal appearance of the body.

Reflection is a cognitive power that comes from using psychological sentences, and as we have seen, when subjects reflect on their psychological states, there is no representation of the self. The self is represented in the reflective neural BGS as a story about a subject who is identical over time and normally aspires to become more like an ideal self. This story is verbal behavior, which includes reports of memories, imaginings, and perceptions as well as reports of the beliefs and desires by which it explains choices made in the situations encountered. Verbal behavior, whether covert or overt, has a phenomenal appearance because it is represented as part of the body in the input scene. Meanings of sentences also have phenomenal appearances since they are constructed in faculties of imagination. But the concept of a subject, like the concept of an object of intuition, is just a kind of understanding built into a faculty of imagination, and their only phenomenal appearance a feeling of confidence in one's understanding. Likewise, feelings and emotions, such as hunger, anger, and pleasure, which occur when certain desires are aroused or satisfied, appear only as bodily qualia caused by activating behavioral dispositions or as covert behavior that fantasize ways of satisfying desires. Thus, even though the psychological states that occur when subjects reflect on their psychological states have phenomenal appearances, nothing immediately present can be interpreted as the self.

Nevertheless, intuitionism presupposes a phenomenal subject. To understand the meanings of metaphysical sentences, intuitionists must assume that there is a subject to which configurations of qualia are immediately present. But since they cannot point to an object of intuition that represents it, they are hard-pressed to explain how they know there is a phenomenal subject, and so they do not always mention it.

The phenomenal subject has an elusive nature because, without a phenomenal appearance that seems to represent the self, intuitionists cannot explain how they know about it in the same way they know about the body and the natural world. But the phenomenal subject is also puzzling because of its practical side. The self, as a reflective neural BGS, guides animal behavior. It uses input to choose goals that are good in the situation, and it pursues them by using input to direct behavior at objects in the natural world. Thus, the phenomenal subject, as the intuitionistic conception of the self, is an agent. And as Reason gives the phenomenal subject a perfect cognitive power, Reason makes the phenomenal subject a perfect agent.

In taking responsibility for choosing goals, one assumes that there is a fact of the matter about which goals are good, and metaphysics is relevant because it explains the Good as part of the True. Beliefs are true when they correspond to Reality, and since its nature explains the essential nature of everything, Reality must explain the nature of the good. Since knowledge of Reality gives Rational subjects an understanding of goodness, metaphysical theories assume that knowledge of the nature of the good causes Rational subjects to choose goals that are good. It enables them to know not only which goals are good in the situation, but also why those goals are good, and so their understanding of why goals are good can cause of their choices. This is not a psychological explanation of the choice because it is not attributed to a desire and to beliefs about the situation and how behavior can satisfy it. The relevant beliefs are about the nature of the good and how it is instantiated in the current situation, not just about the means to an end determined by desire. Indeed, if the goal is desired at all, Rational subjects desire it because it is good. Thus, for subjects with a perfect way of knowing, there is a perfect way of acting. For knowledge of the Good to be what causes Rational subjects to choose goals that are good, they must have self-control. Rational subjects must choose the self-interested good even when opposed by strong animal desires, and since the Good includes morality, they must choose to be moral even when it is opposed to self-interest (and they can get away with it). To be sure, Rational subjects sometimes choose goals that are not good. And intuitionists can explain why by holding that Reason gives the phenomenal subject a free will. But since knowledge of the Good can cause them to do what is right, they hold that Rational subjects deserve to be punished for wrongdoing.

To say that Rational subjects have a free will is to say that, whatever they do, they could have done otherwise. Physicalists believe that complete determinism is incompatible with free will because they believe that every event (that can be explained) is a result of physical causes, and since they are the regularities described by basic laws of physics, choices are ultimately determined by events and conditions that are outside the reflective subject. But in the spatio-material world, complete determinism is not incompatible with free will because what happens depends on both geometrical and physical efficient causes. The reflective brain is BGS, that is, a geometrical cause whose function is to choose goals that are good, and when reflective subjects choose, they could have chosen otherwise because that is what the self does. But this is not known until science is reduced to ontology, and intuitionists explain free will differently because they assume that the self is the phenomenal subject.

Intuitionism makes the belief in free will plausible. When Rational subjects make a choice, they have beliefs and desires, which they would offer as reasons for their choice. But when they do not do what is good, those psychological states cannot be used to excuse them because they know what is good, and since they see the self is the phenomenal subject, they believe that they could have done otherwise. Beliefs about the situation are not an excuse since the only relevant beliefs are about the nature of the good and what is good in the situation. Free will enables them to do what morality requires, even when it is opposed by self-interest, and what self-interest requires, when it is opposed by the strongest desires. Beliefs and desires are just objects of intuition for the phenomenal subject, and when the choice has been made, there is only the phenomenal appearance of the intention formed. Thus, it seems that the choice must have been made by the phenomenal subject. There is no phenomenal appearance of any causal connection between the reasons and the intention. Indeed, it does not even seem possible for an object of intuition to cause the choice since such objects are just the immediate presence of certain structures of faint qualia. Reflection on what it is like to choose makes it seem self-evident, therefore, that the phenomenal subject could have chosen otherwise.

4   Two Kinds of Intuitionistic Metaphysics

Intuitionists have two basically different ways of using metaphysical sentences because there are two basically different ways of understanding how objects of a faculty of intuition can make us aware of the natural world. As we have seen, *direct realists* believe that objects of perceptual intuition *are* the natural world, while *representative realists* recognize that perceptual appearances are just part of the subject who perceives the natural world. In both cases, intuitionists are explaining perceptual phenomenal appearances, which are identical to intrinsic properties of magnetic field matter helping constitute the geometrical action by which the neural BGS constructs the input scene from sensory input. But since there are two different interpretations of

Appearance, there are two different ways of explaining how Reason knows Reality behind Appearance. Thus, there are two kinds of intuitionistic metaphysics, with different beliefs about the phenomenal subject, different theories about the faculty of rational intuition, and different conceptions of the nature of Reality. Since intuitionists defend different kinds of metaphysical theories, they face different challenges in settling on a set of consistent beliefs that all correspond to the same Reality.

The illusion inherent in consciousness makes both ways of interpreting metaphysical sentences plausible. But only representative realists recognize that they are conscious, and even they may not call it *consciousness*. Since direct realism about perception is our naïve attitude, it comes as a surprise to reflective subjects that the phenomenal appearances that occur in perception are basically different from the natural world that causes them. As we have seen, their kinds of unity can show the difference between them. But regardless how intuitionists become representative realists, they discover that they are conscious. They believe that all objects of intuition are part of the knower, and since they are the Appearance, they recognize that Reality exists beyond Appearance. Critical realists know there is a world outside consciousness. For naïve realists, by contrast, everything is inside consciousness, and so they see the difference between Appearance and Reality as just the difference between two kinds of phenomenal appearances, the kind they explain as objects of perceptual intuition and the kind they explain as objects of rational intuition. Since they are direct realists about both, both are public objects, albeit of basically different kinds. To be sure, direct realists recognize that some phenomenal appearances are private. Memories, thoughts, and feelings have phenomenal appearances that are immediately present only to the phenomenal subject who has them. But since they also involve configurations of qualia in phenomenal space, direct realists can believe that private objects of intuition are located in the same space as public objects, for example, like ghosts that haunt them or that in dreaming, they are transported to other parts of phenomenal space.

For metaphysicians that are taken in by the illusion inherent in consciousness, these two forms of realism about perception are the only two ways that perceptual phenomenal appearances can be explained, and ontology uses them to explain the difference between the ancient and modern eras of metaphysics in Western philosophy. In ancient Greece, a paradigm of the direct realist defense metaphysics is Plato, and in the modern era, a paradigm for representative realism is Descartes. Their order in history is inevitable since direct realism is the naïve assumption about perception, and the discovery that it is false is what leads to representative realism. Both are part of the metaphysical stage of spiritual evolution that eventually occurs on any Earth-like planet where life evolves, though, as we shall see, modern philosophy depends on ancient philosophy in another way, which has to do with the practical function of Reason.

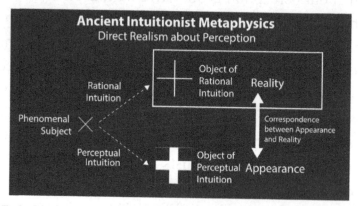

Figure 5 – Relation between Appearance and Reality in Ancient Metaphysics

For direct realists about perception, everything is part of consciousness (represented by the black region in Figure 5). Since direct realists believe that objects of perceptual intuition exist independently of the phenomenal subject, they believe that Appearance is public, and thus, when they show how a faculty of rational intuition discovers Reality behind Appearance, they also take objects of rational intuition to be public. But since Reality is behind Appearance, causing everything found in it, Appearance and Reality are in different public worlds. Plato calls Appearance the realm of *Becoming* and Reality the realm of *Being*. The former is a world of changing visible objects in space, and the latter a world of unchanging Forms. Both are public objects of intuition, and in order to know both Appearance and Reality, the phenomenal subject must somehow be part of both realms. This gives the phenomenal subject a puzzling status in Plato's metaphysical system. It has a faculty of perceptual intuition that depends on an animal body in the realm of in Becoming along with other visible objects. But Reason enables the phenomenal subject to know Forms in the realm of Being, and in order for them to be immediately present, the phenomenal subject must also somehow be part of Being. This is not particularly puzzling to direct realists since everything that exists is inside consciousness. Only some objects of intuition, such as feelings and dreams, are seen as private, and since some of them may seem to be located in phenomenal space like ghosts that others cannot see, it does not seem impossible that objects of intuition not located in phenomenal space are immediately present along with visible objects. But the difference between Appearance and Reality is basic, and since it is not obvious how the phenomenal subject can be part of both a realm of change and an unchanging realm, Plato suggests (in the *Meno*) that the rational intuition of Forms is the recollection of them from memory of a time before having an animal body, when the Forms were immediately present.

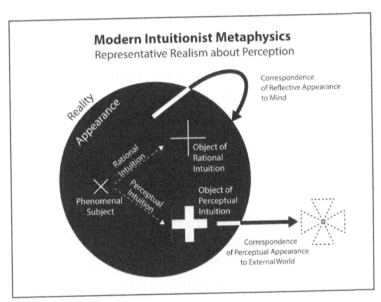

Figure 6 – Relation between Appearance and Reality in Modern Metaphysics

Since representative realists believe that objects of perceptual intuition are parts of the perceiver, they are private, and so this kind of intuitionistic metaphysical argument is based on the point of view of a single phenomenal subject. (The black region in Figure 6 represents consciousness.) Descartes called objects of intuition *ideas* in the mind. Objects of perceptual intuition are interpreted as part of Appearance, and representative realists assume that, besides a faculty of perceptual intuition, the phenomenal subject has a faculty of rational intuition by which it can know the existence and nature of Reality behind Appearance. In the perceptual Appearance, body qualia seem to be located in phenomenal space along with other qualia objects, but since they are ideas *in the mind*, Descartes called the Reality behind the perceptual Appearance the *external world*. Ideas in the mind also include objects of rational intuition that enable the phenomenal subject to know Reality behind the perceptual Appearance, and so they are another part of consciousness as Appearance. Indeed, there are various other kinds of phenomenal appearances, such as those that occur in remembering, dreaming, and feeling, and since the phenomenal subject knows about them in the same way it knows about objects of perceptual and rational intuition, they are also objects of intuition. Thus, representative realism presupposes an all-inclusive faculty of intuition, which might be called the *faculty of reflective intuition*. Since it is how the phenomenal subject knows about itself, Reason must also be able to know the Reality behind this all-inclusive Appearance. Thus, doing metaphysics from the point of view of a phenomenal subject reflecting on its psychological states requires representative realists to show how Reason knows Reality behind Appearance twice. Besides discovering the existence and nature of Reality behind objects of perceptual intuition, representative realists must discover the existence and nature of Reality behind the objects of reflective intuition. The latter Reality is what Descartes calls *mind*.

The difference between direct and representative realism explains why there are two kinds of intuitionistic metaphysics. But to defend their metaphysical arguments, intuitionists had to explain how Reason knows Reality behind Appearance, and that is possible only if Appearance and Reality are both parts of a single coherent metaphysical system. In the context of the pre-Socratic discovery about the first cause, the implicit assumption was that Reality is something self-subsistent (like a substance or substances) that explains the existence of everything found in the world. Hence, a metaphysical system is implicitly committed to an *ontological theory* (though, instead of enduring through time, a substance might be outside time). It assumes the existence of Appearance, and since intuitionistic theories about the nature of Reason are false, their views about the nature of Reality are, at best, faulty, describe a Reality whose nature explains Appearance poses intractable ontological problems. For Plato, it was the problem of finding an ontological theory that can explain coherently how Being and Becoming are related, and for Descartes, it was the problem of finding an ontological theory that can explain how mind and body are related. Indeed, the Achilles heel of intuitionistic metaphysics is the problem of ontological dualism posed by falling for the illusion of intuitionism. Since consciousness is referred to as Appearance, it must be a cause of knowledge about Appearance. But since substances constituting everything are Reality, they must constitute Appearance as part of Reality, and it is hard to describe a world in which substances constitute a natural world in which consciousness is an object of intuition. As we shall see, there are two ways to hide ontological dualisms: one in which Reality is a substance with two essential natures, and another in which Appearance turns out to be Reality. Since both ontological theories are untenable in the end, the history of Western philosophy is largely the story of intuitionistic metaphysicians attempting to overcome ontological dualism and skeptics finding fault with their arguments. Both sides were badly mistaken, and their disputes led eventually to a general recognition of the failure of intuitionistic metaphysics, as *Part Two* describes in detail.

5   Two Views of Objects of Rational Intuition

Philosophers believe that Reason discovers Reality behind Appearance, and since intuitionists are either direct or representative realists, they have different theories about the nature of Reason. In both cases, objects of rational intuition are phenomenal appearances of meanings of linguistic representations constructed in faculties of imagination, which is the way that linguistic geometrical action is embodied in neural geometrical action with an intrinsic phenomenal nature. But in each case, different theories about the nature of rational intuition are plausible. Direct realists defend Reason in a public world, and so they see the faculty of rational intuition as revealing a Reality behind Appearance that is just a different kind of public object. Plato portrays visible objects that move and interact as the realm of Becoming, and so he can plausibly construe objects of reflective intuition, such as the meaning of a word, as unchanging objects of rational intuition, which he calls

Forms and locates in the realm of Being. Representative realists recognize that reflective subjects are conscious, and so they defend Reason from the point of view of a single phenomenal subject. Since Appearance is private, they see Reason as knowing a Reality behind the perceptual Appearance, that is, outside consciousness. Since the external world exists for every Rational subject, it is public. The objects of rational intuition by which Reason has this knowledge of Reality are another part of Appearance, and calling all parts of Appearance *ideas*, Descartes singles out objects of rational intuition by their clarity and distinctness. They are indubitable because they are self-contained compelling arguments for beliefs held together in a single rational intuition, and he uses *clear and distinct ideas* to show how Reason knows not only the Reality behind perceptual ideas but also the Reality behind ideas of all kinds.

The nature of the reflective mammalian brain and the identity of phenomenal properties with an intrinsic property of the magnetic field matter helping constitute its geometrical action give intuitionists two basically different theories about the nature of the faculty of rational intuition to use in making metal arguments. Consider, first, direct realism.

When beings like us understand naturalistic sentences, we construct their meanings in naturalistic imagination, and they have phenomenal appearances. Indeed, the meanings of general words are immediately present. These phenomenal appearances are basically different from qualia objects in phenomenal space. Though both are immediately present, there is nothing hidden about the meanings of the words that name their kinds. The meanings have neither a backside nor an inside, and they are incapable of change. Thus, when we reflect on what naturalistic words mean, *abstract objects* are immediately present in much the same way as qualia objects in phenomenal space. They are a kind of phenomenal appearance that direct realists can plausibly interpret as public objects of rational intuition. Their immediate presence to all phenomenal subjects reveals the existence and nature of Reality behind the public Appearance that direct realists describe. Plato calls them *Forms*.

Since meanings of naturalistic words stand for kinds of objects in the natural world, abstract objects have obvious relations to particular changing qualia objects in phenomenal space, and so they can be portrayed as causing qualia objects to be the kinds they are. For example, since the words *circle* and *triangle* have meanings defined in naturalistic imagination, these abstract objects can be seen as causing the circularity and triangularity of circular and triangular qualia objects in phenomenal space. As 2-D geometrical objects, *circularity* and *triangularity* are the same in how they differ from 3-D geometrical objects, but they are different from one another. Indeed, *sameness* and *difference* are themselves unchanging objects of intuition, though as the meanings of more general words, they even more abstract. *Motion* and *rest* are less abstract than geometrical objects, but abstract, nonetheless. And there are abstract objects of a radically different kind. General terms that characterize reflective subjects have meanings defined in terms of psychological states, such as *knower* and *agent*, *certainty* and *power*, and *wisdom* and *courage*. Since their meanings have phenomenal appearances, they can also be seen as objects of rational intuition that cause Rational subjects to be the kinds of subjects they are. Even meanings of general terms that apply to spiritual organisms, such as *government* and *spiritual authority*, can be interpreted as Forms that explain things found in the commonsense world, where metaphysical arguments begin. And for such metaphysical theories to hold that Reason is a cognitive power with a practical function, they must also show how such objects of rational intuition lead reflective subjects to choose goals that are good, and that is, indeed, a challenge.

Representative realists, on the other hand, realize that all their phenomenal appearances are subjective, and so they must show how a faculty of rational intuition enables the phenomenal subject to know Reality behind Appearance in two ways. One kind of object of rational intuition must reveal the existence and nature of Reality behind the perceptual Appearance, and another kind of object of rational intuition must reveal the existence and nature of Reality behind the reflective Appearance, that is, ideas of all kinds.

The Reality behind the perceptual Appearance is the external world, and some objects of intuition are plausibly interpreted as enabling Reason to know its nature. The objects of perceptual intuition are structures of sensory qualia in phenomenal space. But fainter configurations of qualia occur when we remember what we have perceived or imagine what might exist in the natural world, and since beliefs about some of them seem to be indubitable, they can plausibly be interpreted as objects of rational intuition. For example, the meaning of the sentence, *Triangles have three sides*, seems to be true regardless of what perception might reveal about the external world. But since we use the number of angles of a closed figure with three straight lines in a plane to count the number of its sides, this object of rational intuition is actually an argument. It seems to be indubitable because, in the spatio-material world, it is the phenomenal appearance of a self-contained argument constructed in naturalistic imagination. The certainty of other geometrical arguments can be explained in the same way. They are based on the structure of the faculty of naturalistic imagination, and since they have a phenomenal appearance, they seem to be objects of faculty of rational intuition. We can see that space has exactly three dimensions by orienting as many lines as possible in perpendicular directions from all the others and counting them. In a similar way, we can understand time as a dimension orthogonal to all three dimensions of space. More complex geometrical arguments are also compelling because they are inferences that depend on the structure of naturalistic imagination. Consider the proof that the sum of the interior angles of a triangle is equal to two right angles. It depends on the assumption that lines intersecting parallel lines determine corresponding angles of the same sizes, which describes structures constructed in the faculty of naturalistic imagination. Since this faculty is what enables us to understand the objects we perceive in space, it is plausible that whatever we learn about space and time in this way is an object of rational intuition that represents the Reality behind Appearance. Thus, not only geometry but also arithmetic and mathematics generally can be explained as self-evident truths. This Descartes calls them *clear and distinct ideas of extension* and uses them to explain the essential nature of the external world. To be sure, such objects of rational intuition do not show the existence of such a world external to mind, and that is a problem, as we shall see. But they reveal the essential nature of Reality behind Appearance, if its existence can be shown.

In the spatio-material world, the Reality behind the reflective Appearance is the self. But the self is represented in the neural BGS by the use of psychological sentences to describe psychological states in telling a story told about its identity over time. As we have seen, there is no phenomenal appearance of the self, except the phenomenal subject, which is implicit in the illusion of intuitionism. But the faculty of psychological imagination enables subjects to reflect on their psychological states, and since reflective phenomenal appearances are intrinsic properties of the neural geometrical action of the reflective mammalian brain, they seem to provide indubitable knowledge of the self. Calling objects of rational intuition *clear and distinct ideas*, Descartes uses one of them to show the existence and nature of the Reality behind the reflective Appearance. This is the *Cogito*, his famous argument, *I think, therefore I am.* It makes the illusion of intuitionism explicit, and as a clear and distinct idea, it reveals the existence and nature of the substance constituting the self. Descartes called it *mind*, and since the illusion of intuitionism depends on the unity of consciousness, he defined mind by its unity. The difference between a substance in which many qualia of various kinds are all immediately present at once, and a substance that can always be divided into parts is what saddled modern philosophy with mind-body dualism.

6 Functionality of Intuitionistic Metaphysics

The inevitability of a third minor stage of spiritual evolution depends not only on the *possibility* of a psychological-level culture trying out a third level of linguistic organization as a random cultural variation but also on its *functionality*. It must enable spiritual organisms to acquire new functional powers, and as *Part Two* shows in detail, metaphysics enabled the civilized spiritual organisms in the West to evolve an unprecedented order of functional powers. The functionality of metaphysics is implicit in its nature. Though intuitionism is false, metaphysicians use it as the foundation of their argument, and the belief in Reason motivates them to exchange of arguments with a third level of linguistic organization. That kind of cultural evolution enables spiritual organisms to acquire an entire range of functional powers that were previously out of reach.

As we have seen, since spiritual organisms have a plan-sharing BGS based on the use of language, culture evolves by a form of the reproductive mechanism embodied in its BGS.[38] Beliefs and norms that have accumulated as culture are expressed linguistically, and in spiritual organisms at the psychological level of linguistic organization, situations arise in which members argue about what to do. The linguistic representations they exchange are double-action geometrical causes going through cycles in which they can do both primary and secondary work. Sentences expressing beliefs and desires cause their meanings to be copied from one neural BGS to another, and they do primary work when they make up arguments that are accepted as by another neural BGS. And as spiritual input to neural BGSs, their conclusions do secondary work by helping determine choices of goals by members. These reproductive cycles are constituted by the spiritual BGS, and since language-using subjects can tell when double-action geometrical causes are functional, what determines whether arguments succeed in reproducing is their judgment. Since it is a form of natural selection that depends on the judgment of members of spiritual organisms, culture evolves by *judgmental selection*.[39]

---

[38] This is not the only example of the embodiment of the reproductive mechanism in a BGS. It is also embodied in the mammalian brain as a mechanism that facilitates neurological development, called *plasticity*. Since the basic structure of the mammalian brain is a faculty of imagination, it can internalize regularities discovered in experience, not only physical and mechanical regularities from the natural world, but also language and culture from the spiritual world. As we have seen, the three essential functions of a BGS are served by three kinds of multi-junction circuits of bundles of neurons (through the thalamus, neocortex, and another forebrain structure) that carry picture-grade signals. Pathways along these circuits, tried out randomly, are like double-action geometrical causes going through reproductive cycles. They can do secondary work because they help generate behavior of some kind that depends on imagination, and they can do primary work because, when the pathways are reinforced, they are more likely to be used again. A reward mechanism built into the brain can detect whether they serve functions of imagination in guiding behavior, and thus, its reinforcement of those pathways when they are successful can cause neurological mechanisms in the faculty of imagination to evolve gradually by natural selection in the direction of greater functional power during the development of an individual mammalian brain.

[39] Though the cause of both cultural evolution and neurological development is a reproductive mechanism built into a BGS, let me emphasize the disanalogy between them. The spiritual BGS defines the form of life that evolves on the fourth floor of the edifice of life, whereas the neural BGS is just a part of the animal BGS that has already evolved on the third floor. Subjective neural BGSs are all based on faculties of imagination, and since they all depend on the circuits of bundles of neurons in the subjective neural BGS, a reproductive mechanism is built into them by a reward mechanism that reinforces random variations on pathways around those circuits when it detects that they are functional. But this is just neurological development, which occurs in every animal, one generation after another, during each stage of animal evolution. Of course, it also occurs in each generation of members of spiritual organisms, since each level of linguistic organization is also a level of neural organization. But since the spiritual BGS is the form of life that evolves on the fourth floor of the edifice of life, the cultural evolution that occurs in spiritual organisms by judgmental selection makes an increasing important contribution at each level of linguistic organization (along with natural selection) to the gradual evolution of functional powers that occurs during an entire stage in the overall course of evolution.

Arguments succeed in reproducing when they convince subjects to accept them, and since subjective animals use faculties of imagination to compare them, judgments about which argument to accept are guided by the principle of optimality (where arguments can be better in two ways: using the same premises to conclude more or using fewer premises to conclude as much). Since subjective animals naturally look for what does the most with the least, culture evolves by judgmental selection. But the kinds of judgments involved depend on the levels of linguistic organization of the arguments exchanged.

At the naturalistic level of linguistic organization, sentences have a simple subject-predicate grammar, which can describe only naturalistic states and their causal relation, and as we have seen, culture evolves by *technical selection*. Using input about the situation, members of spiritual organisms can often tell which ways of behaving are the best means to the ends that they are pursuing in the situation, and since the use of naturalistic sentences enables them to refer to causes and their effects, they make judgments based on naturalistic imagination about techniques of attaining immediate goals. As culture evolves, technical judgments accumulate as culture. Tools gradually become more effective, and the tactics used in situations become more effective at promoting conditions that enable spiritual organisms to reproduce. But only some parts of such shared plans evolve. Judgmental selection is about the means to ends pursued in the immediate situation, and the goals that make the ends good are not represented by naturalistic sentences.

The higher level of linguistic organization at the psychological level is evident in the grammatical structure of a new kind of sentence that is used, and since it can represent goals that make ends good, more aspects of the cultural plan evolve in the direction of greater functional power. The use of psychological sentences enables subjects to represent their desires as goals of behavior, and so reflective subjects can think about the goals they pursue. Using input about the immediate situation, they can often tell which end they ought to pursue and which means are best. This causes culture to evolve by *pragmatic selection*. Arguments are about which plan to choose, not just which means to use in pursuit of ends that members find themselves pursuing, and since judgments are based on (psychological and naturalistic) imagination, reflective subjects naturally look for shared plans that do the most with the least. Since the arguments are practical, judgments are ultimately pragmatic, and plans are confirmed by what works. The implicit aim of a practical argument is a plan that maximizes the attainment of more distant shared goals, including everyone's obedience to moral rules that promote cooperation. Members of spiritual organisms at the psychological stage have religions and ceremonies by which they mutually acknowledge the goals they share, and though they still do not know why they share those goals, more aspects of cultural plans evolve by pragmatic selection than would evolve by a purely technical selection of means in immediate situations. In civilized spiritual organisms, there is a further constraint. The only plans that work are those in which a force field of spiritual authority maintains a class structure of some kind. But cultural evolution by pragmatic selection enables civilized spiritual organisms to acquire an order of functional powers that are out of reach for tribal spiritual organisms. Since it includes a class that is freed from manual labor, some members can enjoy the luxury of exchanging more theoretical arguments, and that is how civilization makes another stage of spiritual evolution possible.

During the third minor stage of spiritual evolution, sentences used in metaphysical arguments have a higher level of linguistic organization than psychological sentences, and even more aspects of the shared cultural plan evolve in the direction of greater functional power. At the psychological level, the beliefs that accumulate as culture are various and often contradictory, and as long as they work, there is no point in continuing to argue about what to believe. Metaphysics begins in the commonsense world, where arguments are exchanged, and in a spiritual organism whose members are audacious enough to believe that they are capable of god-like cognitive powers, metaphysical arguments can be tried out. The belief that they have a cognitive power by which they can know Reality behind Appearance imposes a more severe constraint on which beliefs to accept. As we have seen, the intuitionist illusion inherent in what it is like to be a mammalian brain makes the belief in Reason plausible, and since metaphysical arguments aim at knowing the True, rather than merely what works, there are members of spiritual organisms with the goal of discovering which beliefs correspond to Reality. Not every member participates in metaphysical arguments. Most are preoccupied with technical and practical issues that arise in what metaphysicians call Appearance. But some members do, and since metaphysics provides the framework for the accumulation of more specialized arguments, including religion, the internalization of a metaphysical-level culture gives every member a conception of the self as a subject with the power of Reason. As Rational subjects, they see themselves as knowing Reality behind Appearance.

Metaphysical theories assume that Reality is constituted by self-subsistent entities of some kind that can explain every kind of thing found in the commonsense world, and so Rational subjects judge the truth of beliefs by their correspondence to Reality. They are badly mistaken about the nature of Reality, since they use rational intuition to know about it. But even so, belief in Reason imposes a demanding constraint on beliefs that can accumulate as culture because the implicit goal of exchanging metaphysical arguments is to discover the True. True beliefs must all correspond to the same Reality, and so they must all fit together as a consistent system, including even beliefs about Appearance, since they depend in some way on what really exists behind Appearance. Metaphysical imagination enables reflective subjects to compare arguments and judge their coherence according to the principle of optimality, and since the kind of judgmental selection that causes culture to evolve at the metaphysical level is based on the belief in Reason, it is properly called *Rational selection*.

Culture evolves further by Rational selection than pragmatic selection because Reason aims at knowing the True. But Reason has a practical as well as a theoretical function, and the True includes the Good. Regarding the natural world, cultural evolution by Rational selection implicitly aims at a theory about the natural order in which the efficient causes used to explain what happens are reduced to ontological causes. But theoretical arguments have a practical function as well. Since metaphysicians assume that Reason is not only a perfect way of knowing but also a perfect way of choosing, the True includes the Good. When Reason discovers the nature of Reality, it reveals the nature of the good, and when Rational subjects understand its nature, knowledge of goodness causes them to do what is good.

It is good for members of spiritual organisms to submit to spiritual input, and since spiritual input includes moral rules, reflective subjects are required to do what morality requires not only when it is opposed by strong desires but also when it is contrary to self-interest (and wrongdoing would not be known by others). Since they have a spiritual desire to do what is expected of them, they find themselves cooperating in the pursuit of shared goals, and religion claims to explain why they submit to spiritual input. But a psychological-level religion is little more than a myth about the origin of their spiritual organism, and since cooperation in the group is taken for granted, it does not explain goodness in a way that requires reflective subjects to do what moral rules require when wrongdoing would not be known by others and it would not affect their status in their spiritual organism. The basic motive for following a psychological-level cultural plan is avoiding shame. But at the metaphysical level, Reality explain their spiritual nature as something transcendent, and so it can explain the nature of the morally good in a way that enables Rational subjects to know not only what is right but also what makes it good to do what is right rather than what is wrong. Their personal relation to a spiritual Reality behind Appearance gives them a reason to do what is good, even when wrongdoing would not be known by others, and so their motivation for being moral is basically different from reflective subjects during the second stage of spiritual evolution. Since they know that they will be held responsible for doing evil, their basic motive for following the cultural plan is avoiding guilt. This justifies trusting Rational subjects to be moral even when they must act contrary to self-interest or when strong animal desires require self-control. Thus, even though intuitionistic metaphysics is mistaken about the nature of Reason and Reality, cultural evolution by Rational selection is change in the direction of rules and institutions that respect the moral autonomy of Rational subjects.

7 Naturalistic Metaphysics

This explanation of the metaphysical stage of spiritual evolution and its necessary structure is discovered by a science based on ontology. But ontological science has also discovered consciousness and explained how it is part of the natural world. Consciousness is discovered in the natural world because ontological scientists are themselves conscious reflective subjects. Since they explain the natural world as constituted by space and matter, they know that the unity of the natural world depends on all the bits of matter in the world coinciding with parts of the same spatial substance. Thus, when they reflect on their perception of the natural world, they recognize that consciousness has a kind of unity that is radically different from the unity of the natural world. As naturalists, they assume that what they perceive is a world of objects in space, most of which exists independently of their bodies, and as scientists, they have used the empirical method to learn about it. But since they are mammals, experience has a phenomenal appearance, and it can be ignored because they are naturalists following the method of empirical ontology. But when they reflect on what it is like to be a mammalian brain perceiving the natural world, they find that many qualia of various kinds are all immediately present all at once, and they are configured in such a way that they represent what they know about the natural world by perception. Thus, ontologists discover that they are conscious by reflecting on their psychological states and noticing the basic difference between complex phenomenal properties and the natural world that they have explained so completely.

The difference between the unity of consciousness and the unity of the natural world is where the argument of *Chapter 1* began. To show how consciousness is part of the natural world, ontological scientists reduce immediately present complex phenomenal properties to intrinsic properties of magnetic field matter helping constitute the mammalian brain. Since it is a neural BGS, the mammalian brain is a geometrical efficient cause that guides animal behavior, and so they can explain the configurations of qualia in phenomenal space as the geometrical expression of the holistic power of matter. The neural geometrical action of the mammalian brain is magnetic field matter, and assuming that matter has a proto-phenomenal intrinsic property, the intrinsic nature of that magnetic field matter explains the immediate presence of all the qualia to the mammal. That explains how consciousness is part of the natural world, so there is nothing puzzling about it. Neural geometrical action is part of the mammalian cellular geometrical action, and so ontological scientists can explain their own consciousness as what it is like to be a mammal. Knowing that the function of the distinctive structure of the mammalian brain is to serve as a faculty of imagination, they can explain why consciousness comes into existence during biological evolution.

Before discovering that they are conscious, ontological scientists were faced with the puzzle about the unprecedented powers that Western civilization evolved, which now seem to be transforming the entire planet. One obvious difference between the West and other civilizations is philosophy, and though it hardly seems likely at first, the ontological explanation of how consciousness is part of the natural world enables ontological science to explain how it helps metaphysics cause a third stage of spiritual evolution to begin in Western civilization. Their explanation of consciousness reveals an illusion inherent in consciousness that makes it plausible for beings like us to believe that we have a cognitive power called *Reason* that enables us to know Reality behind Appearance. Since configurations of qualia in complex phenomenal properties are intrinsic phenomenal properties of the neural geometrical action by which language-using mammals perceive the natural world and reflect on meanings of linguistic representations, reflective subjects assume that they are aware of their phenomenal properties because of their immediate presence. Thus, ontologists consider the possibility that the illusion inherent in consciousness explains why metaphysical arguments were exchanged in Western culture.

This chapter has shown how the illusion of intuitionism can explain metaphysical arguments as a higher level of linguistic organization than psychological sentences. The reproductive mechanism implies that when a higher level of geometrical organization in a BGS is both possible and functional, another stage of evolution inevitably occurs, during which an entire order of new functional powers evolves. Putting two and two together, therefore, ontological science infers that the exchange of metaphysical arguments is the best explanation of the unprecedented power of Western civilization. As we have seen, there are different kinds of metaphysical arguments, and since they necessarily occur in a certain order, they are part of a necessary series of developments during the metaphysical stage of spiritual evolution by which it can be identified. Thus, if there is enough historical evidence to confirm this hypothesis about Western civilization, philosophy will turn out to be another stage in the evolution of life on Earth, the stage that follows the psychological stage of spiritual evolution. Since metaphysicians try to show that Reason knows Reality behind Appearance, philosophy can be described as the *Study of Appearance*, and since philosophy will be reduced to spatio-materialism in the same way as specialized sciences, philosophy will be explained as part of the *Study of Nature* (see Figure 1). Since the mind is something discovered in the study of Appearance, the ontological reduction of philosophy to spatio-materialism will be the empirical discovery that the mind is identical to the brain.

Philosophy is not, however, a specialized science. Science is based on naturalism and uses the empirical method to study nature. But philosophy uses reflection to study Appearance, and to understand what intuitionistic metaphysicians mean by Appearance, Reason, and Reality, ontological scientists must reflect on their own consciousness. That is, to understand the role of consciousness in ancient and modern intuitionistic metaphysics, ontological scientists must use a faculty of metaphysical imagination, and so their scientific explanation of philosophy depends on reflection as well as perception.

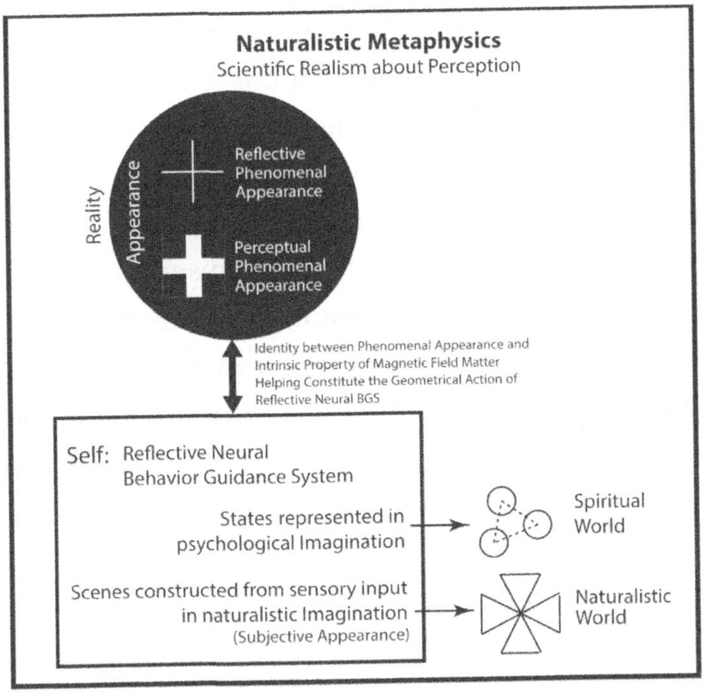

Figure 7 – Relation between Appearance and Reality in Naturalistic Metaphysics

As in previous diagrams, the black region in Figure 7 represents consciousness, where reflective subjects and other mammals find themselves. It is Appearance. But ontological scientists are not taken in by the intuitionist illusion because they reduce consciousness to spatio-materialism. They do not believe that what they know about complex phenomenal properties depends on their immediate presence. They recognize that the self is a reflective neural BGS, and so they understand how perceptual knowledge of the natural world depends on the faculty of naturalistic imagination and how knowledge of the spiritual world depends on the faculty of psychological imagination. To be sure, they know that they are conscious. But as we have seen, they know that they are conscious by contrasting the unity of consciousness with the unity of the natural world, and the difference between them reveals the illusion in inherent in consciousness. Strictly speaking, therefore, ontological scientists do not see *into other minds*, as it has been described here. Rather, they see into the consciousness of other reflective subjects and understand what they mean by calling themselves *minds*. More generally, they understand intuitionistic arguments about Reason knowing Reality behind Appearance by using psychological imagination to simulate the reasoning of intuitionistic metaphysicians in their own brains. But having explained how consciousness is part of the natural world, they know that consciousness is not an efficient cause, and having used the illusion inherent in it to explain metaphysical arguments, they know how consciousness can be a pseudo-efficient cause. Thus, using naturalistic imagination to understand their own reflection, they discount the illusion of intuitionism in themselves and explain what intuitionists are referring to. But since ontological scientists use metaphysical imagination to understand the arguments of intuitionistic metaphysicians, they refer to consciousness, and so they find themselves knowing Reality behind Appearance. Hence, ontological science is a third kind of metaphysical argument. See Figure 8, below, where black areas and letters represent consciousness.

Ontological scientists are naturalists using the empirical method, so they are scientific realists about perception, like physical scientists. Both inherit the concept of mind from their education in Western culture. Though physicalists are baffled about the nature of mind, ontological scientists are not. They use naturalistic imagination to understand how interactions of space and matter constitute everything found in the natural world, and since they understand how consciousness is part of the natural world, they can see it as a pseudo-efficient cause that helps constitute the false intuitionistic belief that mind is a substance with an opposite nature from the brain and other material bodies in the natural world.

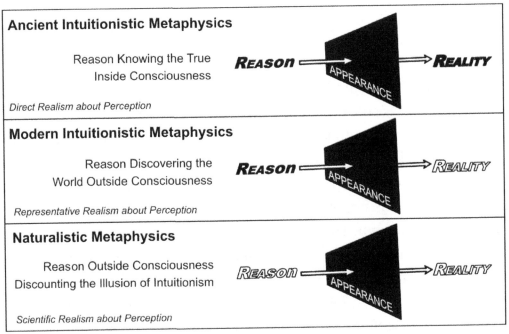

Figure 8 – Three Kinds of Metaphysical Arguments

Knowing that all mammals naturally assume that they know about complex phenomenal properties because they are immediately present, ontological scientists know that the first metaphysicians are direct realists who presuppose intuitionism in order to show how Reason knows Reality behind Appearance. Thus, in ancient metaphysical arguments, both Reason and Reality are inside consciousness. But direct realism is false, and since ontologists can understand the arguments that lead intuitionists to believe that all phenomenal properties are part of the subject, they use the illusion of intuitionism to explain what modern intuitionistic metaphysicians mean by *mind*. Reason is still inside consciousness, but as representative realists, modern intuitionistic metaphysicians believe that the natural world is part of Reality outside consciousness. Thus, modern intuitionistic Reason is inside consciousness looking outside. However, mind is also a substance outside consciousness. It is the substance whose existence is Descartes proves using the *Cogito*, and since that argument describes the illusion of intuitionism, mind has a unity that is opposite to the extended nature of body. The inability to explain how mind interacts with body is the ontological problem of mind-body dualism that dooms the efforts of intuitionists to fulfill the ambition of metaphysics.

There is a third kind of metaphysical argument because the ontological scientists who explain the history of Western civilization as the beginning of the metaphysical stage of spiritual evolution are themselves metaphysicians, discovering Reality behind Appearance. Since ontological science explains the natural world as constituted by space and matter, ontological scientists use naturalistic imagination to know the nature of Reality. Knowing that they are conscious, they know what metaphysicians are referring to as *Appearance*. But since they know how consciousness is part of the natural world, they know that consciousness is impotent as an efficient cause, and so they discount the illusion of intuitionism. Hence, they are reflective mammalian brains in the natural world whose naturalistic imagination has become a cognitive power, called *ontological science*, that enables them to explain Appearance from outside consciousness. Thus, when ontological scientists use naturalistic imagination to discount the intuitionist illusion in their own experience, they find themselves knowing Reality behind Appearance. Hence, they have naturalistic Reason, and ontological science is naturalistic metaphysics. It is the third kind of metaphysical argument, and as scientific realists about perception, they explain consciousness from outside looking in. The discovery that mind is a phantom Reality solves the mind-body problem.

Three kinds of metaphysical arguments evolve in a necessary order during the third minor stage of spiritual evolution, and that is the outline of what I call the *biography of Reason*. On Earth, the story of its life is told as the history of philosophy in Western civilization. But there is more to its biography because what is taught as the history of philosophy in Western civilization is only the beginning of the metaphysical stage. Reason is born as ancient intuitionistic metaphysics, and with help from a religion that explains God as the creator of the natural world, the infant becomes a child in modern intuitionistic metaphysics. It grows up trying to solve the puzzles confronting intuitionistic metaphysics, and despair about ever solving them leads in the modern era to an adolescent identity crisis, which begins and is resolved in three steps. First, Reason renounces the faculty of perceptual intuition as a way of knowing about the natural world, and assuming that the natural world exists, it uses the empirical method to learn about it. When Reason becomes science, it leaves behind its parents' religious explanation of the nature of Good, which survives only as faith in God. But since the evolution of science is led by physics, Reason does not renounce the faculty of rational intuition when it takes up the empirical method. It continues to assume that mathematical truth is known *a priori*, that is, independently of what perception finds in the natural world, and following empirical lawism, it assumes that mathematically formulated laws of nature are the deepest possible empirical knowledge about the natural world. The spectacular success of physics inspires the sciences that study less-general regularities about change in the natural world. But since physics is addicted to its mathoscope, specialized sciences are crippled and unable to explain completely what is found in the study of nature.

The specialized sciences cannot be reduced to laws of physics, and the more those branches of science learn, the more their disunity is a problem. And conclusions about what really exists that cannot be understood in naturalistic imagination are defended in physics. This disillusionment in science is an identity crisis for Reason, and it becomes so intense that Reason takes the second step in its resolution. It admits that laws of physics are not the deepest possible empirical knowledge of the natural world and gives up intuitionistic naturalism in favor of ontological naturalism. By agreeing with the pre-Socratics about substances being the first cause, physics admits that it has become addicted to a mathoscope that filters out the role of space in helping matter generate the regularities on which it focuses, and it is rewarded by solving its puzzles and discovering that matter has a holistic power, expressed as geometrical efficient causes. This reveals how the regularities discovered by specialized sciences can all be reduced to spatio-materialism. This goes a long way towards resolving the identity crisis that began when Reason, in its adolescence, gave up trying to explain the nature of the Good because ontological science explains goodness by the nature of life. It discovers that the difference between good and evil matters to reflective subjects because choosing what is good is essential to leading lives as parts of a spiritual kind of geometrical action aimed at the good. That restores the part of itself that Reason left behind when it took up the empirical method, and that is a portent of a more complete unification of science and religion.

Reason does not fully resolve its adolescent identity crisis until it takes a third step. Though the reduction of physics to ontology unifies science, it is not yet an explanation of everything found in the natural world. For one thing, it does not explain its own existence. And that is part of something else that has yet to be explained: the unprecedented power that has evolved in Western civilization and the globalization of its institutions. Both are explained by showing that the stage at which reflective subjects evolve is followed by the metaphysical stage of spiritual evolution and the unprecedented powers that it gives Western civilization. Thus, as shown in *Chapter 2*, the mind is related to the psychological-level brain in the same way that the psychological-level brain is related to the naturalistic-level brain, in the same way that language-using brains are related to primate brains, and in the same way so on down through all the levels of geometrical organization responsible for the stages of evolution that lead to the existence of beings like us. They are all part-whole relations. But since the part-whole relation between the brain and the mind depends on the illusion of intuitionism, the belief in mind that constitutes it is false, and when ontological science explains the mind as a phantom Reality of modern metaphysics, it discovers how the mind is identical to the brain. This part-whole relation is different from all the others only because the metaphysical level of linguistic organization enlists the help of consciousness in causing a stage of evolution.

This third step is not just a more complete explanation of the course of evolution. It is an explanation of evolution by ontological scientists who are conscious, and it is meant to be understood by other reflective subjects who are conscious. The knowers must understand their own consciousness. The assumption that matter has a proto-phenomenal intrinsic property enables spatio-materialists to understand how their own consciousness is part of the natural world. The assumption that matter has a holistic property enables them to explain the unity of their own consciousness as its phenomenal expression in the mammalian brain, and since they can explain the illusion of intuition as its geometrical expression in the mammalian brain, they can understand what intuitionistic metaphysicians mean when they make metaphysical arguments. But since they understand how consciousness causes the illusion of intuitionism, they discount the illusion and discover that the mind is a phantom Reality. Mind is nothing but a reflective mammalian brain making an intuitionistic metaphysical argument after giving up direct realism in favor of representative realism about perception. This way of discounting the illusion of intuitionism depends on ontological scientists using naturalistic imagination to understand their own reflection. That gives them a kind of *double-sightedness.* Not only can they understand the arguments of intuitionists as intuitionists do, they can also understand how the use of metaphysical sentences depends on an illusion inherent in what it is like to be a mammalian brain. But ontological scientists already know the nature of Reality (that is, how everything in the natural world is constituted by substances). Thus, when they use naturalistic imagination to discount the illusion inherent in their own consciousness in this way, they find themselves knowing Reality behind Appearance. As naturalists, they call it *naturalistic Reason.* Since they can explain everything found in the study of nature and the study of Appearance, they have attained the goal of both science and philosophy. They can even explain naturalistic Reason itself, and since they can explain everything found in the natural world, there are no grounds for doubting naturalistic Reason. When ontological scientists recognize that they have the perfect kind of cognitive power to which philosophy has aspired since ancient Greece, the adolescent identity crisis of Reason is finally resolved. Their self-understanding is how Reason understands its own nature.

PART TWO:
WESTERN PHILOSOPHY

The puzzle left unsolved at the end of *Volume II* of *Naturalistic Reason* was the unprecedented power that Western civilization has accumulated. Instead of falling, like past civilizations, its culture and institutions are spreading to other spiritual organisms on Earth in a largely peaceful way. That puzzle has a solution in a science based on ontology. Knowing how consciousness is part of the natural world, ontological science can explain such a dramatic change in human history as the advent of a third minor stage of spiritual evolution caused by the exchange of metaphysical arguments. That explanation of Western civilization is confirmed in *Part Two* by using the history of philosophy to show how metaphysics caused Western culture to evolve an entire new range of functional powers by Rational selection, including physical science.

To be sure, it hardly seems possible that metaphysics is what caused the West to be different from the rest. Though beginning with the Enlightenment, Westerners generally assumed that their civilization was basically superior to all others, everyone now knows that metaphysics failed, and in the context of the undeniable success of science, a defense of metaphysics seems perverse. Metaphysics promised Absolute Truth, and these days, to be educated is to know that Absolute Truth is not possible. Indeed, it is conventional wisdom that belief in Absolute Truth is the main source of tyranny and genocide. But the theory is not that gradual evolution at the third minor stage of spiritual evolution has been completed in the West. It is, rather, that Western civilization is the beginning of that stage. The history of philosophy can be portrayed as a biography in which Reason was born in ancient Greece and was reared as an intuitionist metaphysician. In the modern era, it rebelled against intuitionistic metaphysics, and beginning with the Enlightenment, a period of unparalleled success in learning about the natural world began. But for Reason, this was an adolescent identity crisis because it kept the faculty of rational intuition, and as physical science, it led to a growing disillusionment with Reason. As late as a few decades ago, it was still possible to be optimistic about the future of civilization on Earth. The globalization of Western institutions could be seen as the *end of history*, in which the Enlightenment was completed as liberal institutions became universal and capitalism made everyone affluent. But, now, it is easier to agree with the pessimists who predicted a *clash of civilizations*. And as disillusionment with Reason is replaced by a popular culture in which it is universally acknowledged that there is no such thing as the True, endarkenment looms ahead. The prospect of the metaphysical stage degenerating to the psychological stage without even a religion to agree about which goals we should all jointly pursue, it is hard to avoid being pessimistic about human destiny.

That is the story told in *Part Two*. But the scientific revolution predicted by this trilogy resolves the identity crisis of reason, and as *Part Three* shows, optimism about human destiny is restored when ontological science becomes naturalistic Reason.

CHAPTER 4:
ANCIENT AND MEDIEVAL PHILOSOPHY

Remarkably, even the statistical methods used in social science can be used to show that human accomplishments in Western civilization far outstrip those of non-Western civilizations. Charles Murray has developed an objective statistical measure of the greatest creative triumphs in science, technology, and art throughout human history, and it points to a basic difference between Western and non-Western civilizations.[40] He traces it to distinctive traits of the West, including its aspiration to realize transcendental goals, that is, its belief in the True, the Good, and the Beautiful. But the difference is also attributed to a curiosity about what is found in the natural world that led to science. This distinctive trait can be seen by comparing the responses of Western and non-Western civilizations to the invention of the telescope by a Dutch spectacle maker in 1608. Nicholas Wade calls it a *controlled experiment in history*.[41]

When Galileo learned of its invention, he built his own telescope and used his discovery of the moons of Jupiter to defend the controversial Copernican hypothesis about the Earth orbiting the Sun. The Church was committed to the ancient Ptolemaic system, which had the Sun circling the Earth, and in the canonical history of science, the Church's punishment of Galileo was just its last-ditch stand against the rise of a new science, which would soon triumph as the Newtonian revolution. The Ptolemaic system had spread around the globe, and Toby E. Huff, a historian of science, used the reception of the telescope in the Muslim world and China at the time to gauge interest in science.[42] In the Mughal Empire in India, scholars were familiar with the astronomical findings of earlier centuries of Islamic civilization, but their

---

[40] Charles Murray (2003).

[41] Nicholas Wade (2014, p. 215).

[42] Toby E Huff (2011).

interest in astronomy stopped with the calendar. The arrival of the telescope in 1628 did not inspire makers of astronomical instruments to fashion their own telescopes, much less question the Ptolemaic system. Nor is there any evidence of telescopes being used for astronomical purposes in the 17th century. The telescope's arrival in the Ottoman Empire around 1626 evoked no greater interest, again, leaving the Ptolemaic system unchallenged. Almost simultaneously in China, Jesuits used the telescope's more accurate predictions of astronomical events, such as an eclipse of the Sun in 1629, to gain credibility in their ongoing attempt to convert Chinese scholars to Christianity. But the Chinese interest in astronomy was only for purposes of divination. Indeed, a Jesuit who touted the telescope as a way of learning about the natural world was even jailed in 1661 for interference in Chinese affairs, escaping execution by dismemberment only because an earthquake the next day prompted his release.

Huff attributes this indifference to the telescope in non-Western civilizations to a "deficit of curiosity," reinforced by educational institutions that mistook memorization for learning about the world. He holds that an "infectious curiosity" inspired by the Newtonian revolution led Europeans to the study anatomy and microbiology, weigh the atmosphere, and explore electricity and magnetism. But like Murray, Huff attributes historical differences to a cultural accident, and Nicholas Wade suggests a more basic cause. As a Darwinist, he believes that genetic differences between Caucasians and Asians played a role in making Europeans "innovative, outward-looking, keen to develop and apply new knowledge, and sufficiently open to prevent the old order from suppressing the new" (219). Ontological science agrees with Wade in looking for a more basic cause of the rise of the West than a cultural accident. But he is on the wrong track in looking for it in genetic differences. Ontological science agrees with Huff and Murray in looking for a cause in history and culture, but it discovers a more basic cause in culture. It explains Western civilization as a third minor stage of spiritual evolution.

The ontological explanation of stages of evolution reveals that the societies studied by historians and social scientists are spiritual organisms. They are a form of life because they have a plan-sharing geometrical cause based on the use of language that guides group-level behavior through cycles in which it does both primary and secondary work. After nomadic bands evolve into agricultural villages, civilization arises because spiritual organisms with a class structure of some kind justified by a religion are able to support a larger population. As a higher level of organization of geometrical action on the fourth floor of the edifice of life, class structure enabled the spiritual BGS to guide group-level behavior to goals that control relevant conditions in large territories with many cities. And as Wade argues, reflective subjects continue to evolve by individual-level natural selection within civilized spiritual organisms. Indeed, genetic changes may have adapted the desire to submit to spiritual input, originally based on kinship loyalties, to the more impersonal spiritual input of the force field of political authority that helps constitute a class structure. But differences between tribal and civilized spiritual organisms do not explain the difference between the West and other great civilizations. To look for the cause of evolutionary change in the frequency of genes in the gene pool is to overlook the basic cause of the evolutionary change that occurs in spiritual organisms. As Huff insists, it is cultural. But *infectious curiosity* is just a symptom of a far more basic cultural cause.

During the second stage of gradual evolution, spiritual organisms at the psychological level of linguistic organization evolve, and as we have seen, a third stage is both possible and functional. Metaphysical sentences are on a higher level of linguistic organization than psychological sentences, and since consciousness makes it possible to believe in a cognitive power that can know Reality behind Appearance, belief in Reason can begin as a random variation in culture without the help of genetic change. The assumption that beliefs are true when they correspond to Reality is functional because it causes culture to evolve by Rational selection. One effect is the coherence of culture. The beliefs that accumulate as culture must fit together consistently so that they all correspond to a single Reality. Since the Good is part of the True, Rational subjects are guided by knowledge of the nature of the Good, and so another effect of the belief in Reason is the evolution of institutions of freedom that respect their autonomy as moral beings. It also gives spiritual organisms greater functional power. Since belief in Reason is both possible and functional, the overall course of evolution includes a third stage of spiritual evolution, the *metaphysical stage*, during which spiritual organisms acquire an order of functional powers that is out of the reach of spiritual organisms at the psychological level.

This prediction of a third stage of spiritual evolution is confirmed by the history of Western civilization. As we have seen, combining the unity of consciousness with its explanation of the self as a reflective neural BGS, ontology distinguishes two ways of basing a metaphysical argument on intuitionism. One depends on direct realism about perception and the other on representative realism. In Western philosophy, the former was introduced by Plato, and the latter was introduced by Descartes. This confirms that the metaphysical level of linguistic organization occurred in the spiritual BGSs of the West, and so the following account of the history of Western philosophy may seem like overkill. But there is a further issue. Ontology must show how intuitionistic metaphysics gave Western civilization the power to cause globalization. As noted in the conclusion of *Volume II*, its power depends on science, liberal political institutions, and capitalism, and this intellectual history shows how they were products of cultural evolution by Rational selection at the metaphysical level of linguistic organization. But intuitionism is false, and so disillusionment with Reason was inevitable. However, that was not the end of the metaphysical stage of spiritual evolution, as explained in *Part Three*.

The metaphysical stage of spiritual evolution began in ancient Greece, and since this was as early as, if not before, the rise of civilizations in the East, it is a fourth instance of a higher level of geometrical organization beginning its stage of evolution before the peak of the evolutionary stage caused by a lower level.[43] And the explanation is the same. Since higher-level geometrical causes are more complex than their lower-level parts, it takes longer for higher-level triple-action geometrical causes to acquire every possible functional power as it becomes possible than for those at the next lower level.

This chapter traces the history of the intuitionistic belief in Reason from

---

[43] Deuterostomes evolved before the heyday of protostomes, mammals evolved very early in the age of dinosaurs, and modern humans evolved before Neanderthals occupied Europe. All four are minor stages because they are caused by levels of organization in BGSs on some floor of the edifice of life.

its onset in ancient Greece, through its marriage with Christian theology, to its offspring in the Middle Ages, leaving the modern era to be described in *Chapter 5*. Philosophy includes not only the defense of metaphysics but also the arguments of its skeptics. Since the skeptics are also intuitionists, they attribute the failure of metaphysics to an epistemological error, called *rationalism*, and so they make more modest claims about Reason. But ontological science supports a contrary interpretation of philosophy. It traces the failure of metaphysics to ontological problems caused by its intuitionistic explanation of the nature of Reason. Their explanations of the nature of Reality were inadequate. But ontological science reveals that confidence in Reason caused Western culture to evolve by Rational selection. It culminated in the Enlightenment, and though its brightest star was the rise of physics and science, it also gave rise to capitalism, another form of the reproductive mechanism based on the spiritual BGS, as well as governments that respect the rights of its citizens. *Chapter 6* shows how confidence in Reason caused the Enlightenment. *Chapter 7* shows how the Enlightenment was followed by disillusionment with Reason. And *Chapter 8* shows it has evolved into our current era of *endarkenment*. But when a science based on ontology explains the course of human history, it reduces reflective subjects and their consciousness to the space and matter constituting the natural world, and as *Part III* explains, science becomes Reason knowing Reality behind Appearance. Being like us everywhere acquire naturalistic Reason.

1 Ancient Philosophy

Arguments about metaphysics began in ancient Greece. It was a civilization whose religion made it possible to believe that human beings were capable of perfection. The Greek Dark Ages (1100 to 800 BC) had an effect on ancient Greek culture like a founder group in biological evolution, in which the traits of a small group are inherited by a large population. But instead of a gene pool beginning a new species, the culture of weaker and more rural spiritual organisms provided the foundation for a new civilization.

The history of a distinctively Greek culture began on Crete with the Minoan civilization (which flourished from 3000 to 1400 BC). It had trade with Egypt and Syria during the Neolithic period, and after 2000 BC, during the Bronze Age, there were great palaces. But around 1600 BC, the Minoan empire was supplanted for some unknown reason by the Mycenaean empire based in Greece. Though there is no trace of metaphysics in either culture, both had a polytheistic religion. The Mycenaean empire fell around 1150 BC as part of the still-unexplained collapse of the Late Bronze Age. But its religion survived for hundreds of years, inseminating classical Greece culture.

Though the Minoan language remains undeciphered, images used in Minoan religious rituals suggest that, besides goddesses, the gods they worshiped were animals, such as snakes and bulls. The Mycenaean gods, however, were all human-like, with Poseidon having a privileged status over many others. There is evidence of temples in which they continued to be worshiped during the Greek Dark Ages. Many are recognizably forerunners of the ancient Greek gods, described in Homer's (800 BC) epic poems, the *Iliad* and the *Odyssey*. The worship of immortal humans with special powers made it conceivable that mortals are capable of perfection.

Culture evolves by judgmental selection, and in a civilization at the psychological stage of spiritual evolution, an autocratic state based on the class structure is stable. Its rule can be imposed over a wide territory by what is aptly called an *ideological mechanism*, an institution that promotes supportive religions and excludes arguments that challenge its authority. Within such ideological constraints, culture can evolve by pragmatic selection. But the civilization around the Aegean Sea was divided into autonomous city-states, and when they were not at war, they were connected by sea-based commerce. This geographical accident was a necessary condition for the evolution of a culture by a different standard.[44] Spiritual input was leavened with the teachings of travelers, such as the sophists, and in the absence of ideological constraints, respect for cogent arguments was able to determine what was believed. Since they shared a polytheistic religion, myths about the supreme powers of immortal gods tempted the pre-Socratic philosophers to believe that they might be able to acquire a perfect understanding of the natural world.

---

[44] I was reminded recently that my colleague and friend, Jon Wisman, uses this condition to explain why the West is different from other civilizations on Earth. But progressive evolution is not a basic law of nature in the spatio-material world, and so it can only be a necessary condition in ontological science.

1.1 Pre-Socratic Philosophy

Pre-Socratic philosophers began by putting aside religious myths. They assumed that human beings have the power to discover the *first cause* (*arché*) of the natural world, and they rejected traditional arguments by refusing to use gods and their intentions to explain what they found. Instead, they tried to become like gods by explaining the natural world in its own terms. In the 6th century BC, Thales and other thinkers living in Miletus, a city-state in Ionia on the western coast of Turkey, defended the first theories. This project, pursued over several generations, discovered that the first cause is substances constituting the world, and their naturalistic conception of substance set a standard that would later be used to judge the success of metaphysical arguments about Reason knowing Reality behind Appearance.

Thales held that everything is made of water, presumably because it is sometimes a solid, sometimes a liquid, and sometimes a gas. If everything were made of water, the self-subsistence of water would explain its existence. But water did not explain all the kinds of things found in the natural world or how they could change, and so Anaximander rejected Thales' theory and held that the first cause was an unlimited entity (called *apeiron*), in which opposite properties competed for existence. But that did not explain where the properties themselves came from, and so Anaximander insisted that the first cause must be air. He attributed changes in observable properties to its condensation and rarefaction, and since air was self-subsistent, it could be a first cause of everything in the world. However, no Ionian offered an adequate explanation of how a first cause gives rise to change, much less all the kinds of regular change found in the world, and so their theories merely laid the foundation on which other pre-Socratic philosophers would pose a dilemma about change.

There were hundreds of city-states sprinkled in and around Greece, more or less independent of one another. They were the fertile ground for traveling teachers to plant the arguments of pre-Socratic philosophers. In a city-state in what is now called *Italy*, Parmenides concluded that change is a mere appearance. He held that what really exists is an extended spherical whole that cannot change. Back in Ionia, Heraclitus defended the opposite view, holding that change itself (or fire) is the first cause.

Parmenides and Heraclitus posed a dilemma for the pre-Socratic project.

It had to choose between a self-subsistent first cause that does not change, which explains nothing that changes, and a first cause that is change, which explains nothing but what is self-subsistent. This dilemma was solved in a city-state in Sicily when Empedocles postulated four different kinds of substances: earth, air, fire and, water. As a direct realist, he used qualia to define their natures: earth is dry and cold, water is wet and cold, air is dry and cold, and fire is dry and hot. They were all self-subsistent, and their natures did not change. But as they endured through time, they could mix and separate, and so these substances could constitute change. This ontology is recognizably a form of materialism, though Empedocles had to postulate powers of *love* and *strife* in order to explain why they mix and separate. But Anaxagoras was skeptical about whether it could explain all the kinds of properties and change found in the natural world, and so he proposed an improvement. Bringing arguments from what is now Turkey to Athens, he held that the natural world is constituted by infinitely many different kinds of basic substances (*seeds*). Since their essential properties included all kinds of qualia, their mixture and separation could explain every kind of thing and how it changes ontologically. But in order to explain why substances mix and separate as they endure through time, Anaxagoras had to postulate a power called *nous* (reason or mind).

Though the pre-Socratics conceived of substance as what we call *matter*, one of the ontologies defended in 5th century BC is more akin to spatio-materialism. Leucippus, an Ionian, and Democritus, a Thracian, used the concept of substance to defend the belief that what exists includes not only atoms but also the *void*. Atoms had geometrical structures that determined how they interacted, and the void separated atoms from one another so that they could move around freely and interact with one another. For example, atoms with hooks could become linked to and unlinked from the eyes of other atoms. Atoms are clearly a kind of matter, and if the void behaved like a frictionless fluid through which the atoms moved, the void can be seen as an opposite kind of matter, playing a space-like role.

Though the pre-Socratics were not metaphysicians, they made a contribution to it because their first cause set a standard by which the success of intuitionistic metaphysics would be judged. The pre-Socratics were naturalists looking for a cause that explained everything, and they discovered that it was just all the substances constituting the natural world. Substances are ontological causes because, as self-subsistent entities, without any deeper cause of their existence, they were the first cause of the existence of what is found in the natural world. And since substances have unchanging ways of existing, their essential natures can explain the kinds of things they constitute. This discovery about the nature of substance was a contribution to metaphysics because it set a standard for judging whether Reason had succeeded in discovering Reality. In the end, a metaphysical theory would have to describe a substance or substances that explain everything found in the world, including Appearance, and failure by that standard is what discredited intuitionistic metaphysics. The mistake was not the belief that Reason can know the nature of Reality, but, rather, the belief that Reason is a faculty of intuition.

To be sure, some pre-Socratic philosophers are interpreted as holding that Reason knows Reality behind Appearance. Parmenides, for example, can be seen as a drawing a distinction between Reality and Appearance. In a fragment of his poem, he defended the existence of something that cannot change, calling it the *way of truth*, and he contrasted knowledge of it with the *way of appearance*. His argument was that *what is, is, and cannot not be, and that what is not, is not, and cannot be*. The necessity of this belief about existence does not depend on what is found in the natural world, and since he attributes knowledge of it to *nous*, or *Reason*, he betrays belief in a faculty of rational intuition. By contrasting the way of truth with the way of appearance, which depends on perception, Parmenides seems, therefore, to hold that Reason is able to know Reality behind Appearance. And his follower, Zeno, is famous for using Reason to pose paradoxes meant to show the illusory nature of Appearance, arguing, for example, that an arrow cannot really move because at every moment it is at rest. There is further evidence of a pre-Socratic belief in knowledge of Reality behind Appearance in a religious cult on a Greek island led by Pythagoras, who can be interpreted as holding that rational intuition reveals that everything is made of numbers.

However, this is not the significance of Parmenides' argument in pre-Socratic philosophy. What he contributed to the pre-Socratic project of discovering the nature of the first cause was making explicit one essential aspect of substance as an ontological cause. To constitute everything in the natural world, it had to be a self-subsistent entity that endures through time, never coming into existence nor going out of existence. This is the assumption that enabled Empedocles to complete the pre-Socratic project by postulating multiple substances and requiring them to exist in some way so that their interaction could constitute all the kinds of things found in the world and all the regular ways they change. The coherence of ontological explanations, in this sense, was the gold standard for judging the success of metaphysical theories. That is the significance of pre-Socratic philosophy for metaphysics.

1.2 Plato

If pre-Socratic philosophy set the standard for judging whether Reason knows Reality behind Appearance, Socrates set the standard for judging how well Reason serves its function of guiding behavior. He insisted that Reality explain the nature of the good in a way that causes Rational subjects who know its nature to lead the good life.

During the 5th century BC, Socrates famously cross-examined Athenians in public places about the good life, embarrassing respected figures by showing their answers to be wanting. This is the crime for which he was ultimately condemned to death, and in his own defense before a jury of his fellow citizens, which is described in Plato's *Apology,* Socrates insisted that his only crime was to be a *lover of wisdom*, a philosopher. His insistence that the unexamined life is not worth living is now commonly understood as meaning that the best life that beings like us can lead is to *ask* what the good life is, since everyone knows that there is no answer. But Socrates' wisdom was that the good life depends on Reason knowing Reality. In *Euthyphro*, an early Platonic dialogue, for example, Socrates compels Euthyphro to give up his belief that the pious is pious because the gods love it in favor of the belief that the gods love what is pious because it is pious, that is, because it is already good. Socrates assumed that knowledge of Reality entails includes knowing the nature of the good, and he believed that to know the Good is to choose the good. That is the perfect way to lead a life, and that is what he meant by *the good life*. In the *Phaedo*, where Socrates explains why he did not accept offers to escape from prison and avoid his death sentence for doing the work of philosophy, he explains that, as a young man, he rejected Anaxagoras' pre-Socratic theory that *mind* governs how *seeds* mix and separate because it would imply that what caused him to remain in his cell were his bones and sinews, rather than knowing the nature of the good. Thus, before the first explicit defense of metaphysics, a practical as well as a theoretical test of its success had been established.

The pre-Socratics and Socrates provided all the pieces that Plato (428-347 B.C.) needed to construct a third level of linguistic organization in the culture of his spiritual organism. He was a direct realist about perception, and as an intuitionist, he assumed that objects of perceptual intuition are the natural world. As we have seen, this made it plausible for Plato to interpret the phenomenal appearances of the meanings of words constructed in (naturalistic and psychological) imagination as Forms that also exist independently of the knower. He called the realm of changing visible objects in space *Becoming* and the realm of unchanging Forms *Being*. In this simple formula for interpreting metaphysical sentences, the world of visible objects is Appearance, and the Reality that Reason (*nous*) is supposed to discover behind Appearance is a separate world of Forms. As phenomenal appearances of meanings of general words, Forms have necessary relations to one another, and since the changing visible objects identified by those meanings can be seen as imitating unchanging Forms, entities in the realm of Being seem to explain all the kinds of things and regular ways of changing found in the realm of Becoming.[45]

Even in Plato's time, ontological problems made it hard to accept this metaphysical system. But it allowed ancient Greeks to believe that mortal humans are capable of a kind of perfection. Reason is the power to know Reality behind Appearance, and thus, not only can humans be perfect knowers, but they can also be perfect doers. Plato built the wisdom that he learned as a follower of Socrates into his metaphysics as the *Form of the Good*. As explained in the *Republic*, the Form of the Good is the Form on which all the other Forms depend, and since visible objects in the realm of Becoming

---

[45] Plato's metaphysical argument posed a problem of ontological dualism that made it difficult to accept, but in the spatio-material world, it is reduced to the relation between the linguistic geometrical action embodied in neural geometrical action and the neural geometrical action by which mammals perceive the natural world.

imitate Forms in the realm of Being, Forms determine what is good for them. By understanding how other Forms depend on the Form of the Good, therefore, Rational subjects know what makes the good for visible objects good. Since they have bodies animated by souls that also imitate Forms, they also know what is good for themselves and why it is good. Among the Forms behind Appearance are the virtues of prudence, justice, courage, and temperance. When it comes to explaining why Rational subjects are virtuous, Plato assumes that rational intuition of the Good Itself causes them to choose the good. But his only explanation of how this works is a metaphor. He holds that Rational subjects are irresistibly attracted to the Form of the Good, as Eros is attracted to physical beauty, but since the desire is attached to an object of rational intuition, it is called *Platonic love*. But this desire is just an assumption, and so Plato never explains how the rational intuition of the Good Itself causes Rational subjects to choose the good.

Plato's explanation of what is good for reflective subjects is not as simplistic as this rendering of his metaphysics suggests. He recognized a basic problem about doing the good when he used the myth of Gyges ring to introduce the issue of justice in the *Republic*. Turning the bezel of the ring inward made its wearer invisible, and since that enabled the wearer to violate moral rules in their self-interest and get away with it, Socrates asked why someone with Gyges ring would do what morality requires when it was contrary to their self-interest. Plato answered this question by describing the nature of the ideal city-state, the *Republic*, as the ideal soul of an individual *writ large*. Like the individual, the city-state needed Reason to guide behavior towards goals that are good, and since Plato did not believe that everyone was capable of Reason, he described the ideal city-state as one in which philosophers were kings and used a *spirited element* to ensure that others obeyed their commands.

Plato held that there are three grades of souls (gold, silver and bronze). Gold souls could learn to know the Forms, and when they knew the nature of the good, they would do the good and lead the good life. Hence, they would have to rule others. But even for them, it was not easy to know the Forms. In his famous *allegory of the cave*, Plato described the extensive training required to turn away from the attractive distractions inside the cave of

Appearance and climb up the arduous mathematical pathway to Reality outside, where Forms were illuminated by the Good Itself, like visible objects in sunlight. The Republic would provide this education to gold souls, and the Good Itself would lead philosophers to turn away from its beauty and to return to the cave, where their choice of goals that are good for the Republic would provide spiritual input that determines goals for other members to follow. Seeing the Form of the city-state as the individual *writ large*, Plato described a three-part hierarchy of classes with an unavoidable tension between them. Philosophers were like the *rational part,* where a faculty of intuition discovers the Good as part of the True. But in order to do what is good, the Republic, like the soul, had to act contrary to the *appetitive part*, or animal desires, which motivate the pursuit of self-interest. They were the merchants, workers, and others with bronze souls, whose pursuit of goals chosen for them was how the Republic followed Reason. Thus, to overcome their resistance, there had to be a third part of the Republic, the auxiliaries of philosophers, or *spirited element*, whose silver souls had the courage to follow spiritual input from the philosopher kings and ensure that appetitive bronze souls did what is good.

Since human societies are spiritual organisms, the relation between the individual soul and the Republic is more than an analogy. Since both are forms of life, both necessarily have a BGS. But when Plato explains the Republic as the individual *writ large*, he fails to recognize the difference between the neural BGSs of individuals with a spiritual desire and the plan-sharing BGS of spiritual organisms that provides the spiritual input for it. He uses the tension between the spiritual desire and other desires in reflective subjects as a model for the ideal city-state, so he fails to recognize the full potential of Reason. His *Republic* is like a naturalistic-level spiritual organism, in which members must follow the commands of a leader, or like a civilized spiritual organism, ruled by an autocrat. A more ideal city-state is already suggested by the basic nature of psychological-level spiritual organisms, where the spiritual desire motivates reflective subjects to cooperate in pursuing goals that they find themselves sharing. Though the natural form of government for a psychological-level civilization, with its class structure, is autocracy, the metaphysical level points to a more ideal Republic in which individuals are autonomous and autocracy is not needed. The spiritual desire enables Rational subjects who understand the nature of the Good to do what is required by the goals that are good for them to pursue jointly. They understand their spiritual nature, and since they know the choices that are required for them to live as members of a spiritual organism, each knows that choosing those goals is good for them. But as Plato knew, his explanation of how Reason passes the Socratic test was merely aspirational. He believed that only a few reflective subjects could become philosophers, and though they had Reason, he could not explain how knowledge of the Form of the Good caused them to choose goals that are good. Thus, he resorted to his myth about the cave, emphasized the arduous training required for gold souls to leave the cave, and used the Sun to stand for the Good Itself that they found outside. Plato's Republic makes it seem that belief in Reason is autocratic.[46]

1.3 Metaphysics

In Alfred North Whitehead's words, "The safest general characterization of the European philosophical tradition is that it consists of a series of footnotes to Plato."[47] As the first full-scale defense of metaphysics, Plato's argument is the random variation with which the metaphysical stage of spiritual evolution began, and it pointed to a kind of perfection about beings like us that inspired many generations in Western civilization. But its offspring are also a model for how intuitionistic metaphysics fails.

Though the pre-Socratics did not defend metaphysics, they showed how the natural world can be explained by substances, and their understanding of ontology set a standard of coherence for judging the success of Reason in knowing Reality behind Appearance. Since Plato's Being is self-subsistent, it is a substance in Parmenides' sense of *what is*. And since there are Forms in the realm of Being, it is a substance in Empedocles sense, whose essential nature can explain the kinds of things found in Becoming. But Being is also unchanging, and since Becoming is change, Plato tried to explain Becoming as simply *less real* than Being. Ontologists would insist, however, that since Becoming exist independently of Being, it must also be a substance, and they

---

[46] Plato's *Republic* was a target (along with Marx and Hegel) of Karl Popper's (1971) denunciation of holism (or collectivism) in the *Open Society and its Enemies*. He was defending a mistaken doctrine called *methodological individualism*, but given the natural perfection of metaphysical-level spiritual organisms, his criticisms are justified.

[47] Alfred North Whitehead (1979, p. 39).

would want to know is how these two substances are related.

In order for both Being and Becoming to be objects of intuition, two substances must constitute the same world. But since Being exists outside space and time, there is no context in which to explain how it can act on the substance constituting space and time, much less how phenomenal subjects can intuit both. Plato addressed this ontological issue in the *Timaeus* (48b-52d), a late dialogue in which Becoming is explained as a *receptacle* in which the Forms appear as *moving images*, that is, with locations in space and time. He uses a myth about a demiurge to explain why there are moving images of Forms in the receptacle, and though this myth suggests that Becoming can be explained in its own terms, like a closed system, it does not solve the ontological problem. Though it is called *metaphysical* dualism, the problem is *ontological*. Their opposite natures preclude understanding in naturalistic imagination how these substances are related as part of a single world. This ontological problem is the Achilles heel of intuitionistic metaphysics.[48]

Ontological dualism was not a problem in pre-Socratic philosophy because their ontological theories all assumed that substances constituting the natural world interact. No such problem confronted Empedocles (or Anaxagoras) because four (or infinitely many) kinds of substances are just varieties of many particular material substances whose mixture and separation explained the change that direct realists find in the natural world. Nor was ontological dualism a problem for Leucippus and Democritus. Though they postulated two opposite kinds of substances, atoms are particular material substances of various sizes and shapes. and their nature as atoms enables them to fit together coherently with the void (presumably seen as a fluid-like matter that separates atoms). But atomism anticipated the explanatory power of geometrical causes. Atomists could explain regularities about change because the sizes and shapes of atoms imposed constraints on what happens as they move and interact in the void.

Since the properties of atoms did not include sensory qualia, atomists had to believe that they were located in the subjects perceiving the natural world.

---

[48] But not all ontological dualisms are problematic. Though ontological science discovers two opposite kinds of substances, spatio-materialism is not problematic because we can understand in naturalistic imagination how space and matter interact.

But it would be misleading to call them representative realists about perception. Atomists explained sensory qualia as special kinds of small spherical atoms that helped constitute the perceiver. But they did not hold that perception of the natural world depended on sensory qualia. No one defended intuitionism until Plato, and the ancient atomists did not try to explain why qualia appear to be configured alongside one another in a 3-D phenomenal space. They were probably direct realists about space who explained what seemed to be qualia objects in space as constituted by atoms. To acknowledge that they were just pre-Socratic *ontological naturalists*, they might be called *critical realists about perception*.[49]

Plato may not even have known about his contemporary, Democritus. But a student in Plato's *Academy* was familiar enough with atomism to reject it explicitly in favor of a naturalistic ontology intended to solve Plato's dualism. Though Aristotle was a direct realist, like Plato, he explained Being and Becoming as two ontological causes in each of the many *particular substances* that make up the natural world. *Matter* helped constitute particular substances, enabling them to exist outside one another and change as time passes, while a *form* helping constitute each substance defined its essential nature. The distinction between matter and form might seem to be the difference between physical and geometrical efficient causes since matter can be seen as tiny particles moving and interacting with one another and since forms include the shapes of particular substances. But Aristotle was defending Plato, and to explain the role of Plato's Forms without postulating a kind of substance that exists outside space and time, forms of particular substances had to be essential forms that filled the role of Plato's Form of the Good. This way of combining matter and form is called *hylomorphism*, and since they had to be postulated separately, like Plato's Being and Becoming, ontologists would consider them two different kinds of substances helping constitute the natural world. Matter enabled particular things to exist outside one another in space, and since Aristotle used matter to explain efficient causes of all kinds,

---

[49] Though the ancient atomists insisted that Reason (nous) knows what is necessary about change, they were not defending rational intuition. They were merely contrasting their genuine explanation of regularities by interactions of the shapes and sizes of atoms to explanations of the mixture and separation of elements (seeds) by the unexplained powers that Empedocles' called *Love* and *Strife* (and Anaxagoras' called *Nous*).

efficient causes were, in effect, expressions of powers by which material substances act on one another. On the other hand, essential forms were substances with a radically different kind of power because they enabled the matter in which they existed to change spontaneously in the direction of a definite end. It was called *natural change*, and since it was supposed to occur for the sake of the end, the end was called its *final cause*. The essential form determined the natural kind of the thing, and assuming that it could exist in matter potentially, Aristotle explained natural change as the *actualization* of its potential form. Its actualization was its *telos*, or end, and since natural change was supposed to occur for the sake of the end, this was a *teleological* explanation of goodness.

Ontological scientists will understand why teleological explanations are easy to understand. Reflective subjects normally explain what they do by the goal that they intend to bring about, called its *purpose*. And the goal is good, since it what their BGS normally chooses in the situation. But since functional changes of all kinds seem to be purposive, Aristotle could plausibly assume that final causes are what is good for all kinds of things found in the natural world. For example, he called the essential forms of living organisms *souls*, and this was plausible because what corresponds to *souls* are the BGSs that define their natural kinds. The *nutritive souls* of plants are the biological BGSs of forms of life at the multicellular level that are responsible for growth and reproduction; the *sensitive souls* of animals are the neural BGS that the biological BGS builds into animal bodies to guide their behavior in the natural world; and the *Rational souls* are the neural BGSs of language-using animals who know the essential forms that are the Reality behind Appearance.

But since Aristotelian teleology turns the purposive explanations that reflective subjects give of their behavior into an ontological cause that entails a puzzling regularity in which potential future states help determine what happens at present, ontological scientists will see it as shallow and mistaken. First, only reflective subjects have purposes because the reflective neural BGS is the only BGS that represents the goals it chooses as goals. Other kinds of BGSs are just geometrical causes that choose goals and generate behavior to pursue them. To be sure, final causes are still a plausible explanation of what it good for other living organisms because the goals normally chosen by a

BGS are good for it. But second, explanations by final causes were mistaken because Aristotle also used them to explain the regularities about natural change in non-living things. For example, the final causes of earth, water, air, and fire were supposed to be responsible for them moving, respectively, to a series of concentric spheres beginning with Earth at the center of the world. (Ether was the fifth substance, *quintessence*, that helps constitute the heavens, explaining their circular motion.) Since these regularities are not kinds of behavior that are chosen by a BGS, their final causes are not good for them. Third, ontological scientists will know that Aristotelian teleology is basically mistaken because there is no such thing as a final cause in the spatio-material world. Efficient causes are responsible for everything that happens in the natural world. Even in reflective subjects, purposes merely seem to cause the behavior aimed at them. The choices are actually caused by beliefs and desires, but they are seen as reasons that identify something in the goals that make them good and worthy of being chosen. Thus, ontological scientists will see Aristotelian teleology as elevating this misleading appearance of purposes to an ontological cause that entails regularities in which future states affect what happens at present and justify explanations by final causes.[50]

Since Aristotle explains the purposive behavior of Rational animals by a basic ontological cause, his explanation of the nature of what is good for them does not pass the Socratic test of practical wisdom. The actualization of what is potential in them defines their goals both as knowers and as doers. Animals perceive the natural world because they have a sensitive soul to which configurations of qualia are immediately present (because of the transparency of the medium between them and objects of perception). Essential forms of substances are also phenomenal properties that are immediately present to them. The Rational soul is a faculty of intuition that discovers essential forms as the Reality behind Appearance by abstracting them from perceptions of particular substances. Since what is good for a substance is the actualization of its essential form, the virtue regarding theoretical Reason is the intuition of

---

[50] Aristotle implicitly acknowledged that essential forms are a distinct ontological cause, or substance, when he argued (*Metaphysics XII*) that an *unmoved mover* was required to explain final causes, or why potential essential forms are actualized. The unmoved mover was located beyond the heavens, and since it was pure actuality, it was supposed to initiate change, starting with the circular motion of the heavens and affecting what happens on Earth, without itself changing. It was like an object of love resembling Plato's Form of the Good, except that it was not located in a separate realm of Being.

essential forms, including the form of Rational subjects. The Good is part of the True, and recognizing that animals are moved by desires, Aristotle describes the virtue of practical Reason as a character trait in which one habitually chooses the mean between extremes determined by desires. (The virtue of courage, for example, is choosing the mean between cowardice, as giving in to fear, and foolhardiness, as ignoring it.)

Though Reason enables Rational animals to know the nature of the good, Aristotle's explanation it fails the Socratic test of practical wisdom. Rational animals know what is good for them because it is part of the essential form that the Rational soul abstracts from the perception of many particular Rational animals. It is a character trait, and Aristotle holds Rational subjects are responsible for their character because it is acquired by practice. But the habit does not depend on spiritual desire because it is acquired by choosing the mean between the extremes in situations where it is easy. Nor is the spiritual desire needed to follow spiritual input when it is opposed by self-interest or strong desires because Aristotle reduces the spiritual organism to a partnership of Rational animals that serves their common good, which includes promoting the virtue of its citizens. These are the final causes by which the goodness of both the individual and the political system are judged. But Rational subjects are not doing what is good because they know *why* the good is good. Natural change in the direction of moderation in choices is just a puzzling kind of regularity about change that holds for the most part in the natural world, and that is not a reason for choosing the end for the sake of which it appears to occur. At most, Rational animals are using their knowledge of the nature of the good to know *what* is good. But since final causes are basic causes, they do not explain why there are Rational souls, much less why they should choose the mean between extremes, and thus, it does explain how knowledge of the nature of the good causes Rational beings to do what is good.

Since Aristotelian teleology must postulate an ontological cause to explain goodness, it fails not only the Socratic test of practical wisdom but also the pre-Socratic test of ontological coherence. His metaphysics appears to be a form of ontological naturalism because particular things are all located outside one another in space. But pre-Socratics, like Empedocles and the atomists, would not accept it. Form and matter are both ontological causes, and though matter can be understood in naturalistic imagination as a substance helping constitute the natural world, forms cannot. Essential forms are the Reality that Reason knows behind Appearance, and since each essential form is supposed to exist completely in all the particulars that have them, they are called *universals*. Plato had to postulate Forms in a separate realm of Being to explain how a single substance could be seen in many particular visible objects. But since Aristotle wanted to be a naturalist, he had to reject the pre-Socratic assumption that particular things are made of many distinct material substances in favor of holding that essential forms divide continuous matter into distinct particular things with different properties (*Metaphysics VII* and *VIII*). Each essential form was also supposed to cause many particular material substances to change in the direction of an end, and belief in them led Aristotle to explore a range of biological phenomena that was not rivaled until modern science. But since we cannot understand in naturalistic imagination how universals do what Aristotle's metaphysics requires, it fails the pre-Socratic test of ontological coherence.

Though final causes explained change in the natural world, Aristotelian teleology was not deep enough to convince Roman philosophers. Though they admired the culture of classical Greece, they were not metaphysicians, and they used naturalistic ontologies defended during the 4th and 3rd centuries BC were to explain how to lead the good life. *Stoicism* was an ethical theory based on (direct realism and) materialism. It postulated a natural order in which every event was a necessary effect of active matter (*Logos*) on passive matter, and believing that virtue required Rational subjects to do their duty within this order, Stoics saw the good life as developing the self-control to avoid the undesirable emotions that an unlucky fate might otherwise arouse. At the other extreme, *Epicureanism* was an ethical theory founded on atomism (and critical realism). The good life was seen as minimizing pain in order to maximize pleasure. Since there was no afterlife, Epicureans were not threatened by punishment in Hades for bad deeds, and so they had no other duties.

By comparison with Plato and Aristotle, what was missing from these ethical theories was the belief that the Good is something that transcends Appearance, and so there was no attempt to show how knowledge of the nature of the good causes Rational subjects to choose goals that are good. Stoics could explain why reflective subjects did their duty because, given the necessity of the natural order, they had no choice but to accept it. And Epicureans could explain why reflective subjects avoided pain and sought pleasure because there was no alternative in a world where that was the ultimate goal of all behavior. This was to reduce the good to natural necessity and to reduce morality to self-interest. But late in the ancient era, a more profound insight into moral virtue was offered by a marriage of Reason with religion. It planted the seed for further progress of culture at the metaphysical level a thousand years later, after another Dark Ages.

2   Marriage of Reason and Faith

Metaphysics was born in a spiritual organism where immortal human beings with various special powers were worshiped as gods. The belief in Reason was the belief that mortals are capable of their own kind of perfection, a cognitive power with practical significance. Since the Good is part of the True, knowledge of the True would enable Rational subjects to lead the good life. But neither Plato nor Aristotle had an adequate explanation of why it is good to do what morality requires when it is contrary to self-interest. Since Plato's *Republic* was the individual soul writ large, it suggested the tension between the spiritual desire and other desires involved in following moral rules. But it did not explain the spiritual nature on which morality depends. Reflective subjects who can see into one another's minds were not seen as equals. Philosopher kings in Plato's *Republic* needed a class of auxiliaries to force ordinary citizen to do what is right. Nor did Aristotle explain our spiritual nature. His city-state was little more than the way that Rational animals manage to live together, and since they were friends, there was no tension between morality and self-interest. Indeed, ontological scientists looking back will notice that Athenian metaphysicians did not even suspect that there was something morally wrong with slavery. Like most civilizations, slaves were taken in war, and they had no moral rights. Since slavery was a fact of life, some reflective subjects were seen as naturally slaves. But slavery became a moral issue before the fall of Rome. It was caused by a marriage of Platonism with Christianity, and that was the foundation of a culture in which slavery would be considered evil.[51]

2.1 The Nature of the Good

Religion evolved in spiritual organisms when language-using mammals acquired the use of psychological sentences. Since they were able to describe their own psychological states as part of the process of guiding their behavior, they recognized that they were cooperating in the pursuit of shared goals. But this is what they *found* themselves doing, and so they could not help but ask why. Part of the cultural plan shared by the use of language was a religion that explained why they followed the spiritual input coordinating their behavior. It was an explanation of the meaning of life, and at the psychological stage of spiritual evolution, it could be just a myth about their origin that explained why they had a shared purpose. But what matters to reflective subjects as members of a spiritual organism includes following moral rules, and at the metaphysical level, religion became an explanation of the meaning of life that explained of why the morally good is good. In Western civilization, an answer was provided by a religion in which the faithful believed that God created the natural world.

Judaism taught that God created the natural world and populated it with beings created in His own image, and those who believed in such a transcendent creator could see confirmation of their religion in Plato's pagan use of Reason to defend the existence of a realm of Being beyond the realm of Becoming. Christianity began as a variation on Judaism that promised salvation from the sorry state of the world not only to Jews but everyone, and when it split off from Judaism, Christ's apostle to the Gentiles, Paul, spread the gospel about the resurrection of Christ to the rest of the Roman Empire in the Greek language. Plato's Form of the Good was replaced by an infinite Rational being for whom Forms were objects of rational intuition and who willed the natural world into existence for a purpose. Since the Christian God was a merciful creator, He sent his Son to atone for the sins of those created in His image by allowing him to be crucified. But Jesus arose from the dead, and those who believed in Christ were promised life in heaven. Since Jesus died like a slave, this included slaves. Though it was not easy to resist

---

[51] The significance of the contribution of Christianity to Western culture is described in Holland (2016, 2019).

temptation, Christianity was an optimistic view of the spiritual world, and it spread throughout the Roman Empire. Christians were persecuted under Jewish and Roman authority until shortly before Christianity was legalized in 313, and in the end, Christianity was the state religion of the Roman Empire. This is how Reason and faith were married in Western civilization.

According to the Socratic practical test of Reason, to know the Good is to choose goals that are good, and if everyone were perfect in this way, Reason would cause heaven on Earth. But Athenian intuitionistic metaphysics had such flawed explanations of the nature of Reality behind Appearance that its explanations of the nature of the good were never adequate. The best that Plato could offer was the *Republic*. Rational subjects were philosopher kings who used auxiliary guardians to force people to do what is good, and as suggested by his recourse to myths, Plato realized that he could not explain how intuition of the Form of the Good caused even philosophers to do what is good. Aristotle's metaphysics explained goodness as the end for the sake of which *natural change* occurs, and Rational subjects were special only because they actualized their essential form by using knowledge of their essential to know what is good. But that did not explain why choosing the mean between extremes is good. Final causes were just regularities found in the natural world in which possible future states determined what happens at present with a necessity akin to efficient causes.

Given the existence of a transcendent creator, however, believers could attribute to God the kind of knowledge of goodness that would cause Rational subjects to choose good goals over bad goals, and so they could see themselves as doing what is good because it is good, even if they did not understand completely why the good is good. This had an appeal in the Roman Empire. Since the creator of the natural world was a Rational being, Christians could believe that life is not just meaningless suffering of pain and evil. It had a meaning, and they knew it had to do with loving one's neighbor as oneself, even though they did not quite understand God's purpose in creating a world in which life had that meaning.

Judaism taught that when God created the world, He created heaven on Earth, called the *Garden of Eden*. He created Adam and Eve in His own image, and he forbade the eating of a certain kind of fruit. But as Rational subjects, they had a free will, and according to the doctrine of original sin, Adam and Eve disobeyed God's commands. Their punishment was the sorry state of a world with death, labor, wrongdoing, and war, which would be inherited by their offspring. When Adam and Eve ate the forbidden fruit of the tree of knowledge of good and evil, they acquired knowledge of the difference between good and evil. This can be explained ontologically as corresponding to the evolution of psychological sentences because spiritual organisms had long warred with one another and that was when reflective subjects first realized that they were choosing whether or not to do what is bad for others because it is bad for them. They had evolved desires that motivated them to do that in some cases, and along with more basic animal desires, they and their offspring would be tempted by desires to sin. These desires could be overridden by the spiritual desire, which motivated them to follow authoritative spiritual input of their culture. But despite knowing that it was wrong, they would sin. In a sense, they lacked the kind of knowledge of goodness that causes Rational subjects to choose the morally good. But as reflective subjects, they understood the predicament they were in, and they believed that they had a free will that enabled them to do what morality requires even when it was opposed to strong animal desires or self-interest.

Judaism had taught that the best way to live was to please God by obeying His detailed commands. That was the price for God's protection of his chosen people. But Christ taught a different lesson. His gospel was that the *kingdom of God* is at hand. God had forgiven original sin, and reflective subjects could have salvation and live in heaven, if only they believed in God and loved their neighbors as themselves. This was an optimistic lesson, which attracted followers, and when Christ was crucified, his followers did not give up this belief. Instead, they saw his death as proof of God's forgiveness of original sin. He had sacrificed His Son, and the *grace* of God was that those who believed in Christ had the free will required to choose to do what is good. But since Christ was God embodied as a mortal reflective subject, he was the model for how to be a Christian. Christ had asked his Father on the cross to forgive those who were sinning against because they did not know what they were doing, and so being a Christian meant forgiving those who sin against them. Forgiveness was required when sinners repented and were willing to be moral. But living life as a Christian did not bring about heaven on Earth, and when that became clear, heaven was postponed to the Day of Judgment. However, seeing Christ's resurrection as proof of his divinity, believers expected him to return and the dead to be resurrected. And when that day did not come, the reward of believing in Christ came to be seen as having an eternal life after death in the presence of God outside space and time.

That is the gist of Christian explanation of the spiritual nature on which moral goodness depends. But as ontological scientists explain it, the morally good necessarily matters to reflective subjects because, as members of a spiritual organism, they have a spiritual nature. Indeed, they have a spiritual desire that enables them to submit to spiritual input even when it is opposed by strong animal desires. But faith in Christ is not quite the rational intuition of the nature of the good that Socrates believed would cause one to choose the good. To be sure, Christianity was based on the belief that such perfect knowledge exists, even if only God has it. God created the natural world for a purpose, and since he must know what makes the good good, that knowledge must have caused him to create a natural world populated with finite beings fashioned in the image of his own infinite Rational power. And since they were created in his image, Christians could expect to share God's knowledge of the Good when their immortal souls were finally in heaven with him. In the meantime, however, finite Rational subjects had to have faith in the Christian gospel and aspire to be morally perfect like Christ. That was not easy because it meant loving one's neighbors like oneself and even forgiving transgressions of others, at least, when they repented their sins. But for a Christian, doing that was the meaning of life, and it seemed possible because they had a free will.

2.2 Free Will

Though God's forgiveness of original sin did not remove the desires and selfish interests that tempted them to do wrong, they could submit to its spiritual input because they had a spiritual desire. It is a unique kind of desire built into the brains of reflective subjects because it helps constitute a neural BGS in which spiritual input can determine the goals that they pursue. It gives linguistic representations of certain kinds the authority to determine which goals are finally chosen in each situation, and thus, moral reasoning can guide behavior. And the neural BGS is a geometrical cause with the function of choosing good goals, and thus, when reflective subjects choose, they clearly have the power to do otherwise. That is the function of all BGSs, even prokaryotes on the first floor of the edifice of life. Reflective subjects are different only because their neural BGS depends on a geometrical cause that is constituted in part by the spiritual desire. Since they can know by reflection whether they choose to act on their spiritual desire, they know that they are responsible for their choices, so they can take responsibility for what they do.

But that is not how it appears to reflective subjects in a culture near the beginning of the metaphysical stage because they have a self-conception based on the belief in intuitionistic Reason, and they think of the self as a phenomenal subject to whom phenomenal properties are objects of intuition. Those phenomenal appearances include representations of the natural world in which they find their bodies and representations of the spiritual world in which they share beliefs and goals with others. And representations of the intentions that are formed and how their bodies behave in the situation also have a phenomenal appearance. But no phenomenal property representing a causal connection between them is immediately present, and so it can seem self-evident to intuitionists that they have a free will.

That is the self-conception of Christians because they believe that they were created in the image of transcendent being who is all-knowing. But given the doctrine of original sin, they conceived of the human predicament as having to resist the temptation to sin, and free will was the power to do so. But they also believed that the will to do what is good depends on the grace of God, which comes from believing in Christ, and since believers knew what is good, they held themselves responsible for doing what is good. Thus, to choose good over evil freely was the kind of perfection to which finite Rational subjects could aspire on Earth.[52] They were able to do what is required to be a Christian even when they did not want to or when they could get away with wronging others, and that is how knowledge of the nature of the good caused them to choose good over evil.

---

[52] God's perfection was assumed to include a free will, but reconciling God's free will with the determinism implicit in holding that to know the good is to do the good is one of the unsolved puzzles of Christian theology.

The gospel is an interpretation of the tension in the reflective neural BGSs between spiritual input and the animal desires or self-interest that may oppose it. When reflective subjects do not submit to what they recognize as spiritual input, they feel the failure to act on their spiritual desire as guilt. This tension is inherent in the individual, and Plato built it into his Republic by interposing the *spirited element* (or auxiliaries) between the philosopher king, who uses Reason to choose goals that are good, and the desires of the citizens, who must pursue it. Indeed, this is the nature that the apostle Paul had in mind when he insisted that everyone has a conscience.[53] Christians shared this view because, even though they believed that they had a duty to serve a good greater than the self, the finite power of human Reason did not enable them to understand completely what makes it good. By accepting Platonic metaphysics, Christians could believe that Reason knows the existence of God beyond the natural world. (Theologians claimed to prove God's existence in various ways, such as showing that the natural world must have a creator, showing that its purposiveness must have a designer, and showing that the notion of a perfect being entails its existence.) But Christians had to rely on revelation for knowledge of God's purpose, and seeing their spiritual desire as free will, life had a meaning for those who accepted the gospel. Life was a trial in which Rational subjects who had faith in Christ could choose freely between submitting to God's spiritual input and giving in to temptation. Though eternal damnation awaited those who freely chose evil, there was forgiveness for those who repented their sins and believed in Christ. They would have an eternal life in heaven. It was never clear, however, why any God would create a world in which being on trial in this way is all that Rational subjects created in his image could understand about the meaning of their lives. But Christians believed that God loved his creatures, and accepting on faith that God had a purpose in creating them, they could hope they would understand his purpose in heaven.

Augustine of Hippo (354-430), a Bishop of the early Christian church, used Reason to fathom the profundity of this faith. Before his conversion to

---

[53] In Romans 2:14-15, Paul wrote, "Indeed, when Gentiles, who do not have the law, do by nature things required by the law, they are a law for themselves, even though they do not have the law. They show that the requirements of the law are written on their hearts, their consciences also bearing witness, and their thoughts sometimes accusing them and at other times even defending them."

Christianity, he was a Manichean who believed that the world was an endless struggle between good and evil. But the existence of a force of evil that God cannot overcome is inconsistent with his omnipotence, and Augustine turned from Manichaeism to an understanding of Christianity based on Neo-Platonism. Instead of seeing the relation between the soul and the body as a struggle between forces of good and evil, he saw human beings as a union of two substances: the body was matter, and the soul was a dimensionless substance with a home outside space and time. It was finite Reason created in the image of God's infinite Reason, and in Augustine's (Neo-Platonist) view, the faculty of rational intuition needs an inner illumination from God to know the True as God does.[54] (In his meditation on the nature of time in his *Confessions*, for example, he claims that rational intuition enabled him to understand how God exists outside time because God showed him how time for finite rational beings is just a subjective appearance of memory of the past and foresight of the future at each moment.) Intuitionistic metaphysics enabled Augustine to transform Manichaeism into a view about original sin. As Manicheanism held, the body and its desires are the cause of sin. But the doctrine of original sin explained the origin of the temptation to sin, and though Augustine believed in free will, he argued that the temptation to sin is so great that finite Rational subjects needed God's grace in order to choose good over evil.[55]

2.3 Idealist Metaphysics

Religion in the Judeo-Christian religion is metaphysical because of the marriage of its Faith to Reason, and so the problems of ancient intuitionistic metaphysics confronted theologians. All Rational subjects were created in God's image, and Christ taught that salvation was open to all, including slaves. This was a lasting contribution of Christianity to Western culture, helping found a class structure that did not depend on slavery. The marriage

---

[54] In *Confessions* (XII.xxv.35), Augustine writes, "If we both see that what you say is true, and we both see that what I say is true, then where do we see that? Not I in you, nor you in me, but both of us in that unalterable truth that is above our minds."

[55] But Augustine's way of marrying intuitionistic metaphysics with Christianity posed the problem of reconciling God's omniscience outside time with free will. God must have known who will be saved and who will be damned as he created the world, and so free will cannot actually be what determines one's destiny. But a just God cannot hold his creatures responsible for doing evil if they could not have done otherwise.

of Platonic metaphysics with the Christian gospel planted the belief in Reason deeply enough in culture to serve as a foundation for cultural evolution by Rational selection in the modern era. It gave individuals a conception of the self as knowing the Good as part of the True and having a free will by which to choose what morality requires. This metaphysical understanding of the meaning of life made Christianity unique among world religions because its theological doctrines required fastidious attention to metaphysical arguments. They are illustrated by disputes about the trinity and struggles to solve the ontological problems of dualism caused by intuitionistic metaphysics.

The belief that God, as the transcendent creator, had sacrificed his Son in the form of a human being on Earth in order to forgive original sin implied that God exists as both Father and Son. Scripture and doctrine led Christians to believe that God also exists as the Holy Spirit, that is, by operating through finite rational beings, for example, as the grace by which God gives them a will that is free to choose between good and evil. Metaphysically, the doctrine of the trinity could be seen as an attempt to solve the Platonic problem of ontological dualism. The Holy Spirit can be seen as an attempt to bridge the gap between two substances as opposite as Plato's realms of Becoming and Being. It enabled Christians to use the Holy Spirit to explain how the two substances interact. But the doctrine of the trinity required theologians to reconcile faith in three Gods with the monotheism entailed by a metaphysics in which the existence of the natural world depends on the will of a God who is outside space and time.

Augustine tried to solve this problem by holding that, while God is one substance, the Father, Son, and Holy Spirit are three *persons* of God. But this resurrected an ontological puzzle that arose in the attempt to reconcile Aristotle's metaphysics with what the pre-Socratics had discovered about the nature of ontological causes. In order to cause what is found in the world by constituting it, substances had to exist self-subsistently, or else they could not cause its existence. But in order to cause its properties, they also had to exist in a certain way (have an essential nature). Thus, to solve Plato's problem of explaining how Being and Becoming can be distinct substances constituting a single world, Aristotelians held that particular substances in space and time are constituted by both form and matter. But in order for each to be an ontological cause, each would have to be a substance, and since they would have opposite essential natures, it would still be impossible to explain how they interact. Aristotelians could insist that it was possible for particular substances to have two different essential natures at once, but that merely hid the inconsistency by spoiling the coherence of ontological explanations. Without an explanation of how the two essential natures are related, it was still a puzzle how form and matter could be combined in each particular substance. Augustine faced the same kind of ontological problem because the Father, as creator, transcended the natural world, the Son was part of the natural world, and the Holy Spirit somehow existed everywhere. Nor did he solve this problem. He did not explain how a substance could have three different essential natures, one each for the Father, Son, and Holy Spirit. Instead, by holding that all three are persons of a single substance, Augustine hid the inconsistency of the trinity and monotheism by sacrificing the coherence of ontological explanation, much as Aristotelians hid Plato's intractable ontological dualism.

Augustine was not alone in struggling with the ontological problem of reconciling the trinity with monotheism. In a series of ecumenical councils after the legalization of Christianity in 313 CE, bishops of the Church settled on a doctrine about the trinity, called the *Nicene Creed*. This attempt to solve the problem of Platonic dualism was based on Neo-Platonism, which had been defended in the ancient era by Plotinus.

Plotinus (205-270 CE) held that Reality is *The One*, an entity whose unity precludes division, multiplicity, and distinction, and like Plato, he identified the One with the Good. He explained everything else as emanations from it. The first emanation was *Intelligence* (the duality of rational intuition and its two objects: the One and the Forms), and emanating from it was the *Soul*, with two aspects: an upper aspect in which Intelligence is divided into many souls, and a lower aspect that makes it seem that they are all located a natural world. This was a coherent first cause since everything had the same basic nature. But with two successive emanations, the One threatened to become three, and to avoid ontological self-contradiction, Plotinus held that all three emanations were aspects of a single underlying principle, and it can be interpreted as the phenomenal subject. Though the One was the cause that Plotinus' used to explain the Intelligence and the Soul, he could not hold that it is a substance without recognizing that the emanations are also substances, and so he postulated something more basic than substance. It was supposed to have a unity that was prior even to the duality of being and non-being, and ontology can explain what Plotinus was referring to as a phenomenal subject. (With objects of intuition, it is Intelligence, which knows not only Forms, but also the One, or itself, as their source.) Since the first cause had an intuitionistic nature, Plotinus was defending a form of idealism.

Plotinus seemed to give the bishops what they needed to reconcile the trinity with monotheism. They explained the Father, the Son, and the Holy Spirit as three aspects of the Neo-Platonist underlying principle, called *hypostases*, and insisted that they were all *substantially identical* (eventually, the formula was *three hypostases in one ousia*). But for those who recognize that what the pre-Socratics discovered was not matter, but, rather, the first cause, or the cause of existence, Plotinus' underlying principle, the phenomenal subject, was a substance with both self-subsistence and a way of existing. By reducing the One, the Intelligence, and the Soul to it, Plotinus defended an idealist ontology because his metaphysics explained all three as objects of intuition for a phenomenal subject. (Since matter was a purely passive principle derived from the phenomenal subject, it replaced Plato's receptacle as the arena where Forms appear as moving images of eternity, called the *natural world*). In these terms, Neo-Platonism solved Plato's ontological dualism by explaining Being as a substance and reducing Becoming to it, as if Becoming were a mere phantom of Reason.

Neo-Platonism entailed an idealist ontology because the phenomenal subject is an intuitionistic substance. Thus, by explaining the Father, Son, and Holy Spirit as hypostases, the bishops solved the ontological problem posed by the trinity by accepting an idealist ontology in which all three were objects of intuition for a phenomenal subject.

Even if this had solved the problem of the trinity, it did not solve all the ontological problems of Christian theology. God created the natural world, populated with many human beings fashioned as images of himself, and the problematic Platonic ontological dualism resurfaced when God became incarnate as one of them. The question was how the divine was related to the human in Jesus. To hold that Jesus was divine was to deny that Jesus was human. But to hold that Jesus was human, despite being immortal, was to accord a lesser status to Jesus than the Father. (The compromise of holding that Jesus was two persons, one divine and one human, was hard to accept because it meant that Mary was the mother of Jesus, but not the mother of God.) In order to express that orthodox doctrine, the Council of Chalcedon in 451 A. D. invoked the concept of hypostasis once again: Jesus was the *hypostatic union* of the divine and human nature. But this is hardly satisfactory, since Jesus, as a substance, would have to be identical to the immortal substance underlying the trinity while at the same time being identical to a particular moral substance in the natural world, even though those substances are not identical to one another. But like other intuitionistic metaphysicians, Christian theologians had something to say for skeptics to argue about.

3   Medieval Philosophy

Around 1330, looking forward to the return of classical culture, Petrarch called the era that followed the fall of Rome *dark*. This may have been unfair, considering the advances accomplished after 800, when Pope Leo III crowned Charlemagne as Emperor of the West. Historians now favor a more neutral description, like *Late Antiquity* or *Early Middle Ages*. But cities did decline, political authority did contract to feudal estates, and the Dark Ages of Europe, like the Dark Ages of ancient Greece, had the effect of a small founder group, beginning the evolution of a culture by Rational selection that would give Western spiritual organisms the power to cause globalization.

It happened in Western Europe because of the fall of Rome. The capital of the Roman Empire had been moved to Constantinople in 330, and as the Byzantine Empire, it survived in the East for over a thousand years (falling to the Ottoman Turks in 1453). But the Western Roman Empire ended with the fall of Rome in 476, leaving the Catholic Church as the only territory-wide institution. The Germanic tribes that invaded the territories of the Western Roman Empire were converted to Christianity, and the remaining territories were converted later when the Church sent missionaries. Spiritual organisms took root in rural territories, and there was a religion to justify a feudal class structure throughout the lands of Europe. Christian theologians had absorbed Neo-Platonism, and with monasteries preserving ancient manuscripts, the culture of the Dark Ages was infected by metaphysics. Thus, belief in Reason helped found institutions in the Late Middle Ages that would enable the West to rise above other civilizations on Earth.

During the Dark Ages, most texts of ancient Greek philosophy were *lost* in the sense that they were written in Greek, and the Greek language died out. There were Latin translations of the first half of Plato's *Timaeus* and Aristotle's *Categories* and *On Interpretation*. The remainder of Aristotle's works was not translated into Latin until the 12th and 13th centuries, and it was the 15th century before Plato's full corpus was translated. In short, Plato and Neo-Platonism dominated Medieval thought through the work of Augustine and other Church fathers until Aristotle's works were available.

Plato's *Timaeus* was the main Platonic text available in translation during the Dark Ages, and it prepared Christians to separate issues about the spiritual world from issues about the natural world. Issues about the origin and purpose or the natural world were addressed in Plato's cosmology by a myth about how the demiurge made Forms appear as moving images of eternity in the receptacle of space and time. Once the natural world was created, there was an order in which every event has a cause, and so finite Rational subjects could expect Reason to explain the natural order by its own causes, like a closed system. Of course, God, as its creator, could intervene in the natural world. But that was an issue in the spiritual domain for theologians to discuss, and separating it from the domain of natural philosophers left room for Reason to read the book of nature as a way of deciphering the mysteries of God's creation.[56]

Since Reason was married to Christianity, students in the educational institutions that arose during the Middle Ages internalized the belief in Reason. From the 6th and 7th centuries, monastic schools and cathedral schools were established to educate children of the nobility and prepare them for the clergy. Indeed, Charlemagne issued decrees requiring monasteries and

---

[56] This did not happen in the Byzantine Empire, and the contrast between this Platonic heritage of the Dark Ages and Islam during the same period is described by Toby E. Huff (2003, Ch. 3, "Reason and rationality in Islam and the West.").

cathedrals to provide education. They taught the seven liberal arts, divided into the *trivium* (grammar, rhetoric, and logic) and the *quadrivium* (arithmetic, geometry, astronomy, and music). But the arts of language and mathematics were applied to the natural world, following the *Timaeus* and the few other ancient texts. With increasing wealth, cities grew, and by the 11th century, the demand for education was sufficient to support individual *masters*, who often traveled from city to city, setting up their own schools and charging students for lessons. As the Church grew, its rules became more complex, and clergy had to be trained in canon law. But more laymen also began to seek admission, and in the 11th and 12th centuries, some cathedral schools became universities. By 1500, when the multiplicity of principalities and countries made the civilization of Western and Central Europe seem far weaker than civilization in the East, more than eighty universities had been established.

Universities were divided into faculties. After six years spent earning a master's degree from the *liberal arts* faculty, a student could move on to the study of *law, medicine,* or *theology*. Masters gave lectures in Latin that were usually organized around a single book, and as Latin translations of ancient texts became available in the 12th and 13th centuries (many by way of Arabic translations), they were incorporated into the arts curriculum. The most important were the extensive works of Aristotle, ranging from topics in physics and astronomy, through the study of animals and the soul, to issues in moral philosophy and metaphysics. Though the new texts included Euclid's *Elements* and Ptolemy's *Almagest*, the quadrivium became a detailed study of natural science based on Aristotelian teleology. The faculty of liberal arts eagerly embraced Reason as a way of discovering the True, as what corresponds to Reality, and though the theology faculty denounced departures from literal readings of the bible and orthodox doctrines as pagan, academics were able to defend themselves as *friends of truth*.[57]

Thomas Aquinas (1225-1274) harmonized Aristotelian teleology with Christian theology by holding that God created a natural world in which change depends on final causes. He defended this grand synthesis in his *Summa Theologica* and similar treatises, and *Thomism* is still the orthodoxy of the Catholic Church. Though it is often identified with *Scholasticism*, that

---

[57] Huff (2003, p. 1870, and for his view of universities, Huff (2003, p. 179-189).

term actually refers to the method of learning used in medieval universities. In classes (and in writings accumulated from them), a question would be posed, a position would be stated, a series of objections would be raised, and each objection would be refuted, one by one. These were mainly metaphysical issues, and arguments about them were exchanged in spiritual organisms. Such *disputations* rewarded conceptual rigor. Careful distinctions had to be articulated in order to resolve contradictions, and students were required to master all the dialectical moves. The goal was to discover the True, and though Scholastics were profoundly mistaken about the nature of Reality, their beliefs about Appearance had to fit together coherently in order to correspond to Reality. Thus, the belief in Reason caused culture to evolve by Rational selection.

In the Renaissance, Scholasticism came to be dismissed by natural philosophers as rigid, formalistic, and sterile. But Scholastics had prepared the way for them by following the method of disputing contrary positions. A central question was the status of the objects of the faculty of rational intuition. Plato's belief that abstract objects are Forms existing outside space and time lost favor with the rediscovery of Aristotle, persisting only as the belief that Reason demonstrated the existence of a transcendent God. But Aristotle's belief that particular substances are constituted by both form and matter also came under attack by nominalists, such as William of Ockham (1280-1349). Essential forms are universals, and the main problem with them is that one and the same entity must exist completely in each and every particular substance of its kind. That does not seem possible unless such entities exist outside space, which betrays the origin of the Aristotelian doctrine of hylomorphism as a way of hiding Plato's intractable ontological dualism of Being and Becoming. Since converts to nominalism had to reject the final causes of Aristotelian teleology, they found themselves believing that particular substances in the natural world are nothing but matter. As direct realists, they agreed with Empedocles and Anaxagoras about qualia being properties of matter. But as materialists, they had to deny that objects of rational intuition are relevant causes in studying the natural world. Scholasticism may be formalistic, but culture had evolved far enough by Rational selection for belief in Aristotelian metaphysics to undermine itself.

However, metaphysics was planted so deeply in medieval culture that the belief in Reason made other contributions to progress that were simply taken for granted. For example, as Toby Huff argues, the recovery of the Justinian Code provided a model that triggered a legal revolution in the 12th and 13th centuries. Roman civil law was based on natural law, the belief that Reason discovers laws governing relations of Rational subjects as part of Reality, and the system of law that was established in Europe by the free consent of scholars debating principles of governance was based on this assumption. Practiced in debates of philosophy, logic, and religious doctrine, these scholars assumed that Reason includes a conscience that, besides revealing what is morally right, caused Rational subjects to choose to do what is right. Thus, Rational subjects were seen as having moral autonomy, and since they were all equal in the eyes of God, the law applied equally to everyone.

As Huff argues, a principal contribution of the legal revolution in the Middle Ages was that a legal system that accorded basic rights not only to individuals but also to associations of them, or *corporations*. That is, associations were treated as rational beings that could own property, have debts, make contracts, be represented in court, sue and be sued, and the like. This status was bestowed generally on cities, towns, charitable organizations, merchant guilds, and professional associations. Indeed, it is what gave universities their autonomy. It authorized associations to create their own rules, select their own leaders, adjudicate internal disputes, and provide for their representation to other groups. This was not *moral autonomy* since associations are not Rational subjects whose knowledge of the Good could cause them to choose what is right. It was, rather, *legal autonomy*, in which administrators chose goals that are good for their associations. Moreover, there was an important difference between administrators and owners. Following Roman civil law, debt owed by the association was not owed by the members individually, and thus, property owned by the association was not owned by its administrators but only administered by them. Hence, the allegiance of its members was to the association, not other individuals.[58]

Huff sees recognition of the legal autonomy of associations as decisive in the development of representative government, the scientific revolution, and

---

[58] Huff (2003, p. 133-146; 2011, p. 147-150).

economic growth. It began with the papal revolution of the late 11th and early 12th centuries.[59] Kings, emperors, and princes had controlled appointments and governance of the clergy, largely because celibate clergy could not bequeath property to offspring, and by reasserting the Pope's authority to administer the clergy, the Church won legal autonomy for itself. This decreased the power of the state, which was already divided among many sovereigns. Reminiscent of the decentralization of power among city-states in ancient Greece, the decentralization of power in Europe at this time is in stark contrast with state power in the Byzantine Empire, Chinese civilization, and the Islamic civilizations in the Middle East and India, where class structure enabled a centralized state to exert its force field of authority everywhere. And as secular associations acquired legal autonomy in Europe, a culture evolved everywhere that facilitated the decentralization of power.

Ontological science can appreciate the significance of this 12th-century development. It recognizes associations as spiritual organisms that are constituted as parts of a more encompassing spiritual organism. Associations are geometrical causes that use a plan-sharing BGS based on language to coordinate the behavior of their parts, for example, by establishing an administrator to choose goals for others to pursue. But since associations are authorized by legal systems, they are parts of a spiritual organism on the fourth floor of the edifice of life, on a par with the class structure of civilization. That is, they are part of the spiritual world constituted by Rational subjects following the cultural plan by which the spiritual BGS of a sovereign spiritual organism coordinates behavior. But they are unlike class structure because associations are voluntary, and they are not territory-wide. Rational subjects form them for a purpose, and when the law respects their legal autonomy in acting for that purpose, they are geometrical causes guiding behavior by constraining the collective effects of physical causes. They are a kind of geometrical action aimed at the good that can even reproduce by inspiring other individuals to form similar associations. But they are parts of the geometrical action of sovereign spiritual organism aimed at the good, and since their geometrical action is at a level of organization higher than the geometrical action of the individual, they are at a level of geometrical

---

[59] Huff (2003, p. 123-127).

organization between the whole spiritual organism and the Rational subjects who are its members.

The transition from the medieval to the modern era, called the *Renaissance,* is often portrayed as the rise of secular humanism, as suggested by the evolution of a more naturalistic painting style. But the *light* that Plutarch anticipated by calling the preceding era the *Dark Ages* was Reason. Underlying the Renaissance was optimism about the power of Reason, inspired by the recovery of ancient culture, and the confidence in Reason that had defended orthodox Thomistic metaphysics in universities spread to ordinary individuals. In 1500, Western civilization had no centralized autocratic state, and without a territory-wide ideological mechanism to censor arguments, culture could evolve by Rational selection. And in 1517, Luther rejected the authority of the Church in favor of salvation by individual faith in Christ. He used the bible to justify marrying Reason with the faith of individuals, and by translating the bible into the vernacular, he made the gospel available to individuals apart from the Church (with help from the newly invented metallic-type printing press). Spread of confidence in the power of Reason gave individuals a conception of the self that was not just their identification with a social role in the spiritual world. Protestants turned away from confessing their sins to priests in the hope that repentance would earn salvation in an afterlife. Instead, they took responsibility for improving their individual lives on Earth. This was done in the eyes of God, and the Protestant Ethic, as Max Weber called it, is evidence of the rise of individualism. But it can also be seen in the respect paid to arguments of single unorthodox individuals. From the beginning of intuitionistic metaphysics in ancient Greece, geometry was the prime example of objects of rational intuition, and a geometrical argument for the heliocentric structure of the heavens introduced by Copernicus in 1543 overthrew the Earth-centered Ptolemaic system, which had been accepted almost everywhere on Earth for nearly 1500 years. Reason was born in ancient Greece, and the Renaissance was its rebirth as the foundation of a culture shared throughout Europe.

CHAPTER 5:
MODERN PHILOSOPHY

Ancient intuitionism survived into the modern era as Platonic metaphysics wedded to Christianity. It was generally taken for granted that Reason proves the existence of God beyond the natural world, and reflective subjects in Western spiritual organisms conceived of the self as having a cognitive power that enabled them to know Reality behind Appearance. That was to know the True, and since the Good is part of the True, Rational subjects also knew the nature of the Good. In the modern era, belief in Reason promoted cultural evolution by Rational selection in two ways. First, it encouraged philosophers who studied nature to resurrect the pre-Socratic project of explaining the natural world by the substances that constitute it. But more adequate ontological theories cast doubt on direct realism about perception. Natural philosophers recognized the subjectivity of qualia, and as critical realists, they explored the consequences of various forms of ontological naturalism. Second, when the philosophers debating metaphysics rejected direct realism, they became representative realists, and as intuitionists, they interpreted metaphysical sentences in a basically different way from ancient intuitionists. This is the second kind of metaphysics that ontological science predicts during the metaphysical stage of spiritual evolution. Hence, modern philosophy confirms its explanation of Western civilization as the beginning of a stage of evolution that follows that represented by other civilizations on Earth.

Interpreting the history of the West as the biography of Reason, the modern era is when Reason rebels against intuitionistic metaphysics and becomes science. That rebellion caused its adolescent identity crisis, and its origin can be traced to natural philosophy as well as modern intuitionistic metaphysics. Both forms of cultural progress gave birth to physics, and its astonishing success along with political institutions based on respect for the moral autonomy of Rational subjects are the most prominent causes of the

Enlightenment, as the next chapter describes.

1 Natural Philosophy

As we have seen, the evolution of culture by Rational selection during the Middle Ages turned scholastics away from the Aristotelian belief in essential forms toward nominalism, and the rejection of final causes led to materialist explanations of the natural world. Natural philosophy did not depend on supernaturalism, and so this led to the revival of the pre-Socratic project of explaining the natural world ontologically. Though ontological naturalism took various forms in the 17th century, they all assumed that what happens is just a result of material bodies moving and interacting with one another, sometimes called *mechanical philosophy*. Thomas Hobbes (1588-1679), along with scientists like Robert Boyle (1627-1691), defended a form of plenum materialism in which everything is constituted by *corpuscles*. Cartesian physics was based on Descartes' belief that the natural world is constituted by extension, a plenum of material substances whose natures can be defined only by 3-D shapes. And Pierre Gassendi (1592-1655) resurrected the ancient belief in atoms and the void.

Ontological naturalists replaced the metaphysicians' faculties of intuition with a faculty built into animal brains that gave them to use language. Mechanical explanation had advanced far enough to reveal that sensory qualia are not the properties of objects in the natural world. Hobbes simply dismissed them as *phantasms* caused by brain events. He was a critical realist about perception, much like the ancient atomists who had explained sensory qualia as special spherical atoms in perceivers. But like other materialists, Hobbes tried to show how the psychological states ordinarily used to explain human behavior could be reduced to brain mechanisms. In the 17th century, no such explanation was available, and it has yet to be discovered in the 21st century. As ontological science reveals, an explanation of how beliefs about psychological states correspond to the motion and interaction of material bodies in the brain depends on recognizing that there are geometrical causes constraining what happens by physical causes.

Nevertheless, Hobbes made a significant contribution to cultural progress because his goal in defending materialism was not merely theoretical. Like the Stoics and Epicureans of the Roman era, he used ontological naturalism as a foundation for explaining the good life. But since the modern era came after the marriage of Reason with Christian faith, the good life was recognized to involve following moral rules, even when it is contrary to self-interest, and so the challenge was to explain morality. Hobbes believed that he could explain morality because, as a materialist, it seemed obvious that mechanisms built into the body and brain could explain the power of reflective subjects to act in their self-interest.

Hobbes saw the issue in terms of political authority. Civilized spiritual organisms use class structure to coordinate behavior over vast territories, and ever since the Pope crowned Charlemagne Emperor, the state's force field of spiritual authority had been justified by the divine right of kings. Hobbes intended to replace the divine right of kings with an explanation of their authority based on a materialist explanation of the behavior of self-interested individuals. His model of the state was an association established by his version of the *social contract*, called the *Leviathan*. But Hobbes was doomed to fail because, without recognizing geometrical causes and how they constrain what happens by physical causes, it is not possible to reduce spiritual organisms on the fourth floor of the edifice of life to the motion and interaction of multicellular animals on the third floor.

To portray reflective subjects as living without spiritual organisms, Hobbes described what he called the *state of nature*. He argued that, since individuals act in their own self-interest, the state of nature was a war of all against all in which life is solitary, poor, nasty, brutish, and short. But since reflective subjects can think about their desires and how they help determine what they do, they know what goals are good for them. And since they can also recognize the mutual benefit of living together in peace and being able to cooperate in pursuit of common goals, Hobbes held that self-interested practical reasoning would lead them to leave the state of nature. They would give up their natural right to act in their own self-interest by agreeing to establish a sovereign with sufficient power to enforce, through punishment, rules that enable them to live at peace and enjoy the benefits of cooperation. Those rules obliged them to refrain from harming others unnecessarily, to keep contracts, and to help others in need, along with other familiar moral duties. Thus, instead of a king with the divine right to rule over other reflective subjects, there was a this-worldly sovereign, whose authority derived from the social contract. But having agreed to the social contract in order to preserve their lives in the war of all against all, they could disobey the sovereign only if their lives were at stake.

Ontological science can recognize the truth of at least two Hobbesian insights. First, Hobbes rightly rejected the intuitionistic belief in free will. By treating consciousness as phantasms in the brain, he discounted the intuitionist illusion about having a free will and explained behavior by efficient causes in the brain. Second, Hobbes rightly rejected the belief that moral rules depend on the purpose of God in creating the natural world. He recognized that the content of morality can be explained as rules that self-interested reflective subjects would agree to if they made a social contract to govern how they treat one another. Since reflective subjects can see into one another's minds, they recognize their basic equality, and so even cultural evolution by pragmatic selection is in the direction of moral equality (though in civilized spiritual organisms evolving during the psychological stage, moral rules must accommodate class structure).

But Hobbes was mistaken in holding that morality can be *reduced* to self-interest. Reflective subjects can see into one another's mind only because they are already members of spiritual organisms pursuing goals that are good for them all, and the social contract explains the content of the rules that reflective subjects would agree to because they are also self-interested. It is not what self-interested individuals are forced to do in a state of nature to avoid a war of all against all. Indeed, Hobbes' reduction of morality to self-interest is ontologically impossible. Self-interest is not acting on the strongest animal desire, as animals do, but rather submitting to spiritual input about how to maximize the attainment of goals determined by various animal desires over a period of time. The spiritual desire that makes that possible depends on animals evolving as parts of spiritual organisms in which they submit to spiritual input and choose goals that coordinate their behavior in pursuit of the good of the group. At the psychological stage, self-interested reflective subjects already follow moral rules.

Hobbes' mistake is, however, understandable. Materialism (like physicalism) promises a naturalistic explanation of the behavior of animals. But since it cannot explain the nature of life, it cannot recognize that self-interested behavior depends on animals participating in a form of life on a higher level of biological organization than animals.

2 Modern Intuitionistic Metaphysics

The modern era differed from the ancient era by its recognition of the subjectivity of qualia.[60] While natural philosophers simply rejected direct realism and got on with explaining the natural world ontologically, intuitionists embraced representative realism and defended metaphysics. Both recognized the existence of sensory qualia, but materialists ignored them, while intuitionists were taken in by the illusion that knowledge of phenomenal appearances is caused by their immediate presence. Focusing on what it is like to reflect on psychological states, representative realists found a new way to argue that Reason is able to know Reality behind Appearance. Descartes was the Plato of the Modern Era. Treating phenomenal appearances as objects of intuition, he found a new way to use metaphysical sentences. Though he was an intuitionistic metaphysician, he was not opposed to natural philosophy. On the contrary, he saw Reason as providing the foundation for it. By revealing the essential nature of the natural world, rational intuition would enable natural philosophers to learn details about its mechanisms empirically, that is, by perception, and eventually, explain everything in the natural world.

When representative realists recognize the difference between perceptual phenomenal appearances and the natural world, they see objects of perceptual intuition as private. All the other phenomenal appearances that occur in reflection are private in the same way, and so they are also objects of a faculty of intuition. Some of them can be treated as objects in a faculty of rational intuition, and as we have seen, representative realists who defend metaphysics must show how Reason knows Reality behind Appearance twice. Behind the perceptual phenomenal Appearance, Reason knows the natural world, and

---

[60] Critical realists are not intuitionists, like representative realists, and so they cannot discover this by noticing that the unity of consciousness is different from the unity of the natural world. But there is other evidence that sensory qualia are subjective. There are dreams and vivid afterimages that sometimes persist after eyes are closed, and for those who notice it, the subjectivity of qualia is evident in gestalt shifts in how qualia seem to be related spatially, for example, when viewing the Necker cube, the Müller-Lyer illusion, or the duck-rabbit.

behind the reflective phenomenal Appearance, it knows the mind. Descartes founded his metaphysics on the latter, the remarkably simple argument: *I think, therefore I am.*

In his *Discourse on Method*, René Descartes (1596-1650) used a *method of doubt* to identify objects of rational intuition, and it showed him the difference between perceptual Appearance and Reality. He put aside whatever he could doubt in order to learn what he knew with certainty. He began with the natural world, and as an intuitionist, he interpreted the phenomenal appearances that depend on the input scene constructed from sensory input in the neural BGS as objects of perceptual intuition. In order to show that they are part of the perceiver, he pointed to dreams. Like objects of perceptual intuition, they are configurations of qualia in phenomenal space, but as parts of the dreamer, they occur without the objects normally represented by them existing. The similarity between dreams and perceptual intuitions showed that it is possible for objects of perceptual intuition to exist without the objects they seem to represent, and since Descartes could not be sure that the natural world exists, the dubitability of its existence showed the difference between the perceptual Appearance and the Reality behind it.

Consciousness includes all the objects of intuition. Descartes calls them *ideas*, and when he reflects on his psychological states, he finds three kinds. Besides objects of perceptual intuition, which he calls *adventitious ideas*, there are objects of reflective intuition, which he calls *factitious ideas,* such as memories and imaginings, and, finally, there are objects of rational intuition, called *innate ideas*. But Descartes needed a criterion to identify innate ideas in the faculty of rational intuition, and he noticed that, when he doubted the existence of bodies outside the mind, he could not doubt his own existence. Thus, he argued, *I think, therefore I am*. This argument is so famous that it is named the *Cogito* after its Latin formulation: *Cogito ergo sum.*

By reflecting on why he could not doubt the *Cogito*, Descartes discovered the criterion for indubitability. He distinguished objects of rational intuition as *clear and distinct ideas*. By *clear*, he meant that the idea is present to mind could be analyzed into its simplest parts, leaving nothing vague or hidden within it, and by *distinct*, he meant that what is known because of the idea does not depend on anything not immediately present to mind. Consider, for example, the way that one seems to know that a triangle must have three sides. Everything needed to know that the belief caused by the idea is true is contained in the idea. Hence, clear and distinct ideas are self-evident.

Metaphysics is an argument that tries to show that Reason knows Reality behind Appearance. Since that is to know both its existence and its nature, Reality must be an ontological cause of the kind discovered by the pre-Socratics. Though intuitionists may not, at first, appreciate its significance, Reality must be a substance (or substances) whose self-subsistence explains the existence of what it constitutes and whose way (or ways) of existing explain its nature, including Appearance.

Ontological science explains why clear and distinct ideas are innate. The Cogito is a description of the illusion of intuitionism. As we have seen, the intuitionist illusion is caused by the unity of consciousness in mammals. Consciousness is identical to the complex phenomenal intrinsic property of magnetic field matter helping constitute the geometrical action of a mammalian brain. Phenomenal properties are immediately present to mammals, and since the mammalian brain uses a faculty of imagination to guide behavior, they seem to be known by a faculty of intuition.

In language-using mammals, the reflective phenomenal appearance depends on the faculty of psychological imagination that enables the mammalian brain to do the thermodynamic work involved in reflection. That is what it is like to be mammals using psychological sentences to reflect on their psychological states. Thus, when Descartes says, *I think, therefore I am*, he is making an argument that is compelling to intuitionists because that is what it is like when they reflect on their psychological states. They are taken in by the illusion of intuitionism. They assume that their beliefs about phenomenal appearances are caused by their immediate presence, and so they believe that the verbal behavior by which they describe them is caused by objects of a faculty of intuition. Given that phenomenal appearances are objects known by intuition, the premise of the *Cogito, I think*, affirms the existence of such objects, and the conclusion, *I am*, affirms the existence of the phenomenal subject to which they are immediately present. Since this idea is clear and distinct, it is an innate idea, and Reason knows the existence of the Reality behind the reflective Appearance. Calling it *mind*, Descartes affirms the *existence* of *res cogitans*, a thinking thing.

The clear and distinct idea of mind also enables Reason to know the *nature* of the Reality behind the reflective Appearance. This idea is *clear* because it is just the immediate presence of all the objects of intuition that the phenomenal subject can describe. And the idea of the mind is *distinct* because it includes everything that is immediately present to the phenomenal subject. Whatever else may exist must lack a phenomenal appearance. Thus, the innate idea of mind reveals not only the existence of *res cogitans* but also its nature. Descartes described mind as having a *unity* that is incapable of division. This is the unity of consciousness, described in *Chapter 1*. Sensory qualia are configured in a 3-D space, and though they have less distinct spatial relations in other kinds of phenomenal appearances, they are parts of complex phenomenal properties. Hence, qualia are all immediately present to a single subject at once, and the mind cannot be divided because if they were located outside phenomenal space, they would not be immediately present at all. Thus, the clear and distinct idea of mind reveals its nature. The mind is the phenomenal subject together with all the objects of its faculties of intuition, and since the Cogito shows its existence, Reason knows that this substance, *res cogitans*, has a kind of unity that is incapable of division. But since its knowledge depends on intuition, mind is a kind of substance that cannot exist in the spatio-material world.

The clear and distinct idea of extension is also innate because it is the kind of phenomenal appearance that depends on the faculty of naturalistic imagination doing the thermodynamic work in which reflective subjects understand the relations of objects in space and how they change as objects move. Perceptual phenomenal appearances depend on naturalistic imagination, and since reflective subjects find arguments based on the structure that it describes compelling, geometry seems to hold of whatever is perceived. The idea of extension is clear because everything immediately present is located in space, and it is distinct because geometrical relations between them do not depend on anything outside their locations in space. Since phenomenal appearances of these arguments have the clarity and distinctness that distinguishes innate ideas, intuitionists like Descartes believe that Reason knows the *nature* of the Reality behind the perceptual

Appearance. It is a substance whose essential nature is to be extended. Thus, if there is a world external to mind, this substance is located everywhere, without any void. This kind of plenum materialism was the indubitable foundation that Descartes meant to provide for natural philosophy. As explained in *Volume I*, a theory about motion enabled Descartes to show how pieces of extension could have the unchanging shapes required for natural philosophers to show how mechanisms generate the regularities found in the natural world. Indeed, Descartes' explanation of gravitation by vortices in extension was so credible that the main hurdle that the Newtonian revolution had to overcome was convincing natural philosophers that action at a distance is even possible.

Since the faculty of rational intuition is part of the mind, it is part of consciousness, and so the rejection of direct realism in favor of representative realism is the discovery of a world outside consciousness. But since Descartes used his method of doubt to begin his argument with the Cogito, he had to show that Reason knows the *existence* of Reality behind the perceptual Appearance, and that is not so easy. He based his argument for the existence of the external world on the existence and nature of God: if God exists, he is a perfect being, and so he could not create finite beings in which perceptual intuitions seem to represent an extended world outside the mind without also creating a world outside the mind that corresponds to them.

This was to invoke theism, the offspring of the marriage of Platonic Reason with faith in Christ by which ancient intuitionistic metaphysics founded the culture that evolved by Rational selection after the Dark Ages into the modern era. Christian theologians did not doubt that Reason can prove the existence of God. Only the meaning of life depended on believing in Christ. Thus, confident in the power of rational intuition, Descartes offered proofs of God's existence. But the cogency of the Cogito set a very high standard, and judging by it, even intuitionists found his proofs wanting.[61] This

---

[61] As Descartes argues, we have the idea of an infinite perfect rational being, and not only does its perfection entail its existence, but also the very existence of this idea of perfection in the mind entails God's existence because the idea itself cannot be caused by the mind of a finite and imperfect rational being. But as Kant showed, perfection does not entail existence because perfection describes the nature of something, whereas existence is about whether it is part of the world. And finite rational beings can invent the idea of an infinite rational being because infinity is just increase without limit and that can be applied to our cognitive powers.

did not immediately derail modern intuitionistic metaphysics because, in a culture based on Christian theology, supernaturalism was taken for granted, and if Descartes' proofs were dubious, it seemed there must be other proofs. However, as we shall see, the inability of Reason to prove the existence of the external world without proving God's existence eventually made intuitionists skeptical about the possibility of all metaphysical arguments in the modern era.

3 Ontological Problems

Descartes expected his metaphysical argument to be welcomed by the Church. In the modern era, the natural world was just one part of the ancient ontological dualism inherited from Plato by way of its marriage with Christianity, and in Descartes' metaphysics, the Reality that Reason discovered behind the perceptual Appearance was Plato's realm of Becoming. It was a natural world in which reflective subjects had bodies alongside other objects in space, and since they could see into one another's minds, there was also a spiritual world constituted by a culture shared as members of a spiritual organism. But in the modern era, reflective subjects were Rational beings with a personal relation to a perfect being that that exists outside space and time, and so their minds were part of transcendent spiritual world. Descartes saw his proof of the existence of God, combined with his proof that mind is distinct from body, as implying the possibility of immortal souls. Since immortality was part of faith in Christ, he promoted his argument to the Church as providing a foundation for the gospel. As we have seen, free will seems self-evident to intuitionists, and thus, Descartes could believe that choosing between good and evil determines whether minds will have eternal life in heaven or suffer eternal damnation. It was still a mystery why a perfect being would create a world that puts individuals on trial in that way. But Descartes expected Christian theologians to welcome his metaphysics for putting faith in God and the possibility of the immortality of the soul on the firm foundation of Reason.

3.1 Mind-Body Dualism

Descartes also expected those sympathetic with natural philosophy to welcome his metaphysics because it put mechanical philosophy on the firm foundation of Reason. But the discovery of an external world in which events are just effects of the motion and interaction of material substances implied that the natural world is constituted by two opposite kinds of substances, and this ontological dualism posed a problem that made Descartes's metaphysics untenable in the end. He called the external world *extension* because it was, by nature, spread out spatially, implying that body is divisible into parts, that is, into smaller bodies that could move relative to one another. On the other hand, mind had a unity that is incapable of division because ideas in the mind are all immediately present to a subject. Both are substances, since one explains the Reality behind the perceptual Appearance, and the other explains the Reality behind reflective Appearance. *Res extensa*, an extended thing, constituted the natural world, and *res cogitans*, a thinking thing with faculties of intuition, helped constitute the Christian spiritual world. Their opposite natures posed an ontological problem for both natural philosophy and metaphysics.[62]

Natural philosophers had taken up the pre-Socratic project of explaining the natural world ontologically, and in order to use Descartes' proof of its nature as a foundation for mechanical explanations, they would have to recognize the existence of minds as well. Like Hobbes, they believed that the body is a machine that generates behavior. But in the Cartesian world, human behavior depends on the interaction of mind and body. Mind depends on body for the kinds of perceptual ideas that occur in it, and body depends on mind to guide its behavior toward goals that are good. But since mind and body are substances with opposite essential natures, they have nothing in common by which they can interact. Descartes claimed that the interaction of mind and body takes place at the pineal gland. But in a world constituted by extension, every event is determined by the motion and interaction of its parts, and thus, if mind is guiding the body's behavior, there are events with no efficient causes in the natural world. Thus, for natural philosophers to accept the foundation provided by Cartesian metaphysics, they would have to abandon

---

[62] In the spatio-material world, there is no problem about the relation between mind and body. Since the clear and distinct idea of the mind *is* the illusion of intuitionism inherent in the neural geometrical action of a language-using mammalian brain, the substance constituting the mind is the mammalian brain whose cellular geometrical action includes the neural geometrical action. Thus, the mind is the part of the mammalian body called the *brain*.

the goal of explaining everything in the natural world mechanically.

The mind-body problem also foiled modern metaphysicians. They had to show how the Reality that Reason knows behind Appearance has a nature that explains everything in the world, including Appearance. A standard for judging the coherence of such explanations had been set by the pre-Socratics because Reality had to be an ontological cause. To explain the existence of what is found in the world, it had to be self-subsistent, and since its way of existing had to explain every kind of thing found in the world, Reality had to be a substance or substances of some kind. Metaphysics assumes that the truth of beliefs depends on their correspondence to Reality. Thus, culture can evolve by Rational Selection even though intuitionism is false. Metaphysicians can accept beliefs only if they are part of a consistent set that corresponds to Reality, and thus, in the end, they would have to show how substances constitute everything in a coherent way. As we have seen, Plato's intuitionistic metaphysics failed for want of a coherent ontology. Being and Becoming had opposite natures, and so one substance had to exist outside space without changing, while the other substance had to be made of many changing parts inside space. The relation between them could not be understood in naturalistic imagination, and Plato had only a myth about the demiurge to explain it. Mind-body dualism posed a similar problem for Cartesian metaphysics.

To be sure, since the interaction between mind and body took place in what had become of Plato's Becoming, it could be explained ontologically. Since Plato's Being had become God, *occasionalists*, like Nicholas Malebranche (1638-1715), could hold that every time the mind must act on the body or the body must act on the mind, God intervenes to make it happen. But this solution to the problem of Cartesian mind-body dualism depended on Plato's dualism of Being and Becoming in the guise of theism, and it merely drew attention to the ontological problems posed by Plato's dualism that Christian theology had failed to solve. Indeed, if the action of an infinite rational being outside time and space mediated the interaction of mind and body in time, each intervention would be a miracle, and in terms of the *Timaeus*, occasionalism vastly increased the domain of the spiritual relative to the natural. The natural world was no longer anything like a closed system.

3.2 Two Ways of Hiding the Mind-Body Dualism

Without an adequate explanation of the interaction of mind and body, the only option was to hide the intractable Cartesian ontological dualism, and there were two ways of hiding it, as there were in the ancient era. Aristotle hid Plato's intractable ontological dualism by treating form and matter as two ontological causes in each particular substance, and Plotinus hid it by postulating a single underlying principle with the nature of a phenomenal subject and reducing The One and its two emanations (the Intelligence and the Soul, including matter) to it. The Aristotle of the modern era was Spinoza, trying to show that a substance can have two opposite essential natures, and the Plotinus of the modern era was Leibniz, trying to show that substances with an intuitionistic essential nature are the first cause.

Baruch Spinoza (1632-1677) believed that everything is constituted by a single infinite substance, which he took to be both nature and God, and he explained the relation between mind and body on the assumption that this substance has two essential natures, called the *attribute of thought* and *the attribute of extension*. He explained the existence of the many particular things found in the world as *finite modes* of this substance. Calling finite modes under the attribute of extension *things* and finite modes under the attribute of thought *ideas*, he held that the order and connection of ideas is the same as the order and connection of things. Thus, Spinoza portrayed ideas as God's way of knowing the bodies they represented, and that meant that ideas were objects of God's intuition. But in order to explain how the idea of the body was a mind in which other ideas were objects known by intuition, Spinoza distinguished the idea of the body as part of the attribute of thought from the *idea of the body as it constitutes the human mind*. The latter included only those ideas that represented parts of the body that were involved in perceiving and knowing objects in space, that is, brain states. As ideas *in* finite minds, they explained the faculties of perceptual and rational intuition. But in order to explain the faculty of reflective intuition whose objects included all the ideas in the mind, Spinoza had to hold that there was also an *idea of the idea of the body insofar as it constitutes the mind;* that is, reflection was an idea *of* the mind (*Ethics, Bk. II, Prop. 21, Scholium*). These objects of intuition were all parts of God's idea of the body insofar as it constitutes the mind, and so Spinoza explained mind and body as a single finite mode under two attributes of a single substance.

Spinoza solved the Cartesian problem of dualism by explaining mind and body in a way that involves no interaction between them. It is a double-aspect theory, called *psychophysical parallelism* But Spinoza's solution to the problem of Cartesian dualism is ontologically incoherent in the same way as Aristotle's solution to the problem of Platonic dualism (called *hylomorphism*). Thought and extension were two different essential natures of the single substance constituting the world in much the same way as (essential) form and matter are two basically different ways that particular substances in space exist. Both would solve the problem of Reality being two substances with opposite natures by treating the two opposite natures as two essential natures of a single kind of substance. But in both cases, it fails because there is no way of existing in itself that would enable a substance to constitute both aspects of a double-aspect theory. Particular substances cannot be constituted by both matter, as a kind of substance that enables them to exist independently of one another, and an essential form, as a single substance whose existence in many particular substances makes them all of the same natural kind. In a similar way, Rational subjects cannot be constituted by both mind and body. Each subject is supposed to be a single finite mode in a substance constituting everything with two attributes. But the mind is supposed to be constituted by God's idea of the body, and so it must have the unity of mind. And body is part of extension, and since it is divisible, it lacks the unity of mind. Simply asserting that a finite mode can have both the unity of mind and the divisibility of body does not explain how it is true. They are opposite ways of existing, and a single substance cannot exist in both ways at once. Such a way of bridging the gap between the unity of consciousness and the unity of the natural world is certainly not something that can be understood in naturalistic imagination. At best, the double-aspect theory of substance is the claim that there is an unknowable first cause of what seems to be two opposite kinds of substances, and that is just the ontological problem to be solved.[63]

---

[63] It is only fair to mention how Spinoza might defend himself against this criticism, though the cost of salvaging intuitionism is great. In his *Ethics*, Spinoza formulates his argument as an axiomatic system,

Gottfried Wilhelm Leibniz (1646-1716) explained how substances with the unity of mind are related to body by eliminating any need to refer to extension. He postulated a coherent first cause, but it had an intuitionistic nature. In his *monadology*, he postulated nothing but minds, which he called *monads*. Monads are phenomenal subjects in which objects of perceptual intuition represent a world of objects in space. But monads are *windowless*, and the external objects turn out to be nothing but other monads, down to their simplest parts, which have more or less blurred perceptual intuitions representing only their immediate neighborhoods. However, beings like us are monads with a faculty of rational intuition as well as faculties of perceptual and reflective intuition, and thus, besides understanding the external world more completely than other animals, we can reflect on ourselves and know the real nature of what exists behind objects of perceptual intuition.

Since Reality is nothing but monads, Leibniz cannot explain what happens in the world by the motion and interaction of extended substances. But metaphysics holds that humans have a perfect way of knowing, and Leibniz makes good on its promise of perfection. Monads are not only windowless, but also unable to interact in any way, and so Leibniz explains what seems to happen in the natural world as the playing out in time of essential natures that are built into each and every monad by an infinite monad. There is a *pre-established harmony* among monads, in which all their objects of intuition fit together as if the monads had different perspectives on a single spatial world where extended substances move and interact. Though it seems to finite monads that what happens in space and time depends on efficient causes, its

---

like geometry, which describes everything as objects of the faculty of rational intuition by which God understands himself. Spinoza defines *attribute* as that which the *intellect* perceives as constituting the essence of substance, and thus, by defining *modes* as that which exists in, and is conceived through something other than itself, he can explain the relationship between mind and body by how the *intellect* perceives the same finite mode under two different attributes. Since the intellect is God's faculty of intuition, this is to attribute the unity of mind to God, as the phenomenal subject. (This does not explain the unity of finite minds, at least, not unless they acquire God's understanding. Finite minds are still ideas of bodies in God's mind, and their unity is not explained by positing an idea of the body in God insofar as it constitutes the mind. Why are there many minds and not just one? Nor is it explained by positing an idea of that idea.) This reading turns Spinoza into a metaphysical idealist, since everything is ultimately constituted by objects of God's infinite rational intuition. If extension is merely how intellect perceives finite modes under one of the attributes, extension is just an object of rational intuition, not a substance with parts located outside one another that can move relative to one another, as Descartes believed. Thus, Spinoza can also be read as resorting to Plotinus' way of hiding the problem of ontological dualism.

ultimate (and sufficient) cause is what it contributes to the perfect world, since God created the *best of all possible worlds*. Leibniz's monadology solved the Cartesian ontological problem because there was no body with which mind had to interact. Indeed, since the infinite monad that created all the finite monads existed, like the finite monads, outside the space and time that appeared to finite monads, Leibniz's monadology also solved the Platonic ontological problem.

3.3 Pre-Socratic Test of Ontological Coherence

Since Descartes was the first to describe the unity of consciousness, he discovered that beings like us are conscious.[64] But an intuitionist, he discovered it in the form of mind, and since it had to interact with body, his metaphysics posed the problem of mind-body dualism. Thus, the challenge to defenders of modern intuitionistic metaphysics was to find an ontological theory that solves the problem of mind-body dualism. Leibniz solved the problem by denying the existence of the body, and since he postulated only substances with the unity of mind, he was an idealist, akin to Plotinus, who reduced matter along with the One and its other emanations to objects of intuition for an underlying phenomenal subject. And Spinoza solved the problem of mind-body dualism by denying that they interact. Since he explained them as different attributes of the same substance, he defended a double-aspect theory, akin to Aristotle, who hid Plato's Being-Becoming dualism as form and matter in the many particular substances.

The similarity between the ancient and modern eras is not an accident. It is part of the ontologically necessary way that the metaphysical stage of evolution unfolds. As explained in *Chapter 3*, there are two basically different kinds of intuitionistic metaphysical arguments because intuitionists can be either direct realists or representative realists about perception. Both assume that Reason is a faculty of intuition, and both try to show how Reason knows Reality behind Appearance. But they are different because direct realists defend a metaphysics that is completely inside consciousness, while representative realists defend a metaphysics that discovers Reality outside consciousness. And both kinds of intuitionistic metaphysics are doomed to

---

[64] Since Plato's metaphysics was inside consciousness, what he discovered was the illusion of intuitionism.

fail because, in the end, their explanations of the world are judged by the pre-Socratic standard of coherence. From the beginning, they recognized that a coherent explanation of everything must have a first cause, and that was not obvious to intuitionists defending metaphysics because they expected to explain everything by using a faculty of rational intuition to discover Reality behind Appearance. They showed that the nature of Reality would explain everything in Appearance, and they took it for granted that it would also explain the existence of Appearance itself. The inability to do that is the Achilles heel of intuitionistic metaphysics. For intuitionists, Reason is inside consciousness, and the Reality that it discovers must not only exist self-subsistently but also have a way of existing that explains both the nature that Reason discovers Reality to have and the Appearance behind which Reason finds Reality. That is not possible, though the obstacle takes a different form in each basic kind of intuitionistic metaphysical argument.

As a direct realist, Plato discovers Reality behind Appearance on the assumption that Reason is a faculty intuition, paralleling the faculty of perceptual intuition, with an opposite kind of phenomenal property as the object that is immediately present. Since the entire metaphysics is inside consciousness, the objects of intuition are the self-subsistent entities constituting them, and there is no way of existing in itself that would enable a substance to explain opposite kinds of objects of intuition. But double-aspect theorists insist that there is such a substance, and idealists can try to reduce Appearance to Reality.

As a representative realist, Descartes uses a faculty of rational intuition to discover a Reality behind Appearance, and it is a world outside consciousness that is made up of substances that exist outside one another in space. But the faculties of reason and perception are both inside consciousness, and there is no way that an extended substance could constitute a substance that uses objects of intuition to know about the external world and to choose how to behave in it. But, again, double-aspect theorists insist that there is such a substance, and idealists can, in this case, try to reduce the substance that seems to constitute Reality to the substance that seems to constitute Appearance and Reason. Only a first cause with an intuitionistic essential nature could seem to solve the problematic ontological dualisms of both eras.

As we shall see, the failure of Cartesian metaphysics leads to a third way that intuitionistic metaphysics turns up a problematic dualism that others try to hide in both ways. After Plato and Descartes, there comes Kant. Since the new metaphysical argument of each era depends on the metaphysical argument of the previous era, they are developments that unfold necessarily during the metaphysical stage of evolution. But as we shall see, Descartes came closest to the metaphysics defended by naturalistic Reason, and as a lesson in the deleterious consequences of trying to solve the ontological problems of intuitionistic metaphysics, consider how the attempts to solve mind-body dualism affected Christian theology. Though Descartes defended the belief in free will on which the Christian meaning of life depends, Spinoza and Leibniz had to deny it. Spinoza scorned free will as an illusion caused by the failure to understand the causes that determine every event. And in a world of windowless monads that simply realize over time the natures they must have as parts of the best of all possible worlds, every choice is predetermined by the infinite monad who created it.

4 Anti-Metaphysical Intuitionism

Descartes, Spinoza, and Leibniz were the great metaphysicians of the modern era. They are called the *Continental Rationalists,* and they did believe that Reason can know Reality behind Appearance. Though ontological problems doomed their metaphysics, there were also problems about their use of rational intuition to know Reality behind Appearance, and they were used to cast doubt on metaphysics. Since they make arguments about metaphysics, skeptics are also philosophers. Indeed, by exposing failures, they helped cause revisions of metaphysical arguments. But they cast doubt on metaphysics, not intuitionism, because their skepticism was based on the illusion inherent in consciousness.

The great skeptics about metaphysics in the modern era are called the *British Empiricists*: Locke, Berkeley, and Hume. Turning away from metaphysics, they used rational intuition to determine the limits of knowledge, a project now called *epistemology.* They assumed that rational intuition affords certainty. They recognized that some kinds of knowledge could not be falsified by perceptual intuitions, but they used Reason to cast doubt on the belief that Reason can know Reality behind Appearance. It began with doubts about knowing the existence and nature of a world external to mind, but it eventually cast doubt on knowledge of the existence and nature of mind itself.

John Locke (1632-1704) took up the project of describing the limits of knowledge by defending the *principle of empiricism*. It held that all our knowledge comes from experience, and assuming that the mind begins as a blank slate, he showed the limits of knowledge by tracing all our ideas to their origins in simple ideas. He did not assume that all our knowledge comes from objects of perceptual intuition, or *sensations*, which he assumed were caused by something outside the mind. He recognized that there are objects of reflective intuition, such as memory, imagination, judgments, passions, and willing, which have an internal cause. His denial that we have innate ideas was not meant to take issue with Descartes, but, rather, to insist that the mind begins as a blank slate. Indeed, Locke used Descartes' criteria of clarity and distinctness to identify the ideas that enter the mind as objects of rational intuition. As phenomenal appearances of arguments caused by the structure of faculties of imagination doing thermodynamic work, they did not seem to be falsifiable by other objects of intuition, and so Locke believed in the certainty of knowledge based on geometry, mathematics, and similar demonstrations, including arguments about God and morality.

Locke's skepticism about knowledge of the natural world was confused. He was sympathetic to mechanical philosophy and shared Boyle's and Hobbes' view of matter as corpuscles. But the explanation of perception by the motion and interaction of material bodies led Locke to recognize that sensory qualia are properties of perceivers. Such causal explanations depend on the primary qualities of bodies, such as extension, solidity, shape, and mobility, which are essential to material bodies, and in order to explain what causes the kinds of sensory qualia in the mind, Locke had to believe that bodies had secondary qualities as well, including color, taste, sound, and temperature. They were dispositions of objects to interact in ways that help determine sensation. Thus, in the mind, there were ideas of secondary qualities and ideas of primary qualities, and corresponding to them outside the mind, there were secondary qualities and primary qualities of bodies. Locke may seem to be a critical realist about perception, like natural philosophers, who accepted the existence of a world external to mind and saw primary qualities as defining the nature of the substance constituting the natural world. To agree with natural philosophers, Locke would have to admit that the ideas of primary qualities enable mind to know the *nature* of the Reality behind the perceptual Appearance. But he parted company from them because his principle of empiricism led him to deny that rational intuition provides knowledge of the *existence* of Reality behind Appearance. A substance, stripped of its way of existing, is just a self-subsistent entity, and calling it a *substratum*, Locke argued that our idea of substratum cannot be traced to any simple object of perceptual intuition. Thus, he rejected *substance* as the confused idea of this something, "we know not what." (*Essay* II xxiii 2) Locke never seriously doubted the existence of the external world. But he was skeptical about our ever knowing what causes the existence of bodies with primary qualities. That is, Locke's principle of empiricism led him to deny that we can even understand what the pre-Socratics tried to do.

For similar reasons, Locke was skeptical about the existence of the Reality behind the reflective Appearance. As an intuitionist, he had a clear and distinct idea of the self as the phenomenal subject to which objects of intuition are immediately present. Indeed, Locke accepted Descartes' *Cogito* as certain proof of his own existence. This is the phenomenal subject, and so Locke understood the essential nature of the substance that Descartes called the mind. But he denied that rational intuition reveals a mind behind objects of reflective intuition, and he denied that we can know this kind of substance because we have no idea of a substratum enduring through time. Again, we know the essential nature of something without being able to know its self-subsistence. Thus, skepticism about metaphysics led Locke to recognize that, when subjects reflect on their psychological states, what they find is a self that can tell a story about its identity over time that leads to the here and now. This is all to which *I* or *me* can refer, if there is no substance constituting the phenomenal subject. But as an intuitionist, Locke explained personal identity over time by the habits, memories, and other reflective phenomenal appearances that enable reflective subject to tell a story about their self.

Locke was skeptical about modern metaphysics, and as an empiricist, he did not expect natural philosophy to discover much about the mechanisms in nature. But Locke was not skeptical about ancient metaphysics. Though he doubted modern metaphysics, he believed that we have certain knowledge of mathematics independently of perceptual intuition. He also used rational intuition to demonstrate the existence of God. Locke held that the *Cogito* enabled Rational subjects to demonstrate the existence of God as the creator of everyone. Indeed, he believed that knowledge of God enables Rational subjects to know with certainty that moral rules have the authority to limit their pursuit of self-interest. What kept Locke from being skeptical about the substances discovered by ancient metaphysics because their existence was built into the culture of the Dark Ages by the marriage of Reason and faith in Christian theology late in the ancient era, providing the foundation for culture to evolve Rational selection into modern metaphysics. Almost everyone in the modern era took it for granted that Reason knows a supernatural world as Reality beyond the natural world as Appearance, and it seemed obvious that God's purpose in creating Rational subjects was the foundation of morality. Locke did not see his rejection of modern metaphysics as much of loss because he saw the main value of Reason as practical.

The contrast between Locke's understanding of the social contract and Hobbes' shows the difference that belief in Reason makes. Hobbes was a natural philosopher, and though he did not deny the existence of God, neither did he use God as a premise. He assumed that morality is founded in the natural world, and as we have seen, he used the social contract to show how it is a consequence of the motion and interaction of self-interested animals with the use of language. But since Locke believed that morality is founded in the Christian spiritual world, he used the social contract to show how morality limits the legitimate political authority of the state. Since Rational subjects were created in the image of God, everyone had an equal right to life, liberty, and property, and since they followed moral rules in the state of nature, it was not a war of all against all. They recognized the goals of their own behavior, and since they could see into one another's minds, they could foresee the benefits of using a social contract to establish a government with limited powers. For example, Rational subjects had a natural right to punish wrongdoers, but by agreeing to alienate this right to a government, they could settle property disputes and restore the moral balance without starting a vendetta. Thus, Locke believed that citizens who had signed the social contract would be justified in overthrowing a misbehaving government long before their lives were at stake, as required to overthrow the sovereign in Hobbes' Leviathan.

George Berkeley (1685-1753) and David Hume (1711-1776) were intuitionists who carried the principle of empiricism to its logical conclusion, recognizing further limits on what the phenomenal subject could learn from objects of intuition. But neither denied that we have a faculty of rational intuition. Indeed, they believed that it gives us indubitable knowledge, such as mathematics. They merely limited its scope. For example, Berkeley denied that we have any idea of the infinitesimally small. Though Hume saw mathematics as demonstrative knowledge, he explained its certainty as just the intuition of relations of ideas in the mind, and so he held that all certain knowledge is analytic, that is, true because of the relations of the ideas denoted by the words used to express it. That is how Hume denied that Reason can know Reality behind Appearance.

Locke's skepticism about the external world was confused because he did not deny that Rational subjects can know the primary qualities of bodies outside the mind. Berkeley avoided this confusion by denying that we have ideas of primary qualities. They are *abstract ideas*, and Berkeley denied that we have any abstract ideas. Shape, for example, is an idea of a primary quality, and since we have no idea of a shape without color, we have no abstract idea of shape. The idea of matter is also abstract, and Berkeley denied any need to believe in matter because the existence of objects of perceptual intuition can be explained by their immediate presence. In his words, *to be is to be perceived*. He understood his denial of matter as entailing an idealist ontology, and as a Bishop in the Anglican Church, he was happy to explain the order found in the natural world by how ideas exist in God's mind. Since God is a phenomenal subject, this was a form of idealism, and Berkeley hoped that idealism would disarm the threat posed to Christian theology by the materialism of natural philosophy.

Though Hume had no such religious motive, he implicitly endorsed Berkeley's idealism by holding that nothing exists but *ideas* and the *impressions* of perception and reflection of which ideas were copies. But by the time he wrote, physics had shown the power of the empirical method and natural philosophy had become science, and Hume mistakenly saw his own philosophy as a contribution to science. The scientific method assumes that the natural world is what exists, and Hume was not a naturalist in that sense. He saw his study of objects of intuition as science, and he believed that it would reveal what science can and cannot know about the world of qualia objects in phenomenal space in which we find our qualia bodies. Indeed, his study of ideas did expose a fatal limitation of science. It implied that we cannot know the necessity of causal relations. We can know only the constant conjunction of ideas (that is, remember the constant conjunction of impressions), and since there is no non-circular reason to believe that the future will be like the past, our belief in causation is just a habit of expecting ideas that have been associated in the past. Hume anticipated the limit that empirical lawism imposes on science, and he was right about laws of physics not explaining the necessity of the efficient causes they entail.

The British empiricists all doubted that Reason knows the Reality behind the reflective Appearance. Since Locke accepted the *Cogito*, he saw objects of reflective intuition as revealing a phenomenal subject, but he denied that we could know that it is constituted by a substance that endures through time. But Berkeley, introspecting more closely, realized that there is no idea of the phenomenal subject itself. Indeed, he denied the possibility of any such idea on the grounds that ideas are passive, while the phenomenal subject is active, that is, a being that judges, imagines, wills freely, and the like. But later, when he acknowledged that we do know about its activity, he held that we have, besides ideas, a *notion* of the mind. The recognition of notions spoiled the simplicity of his skeptical philosophy, and, suspiciously, it is what Berkeley had to hold in order to believe that God exists. Hume would have none of this. When he studied objects of reflective intuition, he found neither an idea of the mind nor a notion of the mind. He explained knowledge of the self as just a bundle of ideas related by their resemblance and association in the past.

Locke and Berkeley both believed that rational intuition reveals the existence of God and, thereby, provided the foundation of morality. They embraced the prevailing theistic view of the spiritual world, including the belief in free will. But as a *scientist* of objects of intuition, Hume extended skepticism to both God and morality. He even denied free will. Though he reduced beliefs about causation to habits of expectation based on past constant conjunctions, he insisted that, since the will is an effect of beliefs and passions, it is not free. Indeed, his analysis of the traditional proof of God's existence based on teleology, that is, the argument from the design evident in nature, is so devastating that it seems he must have been an atheist who was silenced by what was religiously correct at the time. In any case, Hume did not use God or rational intuition to explain morality. His study of ideas revealed that moral judgments about actions are not capable of being true or false. He could find nothing to which moral judgments might correspond. Nor could he find any necessary relation between ideas of actions and the ideas of right and wrong. Thus, Hume argued that statements containing *ought* cannot be derived from statements containing *is*. Since previous philosophers had all held that the Good is part of the True, this was to dismiss them as committing what contemporary analytic philosophers call the *naturalistic fallacy*. What Hume did find is that moral judgments are a way of expressing certain feelings about actions and other objects judged. Thus, nothing kept Hume's skepticism about morality from being a reversion to Hobbes' state of nature except his insistence that we happen to have benevolent passions, which lead us to accept moral judgments and defend political authority when it maximizes happiness.

The rejection of direct realism about perception in favor of representative realism was the beginning of the modern era of philosophy, but since metaphysical arguments were based on intuitionism, they were doomed from the outset. Modern metaphysicians had to defend an ontology that entailed two opposite substances that could not jointly constitute a single world coherently, and the ontological theories proposed to hide the problem of dualism were either ontologically incoherent or preposterous (if only to naturalists). But intuitionism was also the foundation for arguments against metaphysics. Empiricist skeptics cast doubt on both modern claims about Reason knowing Reality behind Appearance. They doubted its claim to know the natural world outside the mind, and they were skeptical about knowledge of the mind itself. Hume was even skeptical about God's existence, the ancient claim of Reason to know Reality behind Appearance.

It might seem, therefore, that the only lasting legacy of modern era was natural philosophy, materialism, and Hobbes' reduction of morality to self-interest. But that is to overlook how modern metaphysics reinforced the level of linguistic organization that had caused Western culture to evolve by Rational selection ever since the ancient world and led to the Enlightenment and its offspring. And the arguments between metaphysicians and skeptics in the modern era inspired another kind of metaphysics in the late modern era. It was disguised as the denial of the possibility of metaphysics, but it led to the predictable attempts of other metaphysicians to hide the problematic dualism that it turned up.

5   Late Modern Philosophy

Hume's skepticism about knowing the necessity of causal connections between events awakened Immanuel Kant (1724-1804) from his "dogmatic slumbers," and he took up the defense of science and the new political order. As an intuitionist, Kant assumed that the self is the phenomenal subject. But instead of assuming that rational intuition is a faculty whose objects are clear and distinct ideas, he explained Reason as a constructive faculty, which uses its own concepts to help determine the objects of perceptual intuition that seem to be the natural world. He called this construct the *phenomenal world*, since he did not deny the existence of Reality behind Appearance. Indeed, he recognized the existence of the *noumenal world* (or *things in themselves*) and acknowledged that it contributes something to the phenomenal world. But what was contributed by things in themselves could not be known. They were simply self-subsistent entities with unknown ways of existing. Somehow, they had effects that were registered in the faculty of perceptual intuition, and since the structure of space and time was contributed by that faculty, they appeared to be objects that move and interact in phenomenal space. Kant held that Reason applied its own concepts (by way of a faculty of understanding that uses imagination) to what was given in perceptual intuition, and thus, all those aspects of the phenomenal world that depended on contributions of Reason and perceptual intuition were universal and necessary. Since they were prior to the particular objects found in the phenomenal world, they were known with certainty. This refuted Hume because the causal relations discovered by science were necessary. Kant called such knowledge *synthetic a prior*. It is *synthetic* because it holds of objects in space and time, and it is *a priori* because, as a result of applying the concepts of Reason to what is given in the forms of space and time, it could not be falsified by objects found in the phenomenal world. Thus, Hume's skepticism about knowledge of causal relation was refuted by replacing his assumption that Reason is just a passive intuition of relations of ideas with a theory about how Reason is a constructive power that helps give ideas their relations as part of the phenomenal world.

Kant intended his *Critique of Pure Reason* to be a refutation of metaphysics. His explanation of the nature of Reason implied that it could not know the nature of Reality behind Appearance, and Kant blamed the belief that it could to an illusion caused by Reason. Kant argued that the belief that Reason could know Reality behind Appearance came from assuming that Reason could apply its concepts to what exists independently of the faculty of perceptual intuition, that is, directly to things in themselves beyond Appearance. Though Rational subjects were naturally inclined to try to use Reason in this way, such metaphysical ambitions were doomed. In Kant's view, it was not possible to show that concepts of Reason hold of the noumenal world outside the mind. His constructivist explanation of the phenomenal world required things in themselves to conform to mind in order to appear as objects of perceptual intuition, and so Kant called his critique of Reason a *Copernican revolution* in philosophy. And his professed goal was to limit the claims to knowledge of Reality in "order to make room for faith."

Kant recognized that Reason has a practical function as well as a theoretical function, though it did not come from knowing the Good as part of True. Reason determines what is morally good by commanding us to act only on those maxims that we can will to be a universal law of nature. This formulation of the golden rule is called the *categorical imperative*, by contrast to Reason's *hypothetical imperatives*, which requires Rational subjects to act in their own self-interest. (It is necessarily true that those who will the end, will the means, and so Reason commands hypothetically that, if Rational subjects will an end, they must pursue the necessary means to it and, more generally, that since they all have the goal of happiness, they ought to be prudent.) Though actions done in one's self-interest may be in accordance with the categorical imperative, they do not show the moral worth of a

Rational subject. In Kant's view, what shows moral worth is a *good will*, which is evident in *action from duty*, that is, actions commanded by the categorical imperative that are contrary to self-interest. In the Christian view, it is possible for Rational subjects to do what is morally right when it is contrary to self-interest or opposed by other temptations because, due to God's grace, they had a free will that enabled them to choose between good and evil. But in Kant's view, Reason not only shows us the difference between right and wrong but also gives us the power to do what morality requires when it is contrary to self-interest. Reason's respect for *law as such* enables Rational subjects to submit to the categorical imperative, and the will is free in that case because the choice is not determined according to laws of nature. Instead, it expresses the *spontaneity* of Reason as a thing in itself, that is, its nature as a self-subsistent entity in the noumenal world. Thus, while self-interested actions are caused by a desire for the end (or the general desire for happiness), free will is caused by the noumenal world, and so actions from duty express a will that is *autonomous*, while self-interested actions express a will that is *heteronomous*.

Kant's Copernican revolution made room for faith because, by explaining science as synthetic *a priori* knowledge with *theoretical validity*, he could explain morality and free will as synthetic *a priori* knowledge with *practical validity*. As Reason helped constitute the phenomenal world, so Reason helped constitute the moral agents who act in it. Thus, Rational subjects could know that the will is free because that was what they had to believe in order to believe that Reason imposes an imperative on them categorically and that a good will is possible. Indeed, Kant's Copernican revolution made room for even more faith because Rational subjects could also know that the soul was immortal and that God existed because that was what they had to believe in order to believe that their will was free.

In Kant's view, the Enlightenment did not depend on Reason's power to know Reality behind Appearance. It depended only on confidence that Reason could know the nature of what exists deeply enough for science to discover universal and necessary laws of nature and that it could understand the nature of the good completely enough to determine which goals are good in the situations that arise. Thus, even though Kant rejected metaphysics, his critique of Reason did not keep intuitionists from claiming credit for the progress in science and the political order during the Enlightenment. Reason was not the simple, immediate presence of self-evident ideas that the illusion of intuitionism first suggests, but, rather, the product of the constructive activity of Reason on a faculty of intuition that provided the forms of space and time. But Kant's constructivist theory of Reason depended on the unity of consciousness in the mammalian brain in the same way previous metaphysics, and so there was a new opening for intuitionistic metaphysics. If Reason constructed both perceptual and reflective Appearances, there was a kind of Reality that Reason might discover behind Appearance, namely, a Reality that was constructed entirely by Reason.

Georg Wilhelm Friedrich Hegel (1770-1831) turned Kant's constructive faculty of Reason into *dialectical Reason*. The dialectic is a three-moment inference, described abstractly as *thesis, antithesis,* and *synthesis*. Each synthesis is a new thesis, and so it can proceed through a series of such three-moment inferences until it reaches the end, where dialectical Reason finds itself. In one form (the *Encyclopedia of Philosophical Sciences*), the series of dialectical inferences explains the nature of everything in the world. Hegel traces it from logic (the idea in itself) through the natural world (the idea outside itself) to spirit (the idea in and for itself), in each of which there are many three-moment inferences. It is an ingenious, even poetic, rendition of all human knowledge accumulated at the time. But in the other form (the *Phenomenology of Mind*), it is the series of dialectical inferences that takes place in the immediate presence of the phenomenal subject, more like a process that unfolds in time. It is an exhilarating ride, and here is a gloss on it in terms of objects of intuition.

The first moment is the object of perceptual intuition, which the phenomenal subject sees as a *thing in itself* (though in the end, it turns out to be just how the phenomenal subject initially appears to itself). The second moment is the negation of the first. This is where Hegel invokes the Kantian constructive nature of Reason. The thing in itself is now seen as an object *for the phenomenal subject* because what is universal and necessary about the object is recognized as the contribution of Reason, using its own concepts. But the second moment does not negate the object of perceptual intuition entirely. An object of intuition remains, and by comparing its own contribution to that object with the object itself, the phenomenal subject negates the negation. This is the third moment, which Hegel sees as a synthesis that turns the original object of intuition into another object of intuition, which is the new thesis for the beginning of another dialectical inference. The object of intuition is the Appearance, which is immediately present to the phenomenal subject, and the trick is that each synthesis reveals something more about how Reason is responsible for Appearance. At the end of the process, the phenomenal subject recognizes that the Reality behind Appearance, the ultimate thing in itself, is Reason. Since the phenomenal subject who carries out the dialectical process is Reason, Reason knows that the Reality behind Appearance is Reason, and thus, Reason turns out to be identical with Reality.

This abstract gloss does not convey the ingenuity of Hegel's detailed elaboration of it, but it shows how Hegel redeployed Kant's constructivist theory of Reason for metaphysical purposes. His conclusion about Reason being identical Reality was not as trivial as it may sound because, when the details of its dialectical path are spelled out, the phenomenal subject also discovers its own nature as *Spirit* (that is, as the *idea in and for itself*, which is the antithesis of the *idea outside itself*, or nature, which is, in turn, the antithesis of the *idea in itself*, or logic). Thus, the lesson that the phenomenal subject has learned in the end is that Spirit and Reason are identical, and as we shall see, something like that is true in naturalistic metaphysics. But Hegel is an intuitionist, and since all that really exists, in the end, is Absolute Spirit, Absolute Reason, Absolute Mind, or whatever term is used to describe the interconnected self-knowing whole that reveals itself to itself by the dialectic, the ontology that Hegel defends is absolute idealism. Thus, while Kant allowed intuitionists to defend the Enlightenment without defending metaphysics, Hegel defended an idealist metaphysics that allowed intuitionists to claim that the Enlightenment was part of the Appearance that unfolds in the process by which dialectical Reason discovers that it is all that really exists.

Like modern philosophy, late modern philosophy was a way of arguing about intuitionistic metaphysics based on representative realism about perception, but since it used a radically different theory about the nature of Reason from Descartes, it was a third way of doing metaphysics. Since ancient, modern, and late-modern metaphysics are all taken in by the intuitionist illusion, the kinds of Reality they discover behind Appearance pose the same problem of ontological dualism when it comes to showing how Reality is a substance (or substances) that constitute everything in the world, including Appearance. Kant replaced Descartes's mind-body dualism with the dualism of the phenomenal and noumenal worlds, but since there was no way to show how substances constitute both worlds, Kant's ontological dualism was just as problematic as Descartes'. Intuitionists, as well as naturalists, balked at it, and so late modern philosophy was a third time that metaphysicians had to hide a problematic ontological dualism.

Hegel solved Kant's dualism as an absolute idealist. He denied the existence of the kind of substance that would explain the natural world by reducing it to the phenomenal subject and what is immediately present, much as Leibniz did in the modern era (by reducing it to monads)[65] and Plotinus did in the ancient era (by reducing it to the One and explaining its two emanations as immediately present to a phenomenal subject). Idealists have a first cause, but it is an intuitionistic first cause rather than a naturalistic first cause, or the kind of substance that the pre-Socratic might believe constitutes the natural world. But given how ontological science uses its explanation of consciousness and the illusion inherent in it to show how metaphysics causes the metaphysical stage of evolution, it expects to find in the late modern period of Western philosophy a third way of hiding Kant's problematic ontological dualism.

When faced with the ontological dualism inherent in intuitionistic metaphysics, it also seems possible to overcome the ontological dualism by postulating a single kind of substance with two essential natures. It was explored by Aristotle in the ancient era (by holding that particular substances are both form and matter), and it was explored by Spinoza in the modern era (by holding that a single substance has both an attribute of thought and an attribute of extension). As ontology predicts, there was a metaphysician who explored this strategy in the late modern era. F. W. J. Schelling (1775-1854)

---

[65] Even Berkeley reduced the natural world to ideas in God's mind.

accepted Kant's constructivist theory of Reason, and instead of reducing everything to Reason, as Hegel did, Schelling hid Kant's dualism by postulating a single substance, the *Absolute*, with two essential natures, one in which it *objectifies* itself as nature, and the other in which it *subjectifies* itself as the phenomenal subject for which nature is the object. In the end, Reason enables the subjectified aspect to recognize the objectified aspects as the other aspect of the Absolute. But like Aristotle and Spinoza, Schelling was not able to explain how a substance can have such opposite natures as subject and object at the same time, that is, with both the unity of mind and the divisibility of the external world. It was the belief in a first cause that is ontologically incoherent, and so it was another ontological theory that failed the pre-Socratic test of coherence.

Though late-modern philosophers claimed credit for the Enlightenment, the Achilles heel of using intuitionistic Reason to know Reality behind Appearance is the ontological problem caused by having to postulate two opposite kinds of substances in order to show how Reality explains everything in the world ontologically, including Appearance. The ontological problem could not be solved. It could only be hidden, and its disguises were either incoherent or incredible. The pre-Socratics came closer to knowing the Truth than intuitionistic metaphysics by seeking the first cause of the natural world. The naturalist rebellion against intuitionistic metaphysics as science was a step in this direction, and in the history of Western philosophy as the biography of Reason, this is the path that enabled it to discover its true identity as naturalistic Reason.

CHAPTER 6:
ENLIGHTENMENT

The history of Western philosophy has been used to confirm the prediction of ontological science of a stage of spiritual evolution after the psychological stage. The ontological explanation of the nature of consciousness revealed that there is an illusion inherent in consciousness that makes it seem that the knowledge of beings like us depends on faculties of intuition. Metaphysics is a third level of linguistic organization, and since consciousness makes metaphysics plausible, it is possible. According to the reproductive mechanism, therefore, if the metaphysical level is functional, a metaphysical stage of spiritual evolution is inevitable. After showing that a series of stages of evolution on Earth lead inevitably to the existence of reflective subjects on Earth, therefore, ontological science predicts that a civilized spiritual organism will eventually begin a metaphysical stage of evolution on Earth. The way that the third level of linguistic organization causes a stage of spiritual evolution implies that events must unfold in a certain order, and *Chapters 4* and *5* have used that regularity to show that Western civilization has the essential traits of the beginning of the metaphysical stage. This also solves the puzzle, left unsolved by *Volume II*, about its rise giving Western civilization unprecedented functional powers and its culture and institutions being globalized. Furthermore, since ontological science completes the study of nature by reducing all the specialized sciences to interactions of space and matter, its own existence is problematic, and the explanation of Western civilization as the beginning of the metaphysical stage solves that problem by showing the origin of the physical science that made it possible for empirical ontology to discover that space is a substance that interacts with matter and uses it to unify physics and science.

This trilogy defends the prediction of an intellectual revolution in which science explains philosophy, the study of Appearance, and discovers that it has become *naturalistic Reason*, after which this trilogy is named. The term *Reason* is capitalized because it refers to the cognitive power that intuitionistic metaphysicians believed enables us to know Reality behind Appearance. Since it began as the ancient Greek belief that beings like us are capable of a cognitive kind of perfection, this prediction that science will attain the goal that metaphysics had from the beginning and explain everything has been portrayed as the biography of Reason. If the argument of this trilogy is on the right track, science will become naturalistic Reason, and the regularity about how events lead to that outcome is the path that Reason will eventually follow on all planets where life can evolve. A metaphysical stage of evolution is inevitable because reflective subjects are conscious, and science will acquire the cognitive perfection that has been the goal of philosophy since ancient Greece. What its lovers called *wisdom* turns out to be naturalistic Reason.

This chapter describes a crucial juncture in the life of Reason on Earth, an adolescent identity crisis. Reason was born in ancient Greece, and after Platonic metaphysics was married with Christianity, it spent its childhood in the family of modern intuitionistic metaphysics. But as we have seen, the attempts of intuitionists to show that Reason knows Reality behind Appearance are doomed because its theory about the nature of Reason is false. The nature of the Reality that metaphysicians found behind Appearance had to be substances of kinds that can explain everything, and no substances could be found that explained everything coherently. In particular, since the kinds of substances that could constitute both Reality and Appearance had opposite natures, metaphysicians were confronted with a problematic ontological dualism that, at best, could only be hidden. But metaphysical culture is founded on the belief in Reason, and after many centuries of cultural evolution, confidence in Reason builds up. The belief that reflective subjects are capable of a distinctive kind of perfection permeates its institutions, and by the time metaphysicians accept representative realism about perception, it is shared universally because the faithful accept a religious explanation of the meaning of life in which they are created in the image of a God that transcends the natural world. Since they were created in the image of a Rational God, they conceive of their self as Rational, and so confidence in Reason builds up popular momentum. Thus, when the prospect of successfully showing that

Reason knows Reality behind Appearance dims and skepticism about metaphysics rises, confidence in Reason has momentum that carries metaphysical-level culture in various directions.

The period when this crisis occurred on Earth is called the *Enlightenment*, which is standardly dated as the 18th-century. In this biography of Reason, this is when the path that leads to naturalistic Reason diverges from intuitionistic metaphysics. This chapter describes three offspring of the Enlightenment that explain the unparalleled rise and globalization of the West: science, liberal political institutions, and capitalism. Ontological science finds its origin in science, and it did not have to solve the problem of ancient dualism because Western culture was beginning to turn away from supernaturalism. After the religious wars of the 16th and 17th centuries, the Enlightenment was the beginning of toleration of different religious commitments. They were mostly Christian, and though traditional theism has survived to this day, it has gradually conceded that belief in a transcendent God cannot be justified by Reason and had to be accepted on faith. Though the theism of Christianity and Judaism is one direction that momentum carried the belief in the basic perfection of beings like us, let us put this remnant from the dualism of ancient intuitionistic metaphysics aside for now because all the relevant currents abandoned supernaturalism in favor of naturalism.

The path that Reason took during the Enlightenment was the naturalism of science. Like the natural philosophy that preceded it, it affirmed the existence of the natural world and used the empirical method to learn more about it. This was to reject the intuitionistic belief that knowledge of the natural world depends on a faculty of perceptual intuition, and this can be considered the beginning of the study of nature. But the rise of science was not just a continuation of natural philosophy. It was the path that Reason took because science depended on modern intuitionistic metaphysics. Indeed, the beginning of science was an adolescent identity crisis for Reason because it depended on Reason rebelling against its intuitionistic family. Philosophy was the study of Appearance that characterizes the beginning of the metaphysical stage, and the scientific study of nature would eventually replace philosophy as the leading edge of Western cultural progress. As we shall see, the rise of science depended on the success of physics, and since its success came from a treasure that Reason took with it when it rebelled against its intuitionistic family, it was an identity crisis for Reason.

Science was only one of the three offspring of the Enlightenment that enabled Western spiritual organisms to acquire an order of functional powers that were out of reach for psychological-level spiritual organisms. Liberal political institution and capitalism were also carried along by the momentum of confidence in Reason, and they also played essential roles. Though they could also abandon traditional supernaturalism, science led the way because it eventually debunked the belief in Reason on which the other offspring of the Enlightenment depended. *Chapter 7, disillusionment with Reason,* describes how the path of scientific naturalism was the self-destruction of Reason.

Science is not the only current that flowed from the momentum of confidence in Reason that had built up at the time of the Enlightenment. What science left behind in Western culture was philosophy, and its various currents are described in *Chapter 8*. What they all had in common was is intuitionism, the belief that knowledge comes from the immediate presence of complex phenomenal properties. Leaving traditional theism aside, they were all basically naturalistic. They did not depend on the belief in a God outside space and time who created the natural world. They did not have to deal with the problematic ontological dualism of Platonic metaphysics. But in the modern era, there was a problem of mind-body dualism in the natural world, and philosophy had to cope with it. Philosophy started off finding ways to hide mind-body dualism, but as it became clear that there was no solution, the momentum of confidence in the belief that there is something perfect about the nature of beings like us petered out and was replaced by confidence in human imperfection. Thus, what ontological science finds when it traces its origin to Western philosophy is *endarkenment*, a metaphysical civilization— and the globe around which its culture has spread—struggling to find its way.

The origin of this dismal outcome of philosophy was the high point of optimism about progress in Western civilization. During the Enlightenment, the Rational pursuit of Truth was expected to lead not only to a complete explanation of the natural world but also to the improvement of the conditions of life on Earth. This progress would come from popular forums where arguments representing all points of view could be heard. Diderot hoped that the publication of his *Encyclopédie*, with contributions from Rousseau, Voltaire, Montesquieu, and other *men of letters*, would sum up the knowledge that had already accumulated and make it available to everyone. Salons, coffee houses, and public spaces provided opportunities for ordinary citizens to participate in the ongoing rational pursuit of the True and the Good.

At the beginning of the late modern era, Kant gave the Enlightenment its motto: *sapere aude* (dare to know). In his 1784 essay, *Answering the Question: What is Enlightenment?*, he defined *Enlightenment* as a change in which reflective subjects, by daring to argue freely and publicly, pass from a state of tutelage by religious and political authorities to maturity, an enlightened state in which freethinking individuals would use their faculty of Reason to judge for themselves what is true and what is good. This justification of the belief in Reason came after the spread of empiricist skepticism about its power to know Reality behind Appearance. Kant saw himself as a skeptic about metaphysics, even though his constructivist theory of Reason provided a foundation for Hegel and Schelling to defend metaphysics. But Kant recognized that the Enlightenment came from philosophy, and as an intuitionist, he meant to give credit where credit is due. Kant justified science, and since he helped put physics on the path to its remarkable success in learning about the natural world, it is ironic that his argument in the *Critique of Pure Reason* about the goal of physics being knowledge of synthetic *a priori* truths defended the very aspect of its method that would eventually lead to the intractable puzzles of modern physics. The rise of science is described in *Section 1*.

Science was only one of three offspring of the Enlightenment that stand out as playing the significant roles in the evolution of the unprecedented power of Western civilization. The rise of science was its offspring on the theoretical side, and on the practical side, its offspring included both a new political order and a new economic order. The new political order was an institution introduced into Western spiritual organisms by the evolution of popular culture. As explained in *Section 2*, it was also an offspring of intuitionistic metaphysics because it depended on the conception of the self as having Reason and a free will that enabled Rational subjects to do what morality requires, even when it is contrary to self-interest or requires self-control. The new economic order was capitalism. It was an indirect offspring of intuitionistic metaphysics because, on the one hand, it depended on the medieval legal revolution and its respect for the legal autonomy of associations and, on the other, it depended on a flow of technological advances from science for its own progressive evolution of production. *Section 3* shows how it contributed to the rise and globalization of the West.

1 Science

The success of science is standardly attributed to the use of the empirical method, which is seen as the rejection of metaphysics. Indeed, the empirical method is often confused with empiricism, the intuitionist argument against metaphysics. But the empirical method is different from intuitionistic metaphysics (and arguments about it) because it rejects perceptual intuitions as the foundation of knowledge of the natural world. The empirical method simply ignores the distinction between direct and representative realism, and taking the existence of the natural world for granted. It uses perception to discover beliefs that are true by corresponding to the natural world. This is the method of both natural philosophy and empirical ontology since both accept the ontological naturalism of the pre-Socratics, and it includes the use of the empirical method. But the use of ordinary perception to learn about the natural world is not what explains the rise of science.

To be sure, Francis Bacon (1561-1628) had proposed a method of induction to replace deductions from Aristotelian teleological metaphysics. It would generalize from observable facts and reduce error by avoiding overgeneralization and by looking for observable facts and generalizations to limit them. But this is just more of what naturalists do as reflective subjects. It can cause cultural evolution by pragmatic selection, but it cannot explain the rise of science as part of the Enlightenment.

Natural philosophy was based on the empirical method, and as the resurrection of the pre-Socratic project, it used the empirical method to discover the substances constituting the natural world. Atomism and forms of plenum materialism had their defenders. Hobbes and Boyle (and even Locke, insofar as he was sympathetic with natural philosophy) believed that the smallest bodies were *corpuscles*, with various shapes and sizes, which, unlike atoms, could be divided and were not separated by the void. Since materialists assumed that what happens is caused by the motion and interaction of material bodies, they favored what is called *mechanical philosophy*. This was to accept the foundation that Descartes expected his metaphysics to provide for natural philosophy. Speaking of passion, memory, and imagination in his *Treatise on Man*, for example, Descartes said, "I should like you to consider that these functions follow from the mere arrangement of the machine's organs every bit as naturally as the movements of a clock or other automaton follow from the arrangement of its counter-weights and wheels."[66] Unlike geometrical causes, which are an effect of space and matter interacting, Descartes' *mechanical causes* were ontological causes because they were geometrical structures of extension, the substance to which he reduced the natural world. But they served as efficient causes because their geometrical structures constrained how they move and interact, and since these regularities can be understood in naturalistic imagination, Descartes treated its phenomenal appearance as a faculty of rational intuition that grasps the necessary connection between causes and effects. But ontological naturalists, both atomists and plenum materialists, took the spatial structure of the natural world for granted, and so the default assumption of mechanical philosophy was that mechanical causes are responsible for what happens

Ontological naturalism and the belief in mechanical causes are not, however, what caused the scientific revolution. On the contrary, physics depended on rejecting them. Their rejection was a consequence of the form of the empirical method that was responsible for the rise of science (and physicalist blindness to geometrical causes). It began with physics, and as we have seen, its method is *empirical lawism*, which assumes that mathematically formulated laws of nature are the deepest possible empirical knowledge of the natural world. But in this context, empirical lawism is called *intuitionistic naturalism* because it is a child of intuitionistic metaphysics. The way that physics used the empirical method depended on mathematics, and since the truth of mathematics was seen as depending on rational intuition, the rise of science was an offspring of intuitionistic metaphysics. Geometrical objects

---

[66] John Cottingham, Robert Stoothoff, Dugald Murdoch (1985, p. 108).

were Plato's prime example of the power of rational intuition to know Forms beyond the visible world, and evolving for centuries, it was still the prime example of indubitable knowledge from rational intuition in the modern era.

As explained in *Chapter 3,* rational intuition is the mistaken belief that the phenomenal appearance of naturalistic imagination is a faculty of intuition. It leads intuitionists who accept representative realism to believe that the truth of mathematics is known independently of perception of the natural world. And using naturalistic imagination to understand the geometrical structure of space, intuitionists can formulate geometry as a deductive system based on axioms. It is just a set of abstract linguistic representations arranged deductively, and the formulation of geometry and arithmetic in this way helps make it seem that rational intuition reveals mathematical truths independently of perception. Rational subjects understand naturalistic sentences by constructing their meanings in naturalistic imagination, and certain very general naturalistic sentences, such as *the shortest distance between two points is a straight line,* and *parallel lines never meet*, seem to be self-evident because they are implicit in the structure of naturalistic imagination. They can be used to derive less general naturalistic sentences describing the structure of space, and since deductive inferences preserve truth, geometry seems to be a system of linguistic representations whose truth can be known by rational intuition.

When pressed, most mathematicians confess to Platonism, the belief that mathematics describes abstract entities that exist independently of themselves. But in the spatio-material world, the meanings of naturalistic sentences determine how they correspond to space, and as explained in *Volumes I* and *II*, that includes mathematical theorems. For example, the truth of geometry seems to be necessary because it corresponds to a substance with an intrinsic geometrical structure whose interaction with matter can generate only quantitative regularities in the natural world. Much the same holds of arithmetic, since its theorems come down to results of counting distinct entities, and they are also determined by the essential natures of space and matter. Since all the branches of mathematics used in physics can be constructed from geometry and arithmetic, mathematics seems true in a way that is different from the truth of equations describing regularities about change. While the latter can be falsified by perception, the former cannot, and so the truth of mathematics is considered self-evident. That is plausible because of the intuitionist illusion inherent in the unity of consciousness. What is understood by reflecting on the structure of naturalistic imagination seems to be known because it is immediately present, and it seems to depend on a faculty of rational intuition. But in the spatio-material world, the apparent certainty of mathematics has the same ontological cause as the unreasonable effectiveness of mathematics in discovering laws of physics. And the birth and continuing advances of physics show that the assumption that mathematics is known *a priori* was essential to the rise of science.

The scientific revolution arguably began with astronomical discoveries, though they hardly show the full power of mathematics. In 1543, Nicolaus Copernicus (1473-1543) used a basically geometrical argument to show the superiority of his heliocentric view of the heavens over the traditional Ptolemaic Earth-centered system. In the early 17th century, the belief that God created the world using a geometrical plan that was intelligible through the *natural light of reason* led to Johannes Kepler's (1571-1630) discovery of three laws of planetary motion, including the elliptical shape of gravitational orbits. When Galileo learned of the invention of the telescope in 1608, he constructed one that was powerful enough for observations of the heavens to confirm the Copernican view. But his work on falling bodies, mentioned in the *Introduction*, is a better illustration of how the use of mathematics facilitated the progressive evolution of scientific culture.

Galileo Galilei (1564–1642) used the empirical method in a new way in defense of his law of falling bodies. This law is a quantitatively precise regularity about change, and using a mathematical description of it, Galileo made precise predictions whose confirmation by careful measurements showed conclusively that this regularity is a law of nature. He discovered that all bodies fall with a velocity that increases at a constant rate as time passes. The quantitative precision of this mathematical description made it possible to use balls rolling down inclined planes to prove that this regularity holds. The change in velocity after each unit of time along the way could be calculated geometrically, and precise measurements of the locations of the balls at certain moments in time tested the regularity. This required Galileo to construct a water clock that measured time with unprecedented precision. Indeed, it was accurate enough to falsify his initial hypothesis. He had assumed that velocity increased with distance, but his measurements showed that the causally relevant factor was time. It increases with the square of the time of falling.

What made Galileo's empirical discovery seminal was his new and compelling way of proving that there *are* laws of nature. It was obvious that there are regularities about change in the natural world. But Galileo showed that they involve quantities that can be predicted precisely. Mathematical predictions are more precise than even the most accurate measurements, and thus, if mathematically described regularities were not *laws of nature*, success in predicting precise measurements would have to be considered sorcery.

Galileo's law of falling bodies was a description of gravitation, and to appreciate the difference between Galileo's new method and mechanical philosophy, consider Descartes' explanation of gravitation. Believing that Reason discovers the nature of the Reality behind the perceptual Appearance, Descartes' clear and distinct idea of geometrical structure showed that it was an extended substance. It was divisible into parts whose properties were figure, size, and motion. There could be no void since that would entail a second kind of substance, and so extension was a kind of *plenum* materialism. Parts of extension can change only by moving relative to one another, and so everything that happens in the natural world is a result of material bodies pushing other bodies out of their way. It was, therefore, a challenge to explain how one body can exert a gravitational effect on bodies at a distance.

The atomists had postulated the void in order to explain how atoms could move, but since Descartes believed that large bodies move around in a *plenum*, he had to hold that much of extension is made up of very small pieces of matter (called *primary matter*). Macroscopic bodies (called *tertiary matter*) could move through primary matter freely since this subtle matter could make room for them by moving around in circular paths. Descartes assumed that astronomical bodies are surrounded by large vortices of primary matter, and he held that atom-sized globules somewhere between primary and tertiary matter in size (called *secondary matter*) were carried along by these vortices. On the assumption that rotating matter tends to flow outward, toward the equator of the vortex surrounding a huge body like Earth, Descartes was able to explain the gravitational attraction of macroscopic bodies (tertiary matter) toward the Earth by the pressure of primary and secondary matter displacing tertiary matter from the outermost regions of the vortex toward the center.

This was an ingenious mechanical explanation, and since Cartesian physics reduced gravitation to a substance with a geometrically defined nature, its necessity could be understood in naturalistic imagination. But Newtonian physics was not based on Cartesian extension. It was based on the Cartesian coordinate system.

Though Galileo was the first to set up experiments that confirmed quantitatively precise predictions, it was Isaac Newton (1642-1726) who established physics as what we now call science. In his masterpiece, the *Mathematical Principles of Natural Philosophy,*[67] Newton showed how mathematics would revolutionize natural philosophy. He assumed that what corresponds to the Cartesian coordinate system is absolute space. Material bodies have locations in this space, and since everything exists at present, he also assumed that time passes everywhere at the same rate. Newton famously announced three laws of motion and a law of gravitation, and using a new branch of mathematics, the *calculus* (which he had constructed as a young man after learning how Descartes used coordinates to describe locations in space and time), he used his laws to derive all three of Kepler's laws of planetary motion and much more. To be sure, like Galileo, Newton used geometrical arguments in his *Principia* out of deference to his readers. But the calculus is what enabled him to predict measurements in a wide variety of gravitational phenomena, from the orbits of the planets, our moon, and the moons of Jupiter to the effect of altitude on weight, the oblate shape of the rotating Earth, and the precession of the Earth's axis of rotation. He could even predict weights on other planets, the paths of comets, and the pattern of tides on Earth. Using only his laws of motion, he could predict quantitative properties precisely in many experimental situations where the relevant forces had to be inferred, such as the change of velocities of material bodies in elastic collisions and the velocity of a body pulled against friction. Each precise

---

[67] Newton's *Principia* was first published as three books in 1687, with further editions published in 1713 and 1726. For translation, see Newton (1999).

prediction provided additional evidence that what happens in the natural world depends on quantitatively precise regularities about change, and combined with the range of predictions entailed by a few simple laws describing them, no one could doubt that physics had found a new way of using the empirical method to learn about the natural world.

Besides the spatial and temporal relations of material bodies, Newton's laws of nature mentioned various non-geometrical, causally relevant quantitative properties, such as *mass* and *force*. But his explanations did not depend on geometrical causes that can be understood in naturalistic imagination. In effect, Newton rejected mechanical philosophy and Cartesian physics in favor of the certainty of mathematics. His law of gravitation was an equation that describes material bodies as exerting forces on one another at a distance *immediately*, regardless of how far apart they may be. In a world where material bodies interact only by contact, it is not possible for a material body at one location to change the motion of material bodies located far away without material bodies in between pushing one another in some way. But in Newton's world, nothing was needed to connect gravitating bodies but the absolute space corresponding to the Cartesian coordinate system. Nor could space itself be a mechanism that mediates their interaction because Newtonian absolute space was immutable. Matter could not change space in any way. But mathematical derivations from his law of gravitation and boundary conditions preserved their necessary truth, and for Newton's followers, confirmation of such predictions was reason enough to accept his law.

Even Newton admitted that immediate action at a distance is puzzling. Without any mechanism behind their interaction, the force of gravity seemed like an occult quality. But he dealt with this puzzle by defending the use of mathematics in physics. In the *General Scholium* of his *Principia*, he refused to speculate about how gravitation might be explained mechanically, insisting that his method did not involve making *hypotheses* about the mechanisms responsible for the regularities about change that laws of nature describe.

> I have not as yet been able to deduce from phenomena the reason for these properties of gravity, and I do not feign hypotheses. For whatever is not deduced from the phenomena must be called a hypothesis; and hypotheses, whether metaphysical or physical, based on occult qualities,

or mechanical, have no place in experimental philosophy. In this experimental philosophy, propositions are deduced from phenomena and are made general by induction.[68]

By *deductions from phenomena*, Newton meant empirical inferences to quantitative regularities about change. But notice that deductions of predictions from them depend on the certainty of mathematics, and that was a contribution of Reason, as the nearly simultaneous invention of the calculus by the metaphysician Leibniz suggests.

Such mathematical descriptions of regularities found in the natural world are called *laws of physics*, and though the physicists who used Newton's method would make many great discoveries, all this method could discover were laws of nature. These laws would be confirmed by careful measurements of what they predict, and when faced with alternatives, physicists would follow the principle of optimality inherent in the faculty of imagination and choose the mathematically simplest law that predicts the widest range of phenomena. The necessity of the regularities would be merely an assumption, as Hume would point out later. But this method assumed that mathematically formulated laws of nature are the deepest possible empirical knowledge of the nature of what is found in the natural world. That is how this argument defined *empirical lawism* at the outset, and it can also be called *intuitionistic naturalism* since the belief in the certainty of mathematics on which it depends was based on the belief in Reason, as shown by tracing this method to its origin during the metaphysical stage of spiritual evolution.

As Galileo justified it, mathematics plays a central role in science because it is the *language of nature*.

> Philosophy [i.e., physics] is written in this grand book—I mean the universe—which stands continually open to our gaze, but it cannot be understood unless one first learns to comprehend the language and interpret the characters in which it is written. It is written in the language of mathematics, and its characters are triangles, circles, and other geometrical figures, without which it is humanly impossible to

---

[68] Newton (1999), p. 943.

understand a single word of it; without these, one is wandering around in a dark labyrinth.[69]

What made it plausible that mathematics is the language of nature was the belief that God had used mathematics to will the natural world into existence. The belief in a transcendent God was not in doubt, and as an object of rational intuition, mathematics seemed to be true in a way that could not be falsified by perception. Physicists had no need for mechanisms that can be understood in naturalistic imagination because the use of mathematics to discover laws of nature was a way of seeing into God's mind. This is akin to what Plato promised in the *Timaeus*, when he explained the order in the natural world as the moving image of eternity: the receptacle was space and time; the Forms were laws of physics, and God was the demiurge. This account of the nature of God derived from the marriage of ancient intuitionistic metaphysics with Christianity, and there is no doubt that the founders of physics took it seriously. Indeed, Newton considered his extensive scholarly work in theology as a more important contribution to progress than his contribution to science.

To be sure, science and Christianity were parting ways. Already in 1633, the Catholic Church forced Galileo to recant the Copernican system (and abjure his defense of it in his *Dialogue Concerning Two Chief World Systems*) under threat of the rack. This was in defense of the political power of the Church during the Reformation, and though it brought an end to the rise of science in regions of Europe under its jurisdiction, science continued to advance in Protestant territories. During the Enlightenment, talk of God dropped out. But the goal of physics was still to discover mathematically formulated laws of nature. And the certainty of mathematics based on rational intuition was the contribution of intuitionistic metaphysics.

After intuitionistic naturalism gave rise to physics, further advances in physics were a form of cultural evolution. But it was not cultural evolution by *Rational selection* because its conclusions were not judged by correspondence to Reality. Though naturalists assume that the natural world is Reality, the truth of laws of physics was judged by their success in predicting

---

[69] From Galileo Galilei, *Il Saggiatore* (*The Assayer*, 1623), translated by Drake (1957, p. 237-8).

measurements. That was the goal shared by physicists, at least, in practice, and advances in physics were culture evolving by a disciplined form of *pragmatic selection*. The shared goal was to reach agreement about the mathematically simplest laws whose predictions cover the widest range of predictions. Correspondence to Reality was a matter of interpretation, in which physicists could indulge while having drinks outside the lab. Given how its practitioners thought of themselves, physics might charitably be described as the rational pursuit of truth. And in the intellectual history of the West as the biography of Reason, it is the path that Reason took. But physics was not the Rational pursuit of Truth.[70]

The discovery of some new laws introduced more sophisticated mathematics. In the mid 19th century, Maxwell summed up all the previously discovered laws of electricity and magnetism as a single set of consistent equations, and using vector calculus, they were later reduced to four equations. Such successes in physics inspired the use its method in other fields. Dalton's measurements of the weights of substances before and after chemical reactions showed that they were made up of atoms, and this led to the periodic table, the classification of atoms into elementary kinds on which the explanation of all chemical reactions is based. Despite Locke's doubts about it, perception revealed unobservable objects, like atoms, on the smallest scale. What Locke did not appreciate was how severely precise measurements would constrain mathematically formulated laws of nature. *All* the quantitative relations that *all* the laws of physics describe must hold in *every* situation. Unobservable entities that are inferred by combining laws in this way are called *theoretical entities*, and physicists generally believe in their existence, at least outside the lab.

In fields where mathematics was less useful, scientists followed a more general form of the empirical method, inferring what to believe as the best explanation of what careful and extensive observations found in the natural world. The study of natural history revealed the enormous scale of geological time. Minerals were analyzed. Fossils were uncovered. Data were gathered about the variety of living organisms. Human anatomy was described. Laws

---

[70] Thus, Hilary Putnam (1990) was correct when he insisted that scientific realism is not metaphysical realism.

of nature were applied when they were relevant, and since explanations could be compared in faculties of imagination, scientists used the principle of optimality, preferring theories that explain more of the phenomena with less in the way of causes. During the Enlightenment, scientists were typically men (and sometimes women) of leisure with confidence in the power of the empirical method to uncover the secrets of nature. Their work was fostered by the establishment of scientific academies. Progress in science encouraged Adam Smith and others to explain human society, that is, spiritual organisms, as a natural phenomenon.

2   Political Order

The new political order that evolved during the Enlightenment recognized the equal rights of citizens to freedom and a say in governmental decisions. Founded on the assumption that citizens are Rational subjects, it was another contribution of intuitionistic metaphysics. The illusion of intuitionism makes it plausible that reflective subjects have a free will, and it was essential to the Christian gospel of salvation because, as Augustine explained, it gave sinners the power to do what morality requires even when it was contrary to self-interest or opposed by temptations to sin. Without free will, eternal damnation of sinners could not be justified. Since free will was built into the conception of the self that members of spiritual organisms internalized during and after the Dark Ages, the assumption that Rational subjects could be trusted to be moral was a contribution of ancient intuitionistic metaphysics by way the marriage of Platonic Reason and Christian faith. But free will also had a firm foundation in the modern intuitionistic conception of the self. Metaphysics assumes that the Good is part of the True, and the Socratic test of practical Reason requires knowledge of the Good to cause Rational subjects to choose goals that are good. The Christian understanding of moral goodness was a reason for being moral only for those with faith in God's purpose in creating Earth as a home for finite beings fashioned in his image. But its effect on behavior was attributed to a free choice between good and evil, and seeing free will as self-evident, modern intuitionists could not deny that individuals are responsible for acting morally. The medieval legal revolution had generalized the autonomy of Rational subjects to cover associations, and as confidence in the moral autonomy of individuals spread, political institutions were seen as legitimate only if they granted Rational subjects as much liberty to pursue their self-interest as is compatible with a like liberty for all.

The difference between the explanation of the social contract by Hobbes and Locke shows the dependence of freedom on modern intuitionistic metaphysics. As a natural philosopher, Hobbes was a materialist. He used the social contract to explain morality as a consequence of the motion and interaction of individuals as machines with the power to act in their own self-interest in a state of nature. It was necessary to keep peace, and individuals had no right to disobey the sovereign established by the social contract unless their lives were at stake. But Locke was a modern intuitionistic philosopher who believed that Reason enables subjects to know what is morally right as part of its knowledge of God, and so he assumed that free will enabled Rational subjects to treat others as moral equals even in the state of nature. Since they could do what is right even when it was opposed by animal desires or self-interest, Locke used the social contract to show that Rational subjects have a duty to obey the law only when governments have limited powers and are legitimate.

In America, Locke's belief that God endowed Rational subjects with an inalienable right to life, liberty, and property became, in the Declaration of Independence, the inalienable right to life, liberty, and pursuit of happiness, and Locke's understanding of the social contract as limiting legitimate political authority was seen as giving government the goal of securing the rights of individuals. In Europe, the divine right of kings did not vanish immediately, though monarchs, like Frederick the Great of Prussia and Catherine the Great of Russia, became so-called *enlightened despots*. And in the French Revolution, the belief that legitimate rule depends on the consent of the governed led to the King's beheading.

The Enlightenment came after the age of religious wars that had devastated Europe in the century following Martin Luther (1483-1546) and the Reformation, and *men of letters* in the 18th century criticized traditional religions for their orthodoxy. Tolerance of religious differences even led to the separation of church and state in the US Constitution. Toleration meant that Enlightenment philosophers could not found freedom and equal rights on

Christianity or any particular religious doctrine. Gone was the part of Christian theism that was based on faith. But the part that depended on Reason was retained as *deism*. Deists believed that God created the world with a purpose, but instead intervening on Earth in order to save us from original sin, they believed that God created an order based on laws of nature that did not require subsequent intervention. The diminution of God's role was a turn toward naturalism. But it was a turn toward natural religion, not an attempt, like Hume's, to reduce moral judgments to expressions of feelings of benevolence. The explanation of why the morally good is good still depended on God's purpose, and since deists assumed that Reason discovered the difference between right and wrong by attending to the natural order, they still believed that individuals choose freely between good and evil. But since the difference between right and wrong was a fact about a natural order, deism was like the worship of nature. Indeed, the replacement of theism by deism opened the way to pantheism, the belief that the world, with its moral order, is God, as Spinoza held. But in one way or another, morality was still founded on Reason knowing that God had a purpose.

Deists had to reject the Augustinian doctrine about original sin. They could not believe salvation depends on believing that Jesus was the Son of God whose death gave us the power to choose freely between good and evil. Though they might believe that Jesus was a great moral teacher, they wanted to show how morality is part of the natural order without following Hobbes and reducing it to self-interest. This Enlightenment project can be seen in Jean-Jacques Rousseau's (1712–1778) interpretation of the social contract. As a deist, he believed that Reason can see from the order in nature that the natural world was created by a transcendent being for a purpose, and this enabled him to come closer than either Hobbes or Locke to the ontological explanation of morality as an essential aspect of spiritual nature that reflective subjects have as members of a living organism on the fourth floor of life.

Rousseau assumed that human beings in the state of nature had desires that led them to pursue goals that promote their survival. But they were not moral in the sense of obeying moral rules. Instead, they treated others as moral equals because of desires that made them compassionate. Rousseau saw spiritual organisms as arising from the benefits of cooperation in the pursuit of common goals on occasions when it obviously benefited everyone. In this primitive state, they acquired the use of language and learned to distinguish right from wrong. But this early occasional social cooperation eventually developed into the kind of civil society that had evolved by the 18th century, and for Rousseau, the state of nature was a model of human virtue by which to criticize its excesses. He saw property rights as giving rise to inequalities among members and turning the virtuous pursuit of goals that serve survival into goals by which individuals acquire more property and power than others. He saw civil society as a source of vanity, leading Rational subjects to care more about the good opinion of others (*amour-propre*) than virtue. The arts that flourished in his day seemed to lead Rational subjects away from natural virtue. He even criticized the sciences for gathering useless knowledge—useless because it does not contribute to natural virtue. In the opening of *The Social Contract*, Rousseau says, "Man is born free, and everywhere he is in chains." He meant that Rational subjects were better off in their first steps out of the state of nature when they began to cooperate in pursuit of common goals. For Rousseau, the social contract defines how much civilization can demand of individuals in the state of nature to enjoy the benefits of cooperation. The social contract determines what Rousseau calls the general will, and though his meaning is contested, ontological science infers that he means to explain the content of the legitimate authority of the group over the individual as the best explanation of his contribution to progress during the metaphysical stage of evolution.

The essential content of the general will is the spiritual input of a spiritual organism in which members cooperate in the pursuit of goals that are good. This includes the rules of morality, and Rousseau and Locke would not disagree about the moral rules. Indeed, both used the social contract to criticize contemporary institutions. But Locke, believing that moral rules bind Rational subjects, as creatures of God, in the state of nature, saw the social contract as limiting the legitimate power of the state, whereas Rousseau, eschewing supernaturalism, saw the social contract as explaining the authority of moral rules as essential to our nature as language-using animals that live by cooperating. He wanted a naturalistic explanation of morality, like ontological science, which explains it as an essential part of the linguistic representations by which a plan-sharing BGS determines the goals for members of a psychological-level spiritual organism to pursue, that is, as basic to spiritual input. But if the social contract represents the evolution of spiritual organisms, the general will is more than the occasional cooperation of otherwise solitary individuals in pursuit of goals that are in everyone's self-interest. It is a form of life in which language-using animals participate, and this spiritual nature is prior to individual self-interest because it is what enables reflective subjects to act in their own self-interest. And Rousseau recognizes that requiring individuals to act contrary to their self-interest is essential to the social contract. He distinguishes it as the general will from the *will of all*. The will of all is just the sum of individual wills, and since they can express self-interest and misleading conventional beliefs, it does not necessarily take priority over the individual will. But the general will does because it is part of our spiritual nature. In effect, Rousseau recognizes that being a member of a spiritual organism requires us to submit to spiritual input because that is a condition of our form of life. It gives individuals autonomy on the condition that they be moral. Since the general will is the will that all members necessarily share, Rousseau insists that when institutions enforce the general will, they force individuals to be free because they are willing what they must will to be autonomous.

In a spiritual organism that is pursuing goals that are good for it, spiritual input has the authority that Rousseau attributes to the general will, and since morality is an essential part of any such cultural plan, Rousseau is justified in using the social contract to criticize the inequalities that arise in civilized society (though he does not recognize that class structure has a function in civilized spiritual organisms).

The political order is the relation between the members of a spiritual organism and the government that chooses goals that are good for the spiritual organism as a whole, and in civilized spiritual organisms, it is the state. It has a monopoly on the legitimate use violence within its territory, and the goals include the use of police to enforce laws internally as well as externally, with a military force. But in order to fuel its thermodynamic work, a spiritual organism must also obtain high-fueling objects, and the institutions that serve that function are the economy. Production is an essential part of the geometrical action of all spiritual organisms.

3   Economic Order

In civilized spiritual organisms, a class structure anchors a force field of spiritual authority that serves both political and economic functions, and a religion explains to members why they cooperate in pursuing goals. During the Dark Ages and medieval era of Western civilization, the shared plan included a feudal class system. But as the population increased during the Renaissance and early modern era, cities and markets grew, and this demographic change combined with the legal revolution of the late Middle Ages to make it possible for the West to try out a new kind of economic institution that replaces class structure.

Given the moral autonomy of Rational subjects, the legal revolution had established the rule of law based on Roman natural law, and within spiritual organisms, it granted legal autonomy to associations. The legal system recognized the right of associations to determine rules for their own administration, to own property, to make legally enforceable contracts, to be held accountable in court, and the like. As groups of individuals whose behavior is guided by a language-based plan-sharing geometrical cause, associations have a spiritual BGS. But since they are constituted by following the shared plan of a civilized spiritual organism, they are just parts of a more inclusive sovereign spiritual organism. By contrast to full-fledged spiritual organisms, they are merely a higher level of geometrical organization in geometrical action on the fourth floor of the edifice of life, much like class structure. That is, the shared plan of a spiritual organism is its culture, and since its members submit to its spiritual input, the coordination of their behavior constitutes a spiritual world. Since civilized spiritual organisms are spread over a vast territory, they need a class structure (or some kind of social stratification that establishes a dominance hierarchy among its members) to coordinate the behavior of their population in pursuit of shared goals, which necessarily includes the acquisition of acceleration fuel for doing thermodynamic work. Since classes are endogamous, they are like distinct spiritual organisms within civilized spiritual organisms. But unlike class structure, associations are a voluntary submission to rules, and since the legal order respects their autonomy in much the same way as it respects individual autonomy, associations are able to serve as a foundation for an economic order in which production evolves by the reproductive mechanism.

3.1 Capitalism

The economic system is a necessary institution that serves the function of providing the material conditions of life for members of a spiritual organism so that it is able to reproduce if the occasion arises. Associations are formed to serve definite functions, and since they can reproduce by inspiring new associations to be formed, they are double-action geometrical causes that can go through reproductive cycles, though they are just parts of civilized spiritual organisms. Thus, if there is a geometrical cause built into the spiritual organism that detects when associations serve the economic function, and if it determines whether they succeed in reproducing, associations necessarily evolve gradually in the direction of greater power to serve the economic function. Thus, even though associations and class structure are both higher levels of organization of geometrical action in civilized spiritual organisms serving the economic function, associations are fundamentally different from class structure because associations reproduce within a civilization spiritual organism, whereas class structure can reproduce only as part of the reproduction of the civilized spiritual organism as a whole.[71]

The historical change by which class structure was replaced in the West is well-known. In the medieval feudal system, direct producers had the right to use the pieces of land and other means of production to supply their own needs. But they had to hand over a certain portion to the lords, and in return, feudal lords protected them from attack by other feudal lords and marauders. Thus, members of both classes had property rights to the same pieces of land, and manors were largely self-sufficient. Though there was little need to

---

[71] As explained in *Volume II*, the feudal class structure depends on a fixed relation to the land that is analogous to use of the hive in bee colonies and eusocial animals generally. Since social signals lack grammar, their meanings are context dependent, and since locating pheromones strategically in the hive determines the context of such social signals, they can determine kinds of behavior in members by their locations in the hive. A geographical structure is also used to constitute the feudal class structure. It depends on members having different property rights to the same pieces of land, and so it reproduces only insofar as the spiritual organism reproduces. There is no such limitation on capitalist associations. Corporations have the same right to own property as individuals, and so they can reproduce within civilized spiritual organisms.

exchange products of their labor, there were markets. Manors with different productive abilities benefited from exchanging products, and lords could purchase luxury goods. As cities grew, merchants and craftsmen formed guilds, money was minted, foreign trade expanded, and banks were formed to loan money, making more money available to flow against commodities in markets. Taking advantage of the legal autonomy of associations, some parts of spiritual organisms tried out a new social relation for coordinating productive behavior. Individuals filling roles in an association produced commodities, and owners of the association, who did not necessarily participate in production, paid them a wage to do that work. There were, therefore, two basically different ways that individuals were related to production. There were *capitalists*, who put forth the money to purchase labor and other means of production, such as raw materials, land, and machinery, in order set up a productive association, and there were *workers* (and managers) who sold their labor to capitalists. When the commodities were sold and the costs of production were covered, the owners had the right to take the income left over as profit for their investment.

Capitalist economic evolution is the effect of a reproductive mechanism that is embodied in the geometrical action of a spiritual BGS that respects the legal autonomy of associations. The associations serving the economic function described above are double-action geometrical causes because they have the power to do both primary and secondary work, and they can be driven through cycles in which they are able to do both. They do secondary work because a shared plan coordinates the behavior of managers and workers in the production of commodities that are useful and can be sold on the market. They do primary work because when the sale of commodities returns a profit, capitalists reinvest in production. At the end of an accounting cycle, some income pays the costs of labor and other means of production, and when it is used to fund another cycle, the productive association reproduces in the sense of continuing to exist. But since there is also a profit, there is capital for additional investment, either to expand existing productive associations or to set up new ones, including the production of modified or different commodities. Thus, when productive associations go through accounting cycles in which profits are earned, investment in new productive associations continues and the production of commodities tends to increase.

The reproductive mechanism is a combination of geometrical and physical causes. Geometrical causes can use acceleration fuel to do thermodynamic work, and double-action geometrical causes are geometrical causes that can do both primary and secondary work. When they go through reproductive cycles in regions with a finite supply of fuel, they evolve gradually toward greater functional power. In this case, the fuel is income from the sale of commodities since that is what productive associations must earn in order to pay the costs of going through another accounting cycle. The supply of this fuel is finite because consumers are members of a spiritual organism and they have limited resources for purchasing commodities. Thus, as production increases, there is a point at which not all commodities can be sold, and some reproductive cycles must come to an end. But it is not just chance which ones succeed, since capitalists reinvest money only in productive associations from which they expect to receive a profit. Furthermore, there are variations among productive associations. Associations are more or less efficient in producing the same commodities. Some may produce modified commodities that are more useful. And taken together, there are associations producing all sorts of commodities that consumers find useful. As productive associations go through reproductive cycles in finite markets, they compete with one another for investments from capitalists who are seeking the greatest profit. Thus, production evolves gradually in the direction of offering all the commodities that consumers find useful enough to pay the costs of their increasingly efficient production.

Though the reproductive mechanism that causes gradual economic evolution by capitalist selection is embodied in the geometrical action of spiritual organisms, it works the same way as the reproductive mechanism causing the gradual evolution of organisms by natural selection. In both cases, it is caused by the existence of reproductive cycles in a region of finite resources. As we have seen, when organisms go through reproductive cycles in a region with finite resources, they impose natural selection on themselves because population growth due to reproduction eventually causes a scarcity that requires some reproductive cycles to come to an end. Resources are finite because they all come down to the flow of acceleration fuel through the planet's surface. Likewise, when capitalist associations go through reproductive cycles in a region with finite resources, they impose capitalist selection on themselves because the growth of production due to reinvestment (and new investments) eventually causes a scarcity that requires some reproductive cycles to come to an end. Resources are finite because they all come down to the flow of money against commodities in market exchanges, and money is a conserved quantity like energy. In both cases, evolution is progressive. Organisms evolve gradually in the direction of greater power to control conditions that enable them to reproduce, and since they must compete for finite resources, species eventually mirror all the available sources of acceleration fuel for doing work. In a capitalist economy, productive associations are double-action geometrical causes, and so their evolution is also progressive. As they go through reproductive cycles within a spiritual organism, *capitalist selection* causes them to acquire every possible functional power as it becomes possible for their kind, and since they are fueled by income from selling the commodities, the relevant condition is producing commodities that can be sold for a profit. Competition with one another for a profit causes associations to evolve in the direction of greater power to produce commodities that consumers are willing and able to buy, and so capitalist associations evolve powers that produce commodities as efficiently as possible. Since there are many kinds of productive associations, the commodities produced eventually mirror all the needs of members of spiritual organisms that can be met by the purchase of commodities.

3.2 Forms of Evolution in Spiritual Organisms

Indeed, capitalist associations can be considered a form of spiritual life because a spiritual BGS guides double-action geometrical causes through reproductive cycles in which they do both kinds of work. That is, they can be considered triple-action geometrical causes. But capitalist associations have a spiritual nature in two ways, one by having a spiritual life of their own and one by participating in and depending on the life of a more encompassing civilized spiritual organism. Beings like us have a spiritual nature in the latter sense, but not the former, because we are not spiritual organisms. We are subjective animals with consciousness that are parts of a spiritual organism.[72]

Though capitalist association are triple-action-geometrical-causes, they are not a new form of life on the fourth floor of the edifice of life because they do not have a new kind of BGS. They use a spiritual BGS, like the spiritual organisms of which they are parts. Instead, they are a higher level of geometrical action in the spiritual organism of which they are part. Much like the class structure of civilized spiritual organisms, capitalist associations are groups within the larger spiritual organism whose behavior is guided by a plan-sharing BGS based on language, and so they can also be considered analogous to insect colonies and other eusocial animals on the third floor of the edifice of life. But capitalist associations are radically different from class structure. Most obviously, capitalist associations are not endogamous, like class structure, because workers can become capitalists, and capitalists can become workers. But it is no less significant that a class structure reproduces only as part of the reproduction of the entire spiritual organism, whereas capitalist associations reproduce within a spiritual organism. Since the quantity of money flowing against commodities is in limited supply in the region, their reproduction causes a scarcity that imposes natural selection on them, and so there is progressive capitalist evolution.

The reproductive mechanism causing economic evolution by capitalist selection is its second embodiment within a spiritual organism because, as we have seen, cultural evolution is the effect of a reproductive mechanism embodied in its spiritual BGS. The arguments exchanged among members in guiding the behavior of a spiritual organism are double-action geometrical causes because they do primary work by being copied from one neural BGS to another and they do secondary work by guiding behavior. The reproductive mechanism works in the same way. When arguments go through reproductive cycle in a region with finite resources, they impose judgmental selection on themselves because their population growth due to reproduction eventually causes a scarcity that requires some reproductive cycles to come to an end. Resources are finite because there are only a finite number of neural BGSs

---

[72] *Capitalist associations* include mom-and-pop business, even though the only workers may be the children. They reinvest their capital as they continue, and so they compete as double-action geometrical causes in the market in the same way as larger capitalist associations.

into which they can be copied. Thus, arguments exchanged tend to evolve in the direction of greater functional power. But unlike capitalist associations, there is no temptation to think of arguments as a new form of life because they are just linguistic representations without any BGS of their own, and since they are driven through reproductive cycles by linguistic interactions of members, they do not impose natural selection on themselves. Nothing is good or bad for the arguments themselves.

As one might expect of reproductive mechanisms embodied in a spiritual organism, psychological-level cultural evolution and capitalist economic evolution are alike in how natural selection depends ultimately on the judgments of its members. For arguments to be copied into a neural BGS in a way that does secondary work, reflective subjects must consider them more cogent than alternative arguments, so culture evolves by judgmental selection. For capitalist associations, the finite resource in the region is the money that flows through markets against the commodities purchased, and for them to go through another accounting cycle, capitalists must believe that enough consumers will consider buying them worth the cost for them to make a profit. Thus, in both cultural and capitalist evolution, the natural selection responsible for the gradual increase in functional powers over generations of reproduction depends on the judgments of reflective subjects about what is good.

Since capitalist economic evolution and cultural evolution depend on different reproductive mechanisms, they can work together in civilized spiritual organisms. Capitalist associations are groups of animals whose behavior is coordinated by a plan-sharing BGS based on language, and since language-based plan-sharing BGSs coordinate the behavior of both capitalist corporations and the spiritual organisms of which they are parts, both can benefit from cultural evolution by judgmental selection. Science was another offspring of intuitionistic metaphysics during the Enlightenment, and since it is cultural evolution in the direction of discovering regularities about change, it keeps providing new kinds of technology. Thus, the range of possible variations on production that can be tried out by imperfect reproduction of capitalist production keeps increasing, and the range of possible commodities that consumers judge to be useful enough to buy with limited resources keeps increasing (while others become less expensive). Indeed, the combination of capitalist and cultural evolution produces positive feedback because the continual improvement of commodities provides technological power that facilitates scientific progress.

3.3 Potential of Capitalist Evolution

Thus, the evolution of productive power of capitalist spiritual organisms is not limited in the same way as the evolution of organisms by natural selection on the planet's surface. Gradual evolution approaches asymptotically a point at which organisms have acquired all the functional powers possible for them, and so stages of gradual evolution come to an end when organisms have the maximum functional power. But if the double-action geometrical causes evolving by capitalist selection approach natural perfection as a limit, the only limit is complete technological control of nature. Even if the scientific explanation of the natural world were complete, advances in technology would not cease until all possible tools had evolved or there was nothing more worth controlling in the natural world.

The evolution of capitalism is a radical change in the nature of civilized spiritual organisms because it serves the same function as class structure. Capitalism coordinates productive behavior throughout the territory of a civilization in a way that provides the material conditions of life for everyone. But class structure is not voluntary since classes are endogamous, and so this Enlightenment offspring of intuitionistic metaphysics replaces class structure with voluntary associations. Indeed, when spiritual organisms evolve capitalism, class structure is replaced by a higher level of spiritual geometrical action that causes itself to evolve by capitalist selection within civilized spiritual organisms. Hence the evolution of the capitalist economic system is the beginning of an indefinitely long gradual increase in the power of production to provide the material conditions of life—unless, of course, the capitalist system is dismantled by government.

Capitalism was not a product of cultural evolution by Rational selection. It began as a random variation on institutions. But it would not have occurred without the respect for the legal autonomy of associations that was born of the marriage of Platonic Reason and Christian faith in the middle ages since that is what provided the spiritual double-action geometrical causes that could go through reproductive cycles within spiritual organisms. The synergy of capitalist evolution with the cultural evolution of science and political principles enabled Western spiritual organisms to acquire functional powers that were out of reach for spiritual organisms at the psychological stage. The liberal political order allowed institutions to evolve that improved the capitalist economic system, such as corporations owned by stockholders with limited liability, markets for exchanging stocks, and banks large enough to fund investments in huge processes of production. The progressive evolution of capitalist production provided the growing affluence and commodities that facilitated new scientific discoveries, which in turn provided new technologies that increased the efficiency of production. These developments and how they work together is the source of the unprecedented power that has enabled Western civilization to cause globalization. But even during the Enlightenment, the cultural progress was recognized as a turning point in human history.

CHAPTER 7:
DISILLUSIONMENT WITH REASON

Science, liberal political institutions, and capitalism stand out among offspring of the Enlightenment. They are the main causes of the unprecedented functional powers that have evolved in the West, and they are the beliefs and institutions that continue to spread as what is called *globalization*. When the history of Western civilization is told as a biography of Reason, this begins the part of its life in which a science based on physics becomes a science based on ontology and recognizes itself as naturalistic Reason. But despite the historical triumph of these three offspring of the Enlightenment, Reason must travel a rocky path before it can defend naturalistic metaphysics. Advances in science lead to disillusionment with Reason, and an era of endarkenment can be seen on the horizon.

Science is the study of nature, and Reason becomes science by splitting off from philosophy, the study of Appearance. This adolescent rebellion against its intuitionistic family was the beginning of an identity crisis. Though science and philosophy both abandoned the supernaturalism that the modern era had inherited from the ontological dualism of ancient metaphysics, both had to cope with the mind-body dualism of modern metaphysics, and the next chapter sketches the dismal fate of intuitionistic philosophy. But science was not just a continuation of natural philosophy because its rise depended on a treasure that Reason carried away from its intuitionistic heritage. As we have seen, physics needed mathematics for its success, and its success is what inspired the scientific study of all kinds of regularities in the natural world. Philosophy justified the belief that mathematics is known *a priori*, and so intuitionism made an essential contribution to the rise of science. But a science based on physics does not provide all the explanatory tools needed to explain everything found in the natural world, and this chapter describes how advances in science during the 19th and early 20th century debunked the belief in Reason on which the other two historically prominent offspring of the Enlightenment depended. This is the story of growing disillusionment with Reason.

Physics was committed to naturalism, and following the method of empirical lawism, it gave science credibility by predicting quantitative properties that could be measured precisely. Though Kant had tried to explain Newton's astonishing success as the discovery of synthetic *a priori* truths, all physics needed was mathematics. Newton himself defended the belief that the deepest possible empirical knowledge of what really exists in the natural world comes from discovering mathematically formulated laws of nature, and the Newtonian revolution encouraged science to aim at explaining everything in the natural world. Physics was seen as discovering that the natural world was constituted by material substances, and materialism was accepted as an adequate foundation for explaining all kinds of regularities in the world. But after making it seem possible for science to explain everything in the natural world, mathematics eventually crushed hope of ever attaining that goal. Though the world in which we find our bodies seems to be a world of objects that change in absolute space and time, modern physics would tell us in the 20th century that the Newtonian 3-D world is just an appearance of a 4-D world in which nothing really changes. This was Einstein's contribution to disillusionment with Reason. But he was just the last of the four horsemen of disillusionment.

From the beginning, science taught us that it was a mistake to think of beings like us as somehow central to the natural order. The first indication that Earth was not created for beings like us to exist was the Copernican revolution. In the 16th century, Copernicus showed that Earth orbits the Sun, and with the help of Galileo, the Sun was recognized as just one of many stars. Though this cast doubt on the Christian explanation of the meaning of life, it was still possible to have confidence in Reason. But beginning with the Cogito, modern intuitionistic metaphysics was egocentric, and in the 19th century, after science had demonstrated the reliability of its knowledge, it laid down further milestones in the disabuse of anthropocentrism. Darwin, Freud, and Marx began, respectively, revolutions in biology, psychology, and social science. They all debunked Reason more frontally. Together with Einstein, they are the *four horsemen of disillusionment*, deflating the assumption that beings like us are capable of cognitive perfection and have the kind of free will that justifies holding us responsible for our choices. These and other advances were undeniable, and as science learned to make modest claims to knowledge, the metaphysical ambitions of Reason seemed even more grandiose. This is the rocky path that Reason traveled after rebelling against its intuitionistic family. Indeed, now, it hardly seems possible that science will ever attain its goal of explaining everything in the natural world.

1 Darwin and the Good

Reason has a practical side. The Enlightenment took the Socratic principle about goodness for granted: *to know the Good is to do the good*. As an inheritance from intuitionistic metaphysics, this conception of the self was based on the belief in Reason. The Good is part of the True, and metaphysical theories assume that understanding the nature of the Good not only enables Rational subjects to know what is good but also causes them to choose goals that are good. This was a test of the success of Reason in serving its practical function from the beginning, when Socrates denied that the good is good because it is desired and insisted that it is desired because it is good. Since intuitionism is false, intuitionistic metaphysics could never fully satisfy the Socratic test. But even the belief that the Good is something that can be known was undermined by the rise of science.

In the early 19th century, scientists discovered that geological features had changed over enormously long periods, and fossils showed that species had changed with them. To a young believer in universal laws of nature like Darwin, the challenge was to explain the change in species. Assuming that variations in the traits of organisms are passed on to their offspring, he explained evolutionary change by the greater reproductive success of those that happened to be better adapted to their environments. *Descent with modification* was evolution by natural selection, a mechanism that materialists (and physicalists) could accept. The environment determines which traits are inherited by offspring, and since the traits of existing organisms fit into their environments, their fitness could explain why organisms have traits that seem to serve a purpose as if designed by an intelligent creator.

During the Enlightenment, Christian theism had given way to the belief that God did not intervene in the natural world after creating it. The laws of nature were designed to carry out his purpose, and since deists believed that Rational subjects could know from the natural order what God's purpose required of them, they could choose to do what is good, confident that there is an explanation of what makes the good. Hence, Darwin's explanation of the cause of evolution did not refute deism. It was still possible to believe in God. Indeed, since there were other proofs of his existence, it was still possible to believe that Reason knows that God exists. When Darwin introduced his explanation of evolution, progress was still taken for granted, and so it was plausible that evolution by natural selection is progressive in the sense of leading, step by step, to the existence of beings like us. Since deists could explain Darwin's mechanism of evolution as God's way of creating Rational subjects in his image, they could give a scientific explanation of what is good. The desires that had evolved in animals identified goals that are good for them, and the fact that human beings have a conscience was compelling evidence that doing what morality requires is good. In effect, since deists worshiped nature, they could hold that knowledge of the nature of the good caused Rational subjects to choose goals that are good. Though Rational subjects identified what is good by what is desired, they desired it because it is good, that is, because Reason recognized it as part of God's purpose in creating the world. In the 19th century, therefore, Darwinism was not necessarily seen as overthrowing the legacy of the Enlightenment.

In the 20th century, however, the implications of Darwinian natural selection were examined more carefully, and evolutionary biologists realized that Darwin's mechanism does not support belief in progressive evolution. Natural selection implies that organisms adapt to their environments, but since Darwinism has nothing to say about changes in the environment, it cannot explain the overall course of evolution. Without recognizing the fundamentality of geometrical causes, there is no reason to believe in stages of gradual evolution, and so Darwinism cannot show that a series of such stages leads inevitably to beings like us. Indeed, it provides no reason to believe that, if evolution on Earth were rolled back to the beginning, some three for four billion years ago, it would unfold again in a similar way. The

Darwinist denial of progressive evolution gave the *four horsemen of atheism* confidence in arguing that the belief in a transcendent creator is irrational and that religion has been the major source of evil in the world.[73]

Darwin's discovery eventually reinforced the argument in Hume's *Dialogues Concerning Natural Religion* (1779) about the apparent purposiveness found in the world having a naturalistic cause. It undercut the argument for a transcendent God from the design evident in the natural world, which was the most popular proof of God's existence. Without the belief that God had created the natural world for a purpose, there was no explanation of the nature of the good, knowledge of which could cause Rational subjects to choose good over evil goals. To be sure, evolutionary biologists could insist that they had an explanation of the nature of the good. Natural selection could explain why desires evolve, and since humans call the goals they determine *good*, they could explain why goals are good by the desires that motivate pursuing them. Indeed, biologists could explain what is good for other species. And sociobiologists could use kin selection to explain morality as an expression of feelings of benevolence, much as Hume believed. But since this was to hold that the good is good because it is desired, it was to deny the Socratic doctrine that the good is desired because it is good. Since desires were the result of a series of evolutionary accidents, humans had no reason to believe that the goals they determined are good in any deeper sense.

After revealing that human beings are not at the center of the universe, therefore, science revealed that their existence on Earth was just the result of a series of accidents. With this understanding of their nature, scientists could explain why humans are inclined to believe that evolution is an inevitable change in the direction of beings like them. That is how it appears to a species that happens to have evolved the power to infer from evidence about what has occurred on Earth over long periods that they are products of evolution by natural selection. But biologists insist that if reflective subjects understand the cause of evolution and they are intellectually honest, they will recognize that their tendency to believe in progressive evolution is just the traditional anthropocentric bias that advances in science have been discrediting ever since Copernicus.

---

[73] See Harris (2004), Dawkins (2005), Hitchens (2007), and Dennett (1995).

The Darwinian revolution illustrates how science caused disillusionment with Reason. In order to explain the good as what is desired, it would have to explain why having those desires is good, and that is not possible if they are just products of an accidental course of evolution. Indeed, scientists deny that science can ever tell us which goals we ought to choose because the scientific method discovers, at bottom, only laws of physics. The causal relations they entail can tell us about the means to goals that we choose, and means-ends reasoning helps us choose goals. But scientists agree with Hume about the difference between fact and value. Science cannot tell us which goals are good because that is not a matter of fact. It is a value judgment, which depends on preferences. Value judgments may be explained scientifically by desires and emotions, but they cannot be justified scientifically. By denying that the Good is part of the True, therefore, science causes disillusionment about practical Reason.

2 Freud and Moral Autonomy

An offspring of intuitionistic metaphysics was Enlightenment respect for the moral autonomy of Rational subjects. But it depended on free will. For the punishment of wrongdoing to be justified, wrongdoers must be responsible for doing what is wrong, and they are not responsible unless they could have done otherwise. But belief in free will was undermined when physics revealed that every event has a cause. As Laplace pointed out, the laws of Newtonian mechanics imply that, if it were possible to know the state of the universe at any time, its state at any time in the future (or in the past) could be predicted. Determinism is not compatible with free will. If choices have a physical cause that is, in turn, the effect of some earlier physical cause, and so on, there is ultimately a cause that lies outside the reflective subject. Hence the subject is not responsible for doing wrong. They could not have done otherwise, and it would be cruel to punish subjects for doing what they cannot help doing. With advances in science, therefore, the belief in determinism challenged the belief in free will. This was a serious challenge for a culture based on modern intuitionistic metaphysics since respect for moral autonomy depended on Rational subjects having free will. They could be permitted to choose their goals for themselves only if they had the free will that justifies holding them responsible for being moral, and there is no way for a science based on physics to explain how they could have chosen otherwise.[74]

The Socratic test was plausibly passed by the intuitionistic metaphysical explanation of practical Reason that evolved after the marriage of Platonic Reason with faith in Christ. Free will explained how knowledge of the nature of the good enabled Rational subjects to be moral even when it was contrary to self-interest or requires self-control. The nature of the Good depended on God's purpose in creating Earth as a home for finite Rational beings, and that presumably was why they were fashioned in his image. Jesus taught that they must love their neighbor as they do themselves, and when they chose between good and evil, they could have done otherwise because they have a free will. Life was a trial in which the fate of immortal souls turned on free choices between good and evil, and the threat of eternal punishment may have helped motivate Rational subjects to be moral. But that did not explain why it was good to be moral because it did not explain why God would create finite Rational beings in his own image and let their free choice determine the eternal fate of their souls outside space and time. This was the great mystery about God's purpose in creating the natural world that required one to have faith in him. Strictly speaking, therefore, Christianity did not pass the Socratic test of practical Reason any more than ancient metaphysics. It gave Rational subjects a limited understanding of the meaning of life, and free will connected this knowledge of the nature of the good with doing the good.[75] It is plausible to believe in free will because intuitionism makes it seem self-evident that choices depend on the phenomenal subject. As we have seen, it seems that reasons or other causes of behavior are just objects of intuition that occur as a choice is made freely. But since God's purpose was a mystery, it was not knowledge of the nature of the good that caused Rational subjects to

---

[74] In the spatio-material world, forms of life are defined by their BGSs, and since they are geometrical causes whose function is to choose goals that are good, all forms of life have the power to choose otherwise. In the case of reflective subjects, some goals are set by spiritual input, and since the BGS represents the states by which it guides behavior as part of the process of guiding behavior, reflective subjects can justifiably be held responsible for wrongdoing. And knowing that they could have chosen otherwise, they feel guilty.

[75] If Augustine was right, it came down to faith in Christ because he held that having a free will depended on believing that Jesus was divine and that, through his death and resurrection of his Son, God had forgiven original sin.

do the good, but only faith in God, and that failed the Socratic test in the same way as Platonic love.

Though it was an imperfect way of passing the Socratic test, the belief that the fate of the immortal soul depends on the exercise of free will was plausible enough for Rational subjects to take responsibility for their choices, much as Max Weber contended when he attributed the rise of capitalism to the *Protestant Ethic*. Belief in free will and moral responsibility was implicit in this intuitionistic conception of the self. But during the Enlightenment, theological doctrines that depended on faith in the divinity of Jesus gave way to deism, and deism eventually led to skepticism about supernaturalism of all kinds. Naturalists denied the existence of anything outside space and time, and scientists assumed that everything, including behavior, could be explained by physical causes. This forced naturalists to reject free will and, along with it, Reason. Free will is how the spiritual desire appears to the phenomenal subject, and after Freud explained the spiritual desire as part of his three-part theory of the psyche, holding reflective subjects morally responsible did not seem justifiable.

Sigmund Freud (1856-1939) began his career as a neurologist, and in the attempt to treat so-called *nervous disorders*, he eventually discovered a naturalistic theory of the psyche that became the foundation of psychoanalysis and, for a time, was widely celebrated for its insight into human nature. Indeed, his theory can be rendered in terms of the ontological explanation of why reflective subjects follow moral rules. Its three parts, the *id, ego*, and *superego*, correspond to parts of reflective neural BGSs of members of spiritual organisms.

In all mammals, desires are attached to representations of objects in the input scene that determine the kinds of behavior that the BGS directs towards them. Freud called this subfunction of the reflective BGS the *id* and explained it as following the *pleasure principle*. But reflective BGSs also use psychological sentences to represent desires as goals relative to objects represented in the input scene, and by comparing plans in psychological imagination, they can identify means to ends that maximize the satisfaction of their desires. This enables reflective subjects to know what is in their own self-interest. Freud calls this function of the reflective BGS the *ego* and explains it as following the *reality principle*. Finally, as members of spiritual organisms, reflective subjects receive spiritual input from the BGS of their spiritual organism that determines the goals they ought to choose. Their desire to submit to spiritual input enables them to act contrary to self-interest and even strong animal desires, and in Freud's explanation of why we do what morality requires, the *superego* corresponds to the spiritual desire. Explaining the psyche from the point of view of the ego, therefore, Freud saw the superego as opposing both the ego and the id.

Freud traced the superego's power to serve this function to its formation during childhood in the *Oedipus complex*. He held that the superego is installed (in boys) as the internalization of the father's punishment of the child's sexual interest in the mother (and in girls, as he explained later, it is the internalization of the mother's punishment of the child's sexual interest in the father, called the *Electra complex*). The superego internalizes parental anger as a desire to punish the self, and since children accept limits imposed by parents as authoritative, the superego is aroused by prohibited behavior and even impulses to disobey rules. Its power to punish the self is what enables the superego to oppose the id and the ego, and its effects are felt as guilt, shame, and remorse. These conflicts of the superego with the ego and id result in the repression of desires (and sometimes even the denial of their existence, or *neurosis*). Thus, intense feelings of guilt and shame are characteristic of the neurotic disorders that Freud identified in his patients.

The psychosexual origin of the superego in the Oedipus complex during childhood can usefully be compared with the evolution of the spiritual desire from the dominance hierarchy found in groups of social animals. In both cases, the desire to submit is an internalization of external anger. When alpha males are defeated in their attempt to overthrow the leader, their aggressive desire is replaced by a desire to submit to the leader. When social animals evolve a plan-sharing BGS based on the use of language, this instinct becomes the spiritual desire, and individual development can be seen as recapitulating this evolutionary history. The child's attachment of this desire to spiritual input from the parent recapitulates the naturalistic stage of spiritual evolution when submission to it motivates members to obey commands of a leader. And the adolescent's internalization of punishment as a conception of the ideal self recapitulates the psychological stage of spiritual evolution when spiritual desires motivate cooperation in the pursuit of common goals. Both developmental stages resemble the Oedipus complex because punishment by authority is internalized as a desire to punish the self for failing to follow spiritual input, which is felt as guilt or shame.[76] Thus, Freud and ontology agree about what causes reflective subjects to be moral when it requires acting contrary to self-interest or strong desires. Nevertheless, Freud's explanation is a milestone on the path to endarkenment.

Since Freud inferred the superego as the best explanation of neuroses, he sees it is as causing irrational guilt and anxiety, and this blinds him to its function in guiding behavior to goals that are good. Spiritual organisms evolved from groups of social animals when language gave them to power to share a plan for attaining goals that are good for the group. Spiritual input determines goals for members to pursue, and their coordinated behavior controls conditions that make it possible for spiritual organisms to reproduce. That is how the spiritual BGS functions. These goals are also good for members because they go through individual-level reproductive cycles as parts of spiritual organisms. Freud recognized, of course, that civilization depends on the superego. But since the superego caused the mental illnesses he treated, he saw it mainly as a source of discontents. Though he admitted that a case could be made for submitting to the necessity of civilization, he believed that a case could also be made for civilization *not* being worth the effort. In the end, he was *impartial* about the value of civilization. What Freud was sure about is that arguments on both sides can be dismissed as rationalizations of feelings.[77]

As explained in ontological science, religion evolves at the psychological stage of spiritual evolution with the function of rationalizing submission to

---

[76] The agreement is not complete. Since Freud traces the superego to the Oedipus complex, he sees the influence of parents on older children as merely refining the identity they acquire by submitting to spiritual authority. But if adolescence recapitulates the transition from the naturalistic to the psychological stage, punishment during adolescence may be as important as during childhood. A new conception of the self is forming, and punishment may be required for some reflective subjects to attach the spiritual desire to the new kind of spiritual input and to repress newly felt desires.

[77] In *Civilization and Its Discontents,* Freud (1994, p. 70) writes that he is "sure only of one thing, that the judgments of value made by mankind are immediately determined by their desires for happiness: in other words, that those judgments are attempts to prop up their illusions with arguments."

spiritual input. But its spiritual input includes both moral rules and prudence, and Freud's disparagement of moral autonomy can be seen in the priority he gives to self-interest. He explained the psyche from the point of view of the ego, and since the ego follows the reality principle, he called it *commonsense* or *reason*. Desires set goals that are good for the self, and in order to do what self-interest requires, the ego opposes the id. It chooses which desires to satisfy and how to satisfy them in any situation, and this might involve deferring gratification or even refusing to satisfy strong desires, like fatigue, fear, and hunger. It serves the interest of the self because it maximizes the satisfaction of desire over a period of time. But when the ego chooses to satisfy desires by following plans that are forbidden, the superego opposes the ego. That enables the ego to do what morality requires when it is contrary to self-interest. But since the ego is rational, Freud saw morality as basically a fear of self-punishment that interferes with reason. Hence the Freudian superego is like the spirited element in the theory of the psyche on which Plato modeled the Republic, except that it is stripped of guidance by Reason. Freud's philosopher king was irrational. Freud assumed that it was rational for the ego to repress libidinal desires contrary to self-interest, and though he admitted that the superego could assist the ego in being rational, he disparaged attempts to show that it is rational to be moral when it is contrary to self-interest. To defend morality was to rationalize irrational feelings caused by the superego.

To be sure, Freud illustrates a deeper cause of disillusionment about Reason serving its practical function. In the physical world, there is no justification for punishing those who violate moral rules. A science based on physics does not necessarily disparage morality, as Freud does, because, like Hume, it can explain moral judgments as expressions of feelings of benevolence, so even atheists would *feel* bound by moral rules. Indeed, scientists expect to explain why human beings are moral when it is contrary to self-interest or requires self-restraint, since that is normal human behavior, and this might be called an explanation of moral goodness. But even if this explained why reflective subjects follow moral rules, it would not justify holding reflective subjects morally responsible. Since their behavior has a physical cause, they could not do otherwise, and thus, when they do what is wrong, they are not responsible. Systematically harming wrongdoers may still be justified, but only in order to deter wrongdoing or to protect others by incarcerating them, much as threats of hellfire deterred some Christians from sinning. But without belief in a free will, punishment does not express respect for the moral autonomy of individuals.

Furthermore, in the physical world, there is no justification of morality. It is always a rationalization. A science based on physics can explain why human beings accept religious justifications for following moral rules. Since every event has a physical cause (except for what is uncertain according to the Heisenberg principle), there must be a cause that explains why religion motivates moral behavior. But no such cause could justify morality. To pass the Socratic test, science would have to explain the nature of the Good in a way that implies that reflective subjects who understand it not only know what is morally right but also have a compelling reason to choose to be moral, even when it is contrary to self-interest (and they can avoid punishment). That is not possible because physical science denies that the good is desired because it is good. Thus, even if a Darwinian explanation of the evolution of human beings could explain how religion gives humans a conscience, it would not explain the nature of the morally good in a way that would explain why they ought to be moral. This is the deeper disillusionment about Reason serving its moral function that makes Freud's theory another milestone on the way to endarkenment.

3 Marx and Freedom

Political progress in the Enlightenment was expected to be change in the direction of maximum equal freedom for all. The Good is part of the True, and since free will enabled Rational subjects to do what they know is morally right even when it is contrary to self-interest, they could be trusted to be moral. The assumption that they have moral autonomy in the state of nature enabled Locke to use the social contract to argue that a legitimate government has only those powers required to do what individuals cannot do when acting independently, such as punishing wrongdoing fairly. The social contract granted everyone an equal right to life, liberty, and property, and since property rights were the basic means of pursuing goals chosen in self-interest, it was the right to happiness. But with the rise of science in the 19th century, absolute idealism gave way to materialism, and as endarkenment set in, the social contract came to be seen as an ideology. While individualists rejected it in favor of libertarianism and even anarchism, the most serious damage to cultural progress and the evolution of a liberal political order came from collectivists who used confidence in Reason to justify governmental power, for example, as the reign of terror in the French revolution. But the most insidious form of collectivism held that the social contract was an ideology that justified one class oppressing another. They used the claim of science to know the underlying cause of history to justify the violent overthrow of capitalism and the use of state power to impose economic equality.

Inequalities of wealth and power in civil society were already criticized in the 18th century. Using the social contract to represent the emergence of morality from a pre-moral state of nature, Rousseau explained its content as the *general will*, and recognizing that it justified equal rights for all, Rousseau famously complained, "Man is born free, but everywhere he is in chains." Seeing the institutions of civil society as encouraging individuals to seek more wealth and power than others, Rousseau urged a political solution. A public exchange of arguments would lead Rational subjects to agree to reforms that curtailed the inequality. This was Enlightenment progress, the offspring of cultural evolution by Rational selection.[78]

However, the evolution of civilization was caused by a higher level of organization in geometrical action that enabled spiritual organisms to coordinate the behavior of a massive population over a vast territory. It took the form of a class structure (or some such social stratification) that enabled members of one class to dominate members of another class, and in the 19th century, Karl Marx (1818-1883) recognized that this inequality had a hidden cause. As a scientist, his goal was to explain history in much the same way that Hobbes, as a materialist, used the social contract to explain the establishment of a sovereign as the result of the motion and interaction of self-interested language-using animals. But Marx was trying to explain civilization, not morality, and the cause he found was a less individualistic mechanism that operated behind the backs of language-using animals.

---

[78] Rousseau helped inspire the French Revolution, and though his notion of a *general will* was used to justify more violent means, that can be attributed to confusion about what he meant by it.

As a student in Germany, Marx had internalized the grand claims of Hegelian idealist metaphysics. Hegel held that freedom, morality, and other political institutions are products of a dialectical process in which spirit emerges from the natural world, and he had assumed that progress toward freedom was already complete. Though the *Young Hegelians* saw traditional religious and political institutions as still posing obstacles to freedom and Reason, they were still idealist metaphysicians who expected these obstacles to be overcome by a dialectical clash of ideas. Marx was a Young Hegelian, but inspired by the rise of science, he who took up the defense of pre-Socrates materialism and tried to *turn Hegel on his head*. He saw human history as a conflict of the material (that is, economic) interests of groups that led dialectically to revolutionary changes in society. But this *motor of history* was hidden from individuals because, instead of unfolding in front of them, like cultural evolution by judgmental selection, the cause was a class struggle happening behind their backs.

During the industrial revolution, many people moved to cities to work for a wage, and recognizing that workers and capitalists have fundamentally different roles in the market, Marx saw the capitalist economy as a form of class structure. His model was the preceding feudal class system in Europe. In both cases, he saw class structure as imposing an ideology on culture that justifies it. Marx saw religion as an ideology that rationalized the inequality between serfs and nobles, and though the capitalist class relation did not depend on religion, Marx saw the social contract as an ideology that rationalized the inequality between workers and capitalists. Marx agreed that everyone is equal, and he did not deny that everyone had equal rights. But they included the right to private property, and since that justified free markets, he saw the liberal political order as allowing capitalists to own the means of production while workers were forced to labor for them. Thus, capitalism, like feudalism, had an ideology that rationalized an unjust class structure, and as a dialectical materialist, Marx believed that a struggle between classes was the cause of basic changes in history. Thus, he denied that the course of history depends on cultural evolution by judgmental selection. On the contrary, he saw certain kinds of cultural change as an effect of class struggle, the motor of history that did not depend on anyone understanding it.

Ontological science recognizes that Marx had a profound insight into the nature of civilization. Civilized spiritual organisms do have a class structure, and instead of being a result of cultural evolution, it does impose a content on cultural plans. In the spatio-material world, the motor of history is the reproductive mechanism. Civilization evolves because a higher level of organization in geometrical action on the fourth floor of the edifice of life is both possible and functional. It is possible because a cultural plan can use the ownership of property to divide members into classes, and it is functional because it can coordinate the behavior of a huge population over a vast territory. Hence, a cultural plan with a religion that justifies the class structure is an essential part of civilization. But Marx did not explain history by the reproductive mechanism. Since he meant to turn Hegel on his head, his motor of history was class struggle. While idealists attributed historical change to a dialectic of ideas, he was a materialist who believed that the course of history depends on a class struggle in the economic system, and his materialist dialectic included the dominant class protecting its economic interest by imposing a religious ideology on culture. This can be seen as a blurred insight in the essential nature of civilization at the psychological level. But Marx's use of his motor of history to explain the origin of capitalism is profoundly mistaken.

According to Marx's materialist dialectic, an economic system is a class-based *mode of production*, and the increasing power of the technology used in production (the *forces of production*) eventually frees the oppressed class by overthrowing the class structure (the *relations of production*). Accordingly, during the feudal period, the forces of production became so powerful that serfs could escape domination by lords, and the feudal class structure gave way to the new capitalist social relation. But they became enslaved in a new way by capitalists, and the ideology that arose dialectically to defend the interest of capitalists was the liberal political order. Marx saw the Lockean belief that everyone has equal rights as fooling people into believing that there was no class structure after the demise of the feudal relations of production. But Marx fails to appreciate how the roles of capitalists and workers in a capitalist spiritual organism are different from class structure. In the spatio-material world, class structure is a division into different endogamous groups that is tied to the land by property right because it must be territory-wide to coordinate production. But capitalist associations are voluntary, and they can have limited footprints since only the legal order needs to be territory-wide for markets to facilitate the exchange of commodities against money. And without recognizing how geometrical causes can constrain what happens by physical causes, he could not recognize that feudalism was replaced by a new form of spiritual life contained within civilized spiritual organisms that evolves gradually by imposing capitalist selection on itself in the direction of greater power to produce all the commodities that consumers are willing to buy.

Marx recognized the increase in productive power after replacing feudalism, but he did not attribute it to capitalism. His motor of history assumed that it was just the increase in forces of production that always occurs, presumably because of human ingenuity (cultural evolution by technical selection), and so he saw the growth in production as just an increase in capitalist exploitation of workers. Specialized sciences try to imitate physics, and seeing himself as the first scientist of capitalism, he used the *labor theory of value* to measure its rate.

The labor theory of value holds that the value of commodities comes from the labor needed to produce them, and in the spatio-material world, this true in the sense that production in spiritual organisms is necessarily just the coordinated behavior of their members. In the feudal system, the labor of one class is responsible for the agricultural production that members of both classes consume, and in the capitalist system, workers contribute the labor while the means of production are owned by capitalists. Thus, Marx saw capitalism as just another way that one class exploits another class. Talk of exploitation arouses resentment about unequal rights, but seeing himself as a scientist, Marx could claim that his labor theory of value was just a law of nature about the rate of exploitation in the capitalist economic system. Markets determined the *exchange value* of commodities (including the value of labor exchanged on the labor market), and Marx used the labor theory of value (the assumption that *labor time* is the true measure of value), to argue that the profit from the sale of commodities is a measure of the *surplus value* that capitalists took from workers. Since this was a quantitative description of the regularity about the exploitation of workers by capitalists, Marx could think of himself as a scientist.

Moreover, as a scientist, Marx saw his explanation of capitalism, like other scientific theories, as entailing predictions. Dialectical materialism explained history as a regularity about changes in class structures in which the natural increase in forces of production eventually leads to the overthrow of the class relations that organized production, and so Marx could predict what would happen under capitalism. Capitalists would keep workers at a subsistence level in order to maximize surplus value, and since this meant that economic growth would lead to overproduction (that is, the problem of producing more commodities than workers could buy), capitalists would have to develop markets in other countries, spreading its class struggle internationally. Marx predicted that, as capital grew, it would become concentrated in fewer and fewer hands, and since more and more people would be forced to work for a subsistence wage, the polarization of capitalists and workers and the pauperization of the workers would be so obvious that it would lead to an inevitable worldwide crisis. Eventually, the falling rate of profit would cause an economic crisis that triggers a violent revolution, and the capitalist class relation would be overthrown. Workers would be freed from capitalist oppression by abolishing the right to private property on which the class structure was based.

Das Kapital (1867) was Marx's attempt to establish a science of capitalism. It was the description of a regularity that predicted an economic crisis that would lead to the violent overthrow of capitalism. But as a scientific explanation, it could not condemn capitalism or praise its overthrow. It could only predict the inevitable future of civilization. However, no one can read *Das Kapital* without sensing Marx's righteous indignation about capitalist exploitation, and his goal in establishing this science is revealed more accurately in the *Communist Manifesto* which he wrote with Friedrich Engels in 1848. There is an instinctive animal anger at unjustified unequal treatment. It can be seen in apes who are treated unequally, and it can even be seen in chicks that protest loudly when they have not been fed, and other chicks have.[79] And seeing themselves on the side of history, political Marxists intended to use this instinct to help history along. They railed against capitalism, and after its overthrow, they predicted a rosy future. For a while, the means of production would be owned by the state, and workers would manage it following the socialist principle: *from each according to their ability and to each according to their needs*. But the power of the forces of production would continue to increase, as they always do, and socialism would eventually be replaced by communism, an economic system in which there would be no state, everyone would be equal, and since everyone work only when they wanted to, they would be truly free.

The *Communist Manifesto* expressed Marx's motive in establishing a science of capitalism (and the motive of Engels in supporting him). He looked forward to the overthrow of capitalism, and he hoped to inspire others to help in bringing it about. Thus, his work was another milestone in disillusionment with Reason. He embraced the liberal political offspring, in which government would respect the equal rights of everyone, but since he believed that property rights are a tool of oppression, he intended to promote the equality of individuals at the cost of their freedom. He also embraced the scientific offspring of the Enlightenment, since science was seen as the only reliable way of knowing about the natural world. But science is not Reason knowing Reality behind Appearance. It is a method that can discover what is true without it being self-evident to every Rational subject, as the use of mathematics in physics illustrates. That is how Marx and his followers saw Marx's explanation of the motor of history. They did not expect *Das Kapital* to change history by affecting the evolution of culture by judgmental selection. Indeed, his motor of history implies that culture has an ideology that would prevent it from making that kind of contribution. But Marx expected the recognition of the unjust inequality of class structure to arouse righteous indignation in those who did accept his theory, and Enlightenment confidence in science eventually explaining everything in the natural world justified them

---

[79] See YouTube demonstration of "inequity aversion" with capuchin monkeys at https://youtu.be/meiU6TxysCg. The primatologist, Frans de Waal, argues that this regularity is evidence of empathy between mammals generally, but it can be explained more simply as a consequence of having a faculty of imagination that enables mammals to perceive themselves as one animal body among other bodies as part of a world of objects in space. Inequity aversion can evolve as a desire that is aroused when animal bodies in certain similar situations are treated in different ways.

in helping overthrow capitalism and establishing a socialist stage, even if they had to act contrary to the expressed wills of morally autonomous individuals. Since they would be acting for the good of those who did not recognize their oppression, the end would justify the means.

Marx's revolution was a scientific revolution that justified a political revolution. It was a third milestone on the path from the Enlightenment to the era of endarkenment. It used science and a belief in the equality of everyone to justify overthrowing capitalism by force, if necessary. It turned the individualism derived from the belief that everyone has the power of Reason into collectivism. Locke meant the social contract to limit government to the pursuit of goals that respect the sovereignty and responsibility of individuals, but the socialist revolution would set up a state to end the inequality of workers and capitalists by taking over the management of production. But civilized spiritual organisms need to coordinate productive behavior on a massive scale, and thus, by replacing the capitalist class structure with the state, socialism would put another class in power. As scientists with the expertise to know about the motor of history and its ideal outcome, socialists did not need the consent of the governed to rule. They were on the side of history, and without a culture that justified their rule, like a religion or the social contract, Marxists would have to use the state's monopoly on violence to force reluctant individuals to comply with their social engineering. The other class would bear the cost of Marxism, as history teaches those who study socialist revolutions on Earth, beginning with the Russian revolution and including not only the socialist revolutions in China, Cambodia, North Korea, and Cuba and, possibly, Venezuela, but also the national socialism of Hitler's Germany.[80]

Thus, Marx was one of the four horsemen of disillusionment with Reason. By using respect for science to impugn the liberal political order, he turned two offspring of the Enlightenment into weapons for destroying the third. Using the claim of science to know about the natural world, he justified giving social engineers the power of the state so that political power would be used

---

[80] Notice that, except for national socialism, these socialist revolutions did not occur in capitalist spiritual organisms, but, rather, in spiritual organisms that were still at the psychological state of spiritual evolution.

to ensure equality of economic outcome, whatever the cost to the respect for the moral autonomy of Rational subjects that the West had inherited from intuitionistic metaphysics. But the power of the state was given to the communist party, and since history exposes it as an endogamous territory-wide class that rules over the rest, the politically imposed equality was a return to a feudal class structure similar to the one that capitalism was replacing. This is the collectivistic form of political power that Plato had defended in the *Republic*. Believing that only philosophers had the rational intuition that knows the Good, he justified giving philosophers the power of the state, enforced by the spirited element, to rule of those who were unable to know which goals are good. But Marxists were motivated by righteous indignation about the economic inequality between workers and capitalists, and their form of collectivism would make everyone equal by destroying a system of production whose evolution within civilized spiritual organisms increased their power to produce.[81] When many distinct voluntary capitalist associations go through reproductive cycles, competing to provide commodities that consumers are willing to buy, they impose capitalist selection on themselves, and besides not respecting the moral autonomy of individuals, it would destroy a kind of geometrical action aimed at the good evolves gradually in the direction of providing ever more efficiently all the kinds of commodities that consumers want—not to mention how it contributes to the advance of science and growing power over nature.

4 Einstein and the True

Science was an offspring of intuitionistic metaphysics. Though physicists confirmed mathematically formulated laws of nature by measurements of predictions, they assumed that the truth of mathematics was known by rational intuition. At first, this seemed to be just a form of natural philosophy because they used perception, rather than perceptual intuitions, to know about the natural world, and they explained what happens in the natural world in a way that could be understood in naturalistic imagination. But in the 20th century, modern physics undermined Enlightenment confidence in science discovering

---

[81] The classical critique of Marxian collectivism is Karl Popper (1945) *The Open Society and Its Enemies* (London: Routledge). While the first volume is titled *The Spell of Plato*, the second volume is titled *The High Tide of Prophesy: Hegel, Marx, and the Aftermath*.

the nature of what really exists, even if it is just the natural world.

After Newton discovered the laws of motion and gravitation, the other basic discoveries of classical physics were summed up in the 19th century as Maxwell's laws of electromagnetism (and the Lorentz force law). They were formulated as equations that use Cartesian coordinate systems to describe regularities about change, and mathematics was still used in this way to formulate laws about the motion and interaction of particles on the smallest scale in the 20th century. But laws of quantum physics were revolutionary because, unlike the deterministic laws of classical physics, they had a probabilistic character that could not be eliminated. This did not prevent physics from using them to discover the corpuscles that Locke doubted would ever be discovered. Even probabilistic quantum laws entailed quantitatively precise predictions about how particles move and interact by which could be confirmed, and since all the quantitative properties had to be consistent with one another, physicists were able to attribute a geometrical structure of micro-level composite bodies, such as atoms and molecule. Eventually, the Standard Model of quantum physics identified all the subatomic particles. With the help of mathematics, science has continued to foster new kinds of technology, from digital technology and the extraction of information from vast data collections to nanotechnology and biological engineering. The increasing control over the natural world is clearly progress, and it continues to fuel the evolution of production by capitalist selection that has propelled the rise of the West and globalization.

But a puzzle turned up by the Einsteinian revolution in 20th-century physics disabused naturalists of the expectation that science would give them an explanation of everything that they could understand in naturalistic imagination. Physics uses the method of inferring laws of nature as the simplest mathematically formulated description of regularities that cover the widest range of precise predictions.[82] Though physics was an offspring of intuitionistic metaphysics, its progress was not cultural evolution by *Rational*

---

[82] To contrast it with ontological naturalism, the method of the natural philosophers, like Boyle, I called it *intuitionistic naturalism*. But that is just another name for empirical lawism, the method by which physics discovers mathematical formulated laws of nature, which I used to contrast it with empirical ontology, the method of inferring powers of space and matter as the best ontological explanation of the laws of physics.

selection. The method of physics is empirical lawism, which is a sophisticated, rigorous form of *pragmatic selection*. Physicists accept conclusions about laws when they work, that is, when they help reach their shared goal of predicting measurements. Questions about how the equations correspond to Reality are a matter of interpretation, left for discussion later, in a more philosophical mood. But the truth of the mathematics employed was not at stake, and thus, when Einstein's way of using mathematics to describe two of the most basic regularities about change ever discovered were confirmed by careful measurements, what seemed to correspond to the equations was profoundly puzzling.

Volumes I and *II* show how ontology solves all the puzzles of modern physics, both quantum and gravitational physics, and it shows how they are all caused by its reliance on mathoscopes. That is, the assumption that the deepest possible empirical knowledge of what really exists are mathematically formulated laws of nature filters out the role of space in helping matter generate the regularities describes by them. Laws of classical physics were formulated as equations in Cartesian coordinate systems, and for equations to describe what is regular about change, time was treated as a fourth dimension. This is the reference frame used in classical physics. But Einstein used *transformation equations* to describe regularities about change as regularities about relations between as reference frames. In his special theory of relativity, he used transformation equations to describe the regular relation between the coordinates for the same events used in different reference frames in constant motion relative to one another, called *inertial reference frames*. (They were called the Lorentz transformation equations.) In his general theory of relativity, an explanation of gravitation based on his special theory, he used transformation equations to describe how coordinates change in *arbitrary reference frames* following trajectories in a gravitational field. (They were entailed by the *Einstein field equations*.) Both sets of transformation equations describe regularities found in the natural world, and they have been confirmed by measurements of quantitative predictions. But neither set can be derived from the laws of classical physics. Indeed, they are incompatible with Newtonian *absolute space* and *absolute time*, which is our ordinary way of thinking about the natural world as a world of objects in space and time. That is what makes the regularities described so disconcerting.

The equations that Einstein used in special relativity can correspond to the world only if the present moment of objects located at a distance from the origin of a reference frame depends on a reference frame's velocity. That is, if two inertial reference frames moving at different velocities pass one another at some point in space, they will disagree about which moment in the history of the distant object is simultaneous with them at the moment of their passing. They will also disagree about its location. The dependence of an event's location in time and space on its relation to the reference frame used by an observer is the *relativity* after which Einstein's theories are named. But Einstein's relativity theories imply that all inertial reference frames are equally correct, and thus, in order to believe that his theories are true by corresponding to the natural world, like other laws of physics, absolute space and absolute time must be replaced by *spacetime*. What really exists is spacetime. It is a four-dimensional geometrical structure in which the relations of all possible inertial reference frames at a point in spacetime can be described at once, and Einstein's general theory of relativity uses the curvature of four-dimensional spacetime at a point in spacetime to describe the gravitational field at that point. Interpreting Einsteinian relativity ontologically, that is, as a description of what really exists, spacetime is an entity that is downright puzzling. It does not seem possible that spacetime is what really exists in the natural world because it contradicts our commonsense belief that existence is what distinguishes the present from the past and the future. Since Einstein's relativity theories hold everywhere, they imply that every event in the history of the universe exists in exactly the same sense as every other event. This is an ontological theory about the nature of time and existence that is aptly called *eternalism*. Besides being incompatible with the passage of time, spacetime ontology has other puzzling implications. It has led physics to conclude that the universe began with the Big Bang. Indeed, many physicists now defend *multiverse* theories, in which many Big Bangs and many universes are what exist. Some physicists suggest that there are wormholes in curved spacetime that connect enormously distant locations in the universe directly. And some even seem to believe that time travel is possible.

Though the mathematics describing spacetime is consistent, spacetime ontology is utterly incredible to reflective subjects. They are congenital presentists because the faculty of naturalistic imagination uses the passage of time to represent change. They cannot tell a story about their self as something that is identical over time without assuming that time passes. They assume that the choices they made in the past cannot be changed because they are over with and no longer exist, and they assume that their choices at present determine a future that does not yet exist. Thus, whereas classical physics implied that the natural world is nothing but a motion and interaction of particles that can be pictured in naturalistic imagination all the way down, 20th-century physics has concluded that, at bottom, the natural world has a truly puzzling nature. Since beings like us cannot begin to understand how we are parts of such a natural world, spacetime is as ontologically problematic as any Reality that intuitionistic metaphysicians claimed to know behind Appearance.

Indeed, spacetime ontology is so unbelievable that it might have been used to cast doubt on the empirical method of physics and science generally, much as mind-body dualism and absolute idealism discredited modern intuitionistic metaphysics. But physics is not cultural evolution by Rational selection. It is not trying to understand how all its beliefs fit together as representations of a single Reality. Instead, it is cultural evolution by a quantitatively rigorous form of pragmatic selection. Since the method of physics is empirical lawism, agreement depends on finding the simplest laws with the widest range of quantitative predictions that are confirmed by measurements. What works in that way is true. To be sure, laws of physics must fit together. But that is just the logical consistency of the equations used to all formulate them. Though puzzles about spacetime ontology may turn up when physicists offer interpretations of their equations in their spare time, confirmation of mathematically formulated laws of nature by precise measurements of quantitative predictions is more compelling than what can be understood in naturalistic imagination, and when they see Einsteinian relativity as the discovery of spacetime, confidence in empirical lawism leads them to portray physics as confirming a Darwinian lesson about Reason. Though mathematics enables physics to discover the deepest possible empirical knowledge about what exists, we should not expect to be able to understand its nature in naturalistic imagination because our cognitive powers are adaptations to a series of environments that our ancestors happened to occupy. There is no doubt that mathematics enables physics to see something about the nature of what really exists behind the world of objects in space in which our animal bodies around, but since mathematics is *a priori* knowledge, it depends on our brains in some unknown way, and beings like us cannot understand how it works.

Einsteinian relativity is portrayed as confirming the belief that all truth is relative. But relativity is not the same as relativism. Einstein's relativity theories describe an absolute truth since spacetime is a world in which all possible reference frames are true in the same way. However, when Reason rebelled against its intuitionistic parents and became science, it expected to explain everything in the natural world, and though Newtonian physics seemed to provide the foundation for such an explanation, Einsteinian physics implies that science cannot even begin to attain its original goal. If there were no technology testifying to its credibility, science would seem to be a fool's errand. Hence, modern physics is a fourth milestone on the path to endarkenment.

CHAPTER 8:
ENDARKENMENT

Arguments about metaphysics are at the third level of linguistic organization, and when they are exchanged, culture evolves by Rational selection. Confidence in Reason blossomed as the Enlightenment, and the power and influence of Western civilization were due mainly to three of its offspring. Science was one of them, but since it debunked the other two, belief in Reason was self-destructive. And while physical science was leading to disillusionment with Reason, the intuitionistic family that Reason left behind was also evolving. Confidence in Reason had built up momentum for centuries in Western culture, and it carried philosophy into the 19th century in other ways. But they were all founded on intuitionism, and since all the forms of intuitionistic metaphysics had been discovered, confidence in Reason petered out. This chapter describes how Reason was replaced by relativism and began an era in Western history that is indistinguishable from a psych-level spiritual organism without the benefit of a shared religion called endarkenment.

Though this era is not the path that leads to Reason understanding its own nature, it is part of the biography of Reason. The resolution of its identity crisis depends on tracing its origin back through physical science to Western philosophy, and by the time that empirical ontology discovers that space is a substance, solves the puzzles of modern physics, and unifies science, the era of endarkenment has already set in. To show that Reason evolved from intuitionistic metaphysics by way of the Enlightenment offspring that were responsible for the unprecedented power and influence of the West, ontological science must explain how the philosophical movements that science left behind arrived at this dismal outcome.

What the disillusionment with Reason in science and the rise of relativism in philosophy have in common is the rejection of supernaturalism, and so it is relevant to notice that even in the rising tide era of endarkenment, a more positive voice can be heard . The belief that God created the natural world and populated it with beings like us for a purpose plays no role in either science or philosophy. But it has survived on its own as the religion of Christians and Jews. Theologians have given up claiming to have proofs of God's existence outside space and time, and they admit that belief in God depends on faith. But as we shall see, the survival of Judeo-Christian religion is a positive voice in the era of endarkenment because it reminds us of the possibility of a transcendental foundation of the Good. At least, it promises that there will be an illuminating and satisfying explanation of the meaning of life, and this argument leaves open the possibility of discovering such an explanation in a world constituted by substances that endure through time.

Since naturalists hold that nothing exists outside space and time, they do not have to solve the problematic ontological dualism inherited from ancient intuitionistic metaphysics. But in the modern era, the belief that Reason can know Reality behind Appearance led to mind-body dualism, and since that ontological problem turns up in the natural world, naturalists must solve it. A naturalistic solution to that problem might provide a kind of explanation of meaning of life that would satisfy theists.

But if so, it could not be discovered by any current that the momentum of Enlightenment confidence in Reason carried into philosophy because they were kinds of intuitionism that accepted naturalism and did not try to use Reason to solve the problem of mind-body dualism.

In popular culture, philosophical currents had another way of handling that problem, called *romanticism*. And in academic culture, philosophical currents continued to hide the ontological problem of mind-body dualism until they petered out and philosophers decided that metaphysics is meaningless— or denied that there is any such thing as the True and the Good.

1 Romanticism

The popular philosophical currents after the Enlightenment are called *romanticism*. Romantics rejected argument in favor of feelings, will, and even the beliefs and values shared by a group as culture. They explicitly rejected the developments heralded as progress during the Enlightenment, and some romantics did relapse into making arguments. Though expressions of romanticism are usually easy to recognize, *romanticism* has the reputation of being hard to define. But as an inevitable development during the beginning of the metaphysical stage, this part of the history of Western culture can be explained ontologically

Except for traditional theism, all the currents flowing from the Enlightenment were naturalistic, and the one generally praised as progress during the 18th century was not beyond criticism. Without an explanation of the meaning of life that depends on God's purpose, it was criticized as being too this-worldly. The Enlightenment asked reflective subjects to be content with the goodness of the kinds of goals that could be reached by science studying nature, by governments respecting the moral autonomy of Rational subjects, and by capitalist economic progress. But the latter took the form of the industrial revolution, and it included the enclosure movement. The division of communal lands into the private property of capitalists forced a migration of rural populations to industrial cities and towns looking for work in factories. Even children were forced to work. Rural landscapes were invaded by railroads. The scenic countryside was blemished with mines and mills.

Believers in Reason tried to defend progress by pointing to the increase in knowledge, the protection against the monarchical autocratic state, and the growing power to provide the material conditions of life. But even those who appreciated these benefits could not help but sense a shallowness about what Enlightenment progress had to offer. The most telling objections to progress by defenders of romanticism were voiced in literature. For example, a warning about the monsters that science would create by tampering with nature came from Mary Shelly's *Frankenstein.* But romanticism was not just opposition to the classical standards. It affirmed something that was missing from Enlightenment progress.

The romantic movement is usually identified from its expressions in the fine arts, as changes of style or content in literature, painting, and music. It is commonly illustrated by the English romantic poets around the beginning of the 19th century, from Wordsworth and Coleridge to Keats, Shelly, and Lord Byron. They celebrated the beauty of nature and the experience of being part of it. They admired the courage of individual heroes, mourned the loss of past glories in medieval ruins, and wondered at the passage of time and death. Gothic novels told horror stories about ghosts in ancient mansions. The most famous novel of the time, Goethe's *Sorrows of Young Werther*, sympathized with a young man who killed himself because the woman he loved was married and could not spend her life with him. Romanticism can be seen in paintings of the sublime beauty of nature—and paintings of individuals awestruck by it. It can also be seen in the intense negative passions evoked by paintings of the suffering of courageous heroes and monsters unleashed by science and Reason. Beethoven used the art of *music* to arouse deep passions in listeners, and his influence resounds in Brahms, Chopin, Schubert, and other composers in the early 19th century.

Though these works of art are recognizably romantic, *romanticism* is notoriously hard to define, and one is offered by this explanation of the West as the beginning of a metaphysical stage of evolution. As a current that flowed from the metaphysical belief in a Reality behind Appearance, romantics continued to believe in something that exists beyond normal life. In the ordinary world, normal life is caught up in Enlightenment progress, and sensing that it is shallow, romantics wanted to be in touch with something deeper, something more in keeping with what they felt, something more real. Since what they were looking for was necessarily part of Appearance, they had a transcendental goal. But their goal was not knowing the True. Nor was it knowing the Good. It was not even knowing the Beautiful. *Knowing* them is the transcendental goal of Reason, and that is what romantics rejected. Romanticism was the replacement of Reason with the enjoyment of beauty and intense feelings and the replacement of knowledge with will and virtue.

The momentum that had built up from centuries of arguments about metaphysics flowed into romanticism as the belief that beings like us are capable of a distinctively human perfection. But romantics denied that perfection is cognitive. Reflective subjects are not merely knowers of the world but also doers in the world, and they are guided by feelings. They saw the perfection of other faculties of mind as vehicles for reaching transcendental goals. Like Plato, romantics believed that what is most real lies somehow beyond Appearance. But instead of knowing it, they wanted to experience it in feelings. They replaced metaphysical arguments with poems and other works of art, and their beauty was supposed to arouse an intense aesthetic enjoyment that would make what is most real immediately present. It was still an intuition of Reality, but it was a non-cognitive faculty. The objects were felt rather than known. It had a non-Rational transcendental goal.

Ontological science defines romanticism by its belief in a transcendental goal and its rejection of Reason as a way of attaining it. That is what is meant by describing it as believing in art for art's sake. By contrast to modern intuitionistic metaphysics, which began with the Cogito, *I think, therefore I am*, romanticism might be described as beginning with *I feel, therefore I am*. But romantics would bristle at any such comparison because the Cogito was an argument aimed at knowing the True. Romantics did not believe in argument. *Sapere Aude,* or dare to know the True, was the motto of the Enlightenment, and if romanticism is to be described in terms of truth, it ought to be given the motto: *Beauty is truth and truth beauty*.

Since the Enlightenment and romanticism both abandoned supernaturalism, both focused on the natural world. But while the Enlightenment replaced theism with deism, romanticism replaced knowledge of nature with the worship of nature. Rousseau can be seen as a pivotal figure because he was drawn in both directions. Since God did not intervene in the natural world after creating it, deists did not believe that we have a personal relation to God. Instead, they expected to learn the nature of the Good from the study of nature. This is how Rousseau saw nature in his use of the social contract to define the general will. And since Rousseau held that moral goodness evolved from the state of nature as our compassionate ancestors learned how to benefit from cooperation in the pursuit of common goals, science sees Rousseau as anticipating its ontological explanation of our spiritual nature as our participation in the form of life on the fourth floor of the edifice of life. But romantics see Rousseau as anticipating their movement because Rousseau used the childlike innocence of our ancestors as the model of virtue to criticize the corruption of embracing the false values we have acquired with the rise of civilization. Rousseau would probably not resist this appropriation by romanticism, judging by *Emile*, his treatise on child-rearing that aimed at returning to more primitive virtues. But as explained ontologically, the difference could not be more basic. Rousseau's social contract was aimed at knowledge of the Good, and romantics would reject his cognitive way of relating to nature as the worship of a false idol. The proper worship of nature is to express the real nature of nature more perfectly in feeling and action.

The transcendental goal of knowing the True was replaced by the transcendental goal of authenticity. Beings like us are part of nature, and intense feelings, especially aesthetic enjoyment, can be seen as expressions of the real nature of nature through us. Like feelings, the will is a faculty of the mind, and individuals who will actions from their innermost being can be seen as expressing the nature of what exists most basically. Romantics celebrated it not only in venerating medieval chivalry but also in stories of individual acts of heroism. Indeed, as romantics see it, what makes the will authentic is not its goal but, rather, how it was willed. This was a rejection of classical standards that described the difference between good and evil goals as inherent in the nature of what exists because the goals willed by different individuals could be different, even opposite, and the wills would still approach perfection in the same way. Authentic feelings and actions are expressions of one's real nature, indeed, a way of being at one with what is most real in nature.

German romantics tried to explain why authenticity is good by how it fits into an idealist ontology. But they verged on betrayal of the Enlightenment belief in the moral autonomy of individuals because authenticity did not have to be in the individual. For example, according to Herder (1744-1803), a leader in German romanticism, nature expresses its real nature in our sharing a language and culture. Since the beliefs shared in any culture replaced knowledge of Reality behind Appearance, Herder's romanticism was the foundation of *historicism*, the doctrine that truth is nothing but nature expressing its real nature as the plan shared in members of a spiritual organism. And it is not a big step from the celebration of collective belief to the celebration of collective will. The French revolution, for example, culminated in the reign of terror, and though it was done in the name of Reason, it was an authentic expression of nature as collective will.

2 Nineteenth-Century Idealism

Philosophy was left behind when Reason rebelled against its intuitionistic family as science, and while its overflowing confidence in a distinctively human perfection of beings like us flowed in the direction of romanticism in popular culture, it took an opposite direction in academic culture. What these flows had in common was intuitionism, the belief that consciousness is objects of intuition. But whereas in romanticism, the flow rejected the cognitive perfection of Reason in favor of feeling and will while keeping the belief in a Reality behind Appearance, in academic philosophy, the flow continued as argument while abandoning belief in the existence of a Reality that lies behind Appearance. As we have seen, absolute idealism is a metaphysical system that reduces both Reality and Appearance to an intuitionistic substance known by Reason, and thus, when science rejected intuitionistic metaphysics, what it left behind was an intuitionistic kind of academic philosophy that is defined ontologically as absolute idealism. But in the end, the claims that philosophy could make on behalf of Reason became so modest and self-destructive that absolute idealist ontology had all but vanished. It was replaced by a bland and meek belief in the existence of what is immediately present, like what is assumed in spiritual organisms during the psychological stage.

Since absolute idealism was one of the two ways of hiding the problematic ontological dualism inherited from Kant's distinction between the phenomenal and noumenal worlds, it was inevitable. In *Chapter 5*, it was represented by Hegel, and it is also called *objective idealism* to contrast it with the *subjective idealism* of Berkeley and Hume. Interpreted ontologically, empiricism was the reduction of Reality to Appearance because strict adherence to Locke's principle of empiricism entails skepticism about Cartesian metaphysics. As an epistemological theory, it holds that all knowledge can be reduced to objects of intuition that originate from either the faculty of perception or the faculty of reflection built into the mind. Hence, it winds up denying that we can know that there is a world external to mind. But absolute idealists use a Kantian constructive account of Reason to show how it knows Reality even though Reality is not *behind* Appearance. They argue that Reality and Appearance are constituted by the same intuitionistic substance, and so they believe that nothing exists but consciousness.

This kind of idealism cannot defend the criterion of truth implicit in metaphysical arguments as the claim to show that Reason knows the nature of a Reality that exists behind Appearance. That is the kind of metaphysics that begins the ancient, modern, and late modern eras, and it implies that the criterion of truth is correspondence to a Reality that is different from Appearance. But idealism hides its unavoidable problematic ontological dualism by denying that anything transcends the world in which perception finds our bodies, and so the correspondence criterion of truth is trivial. Beliefs that correspond to Appearance necessarily correspond to Reality. The criterion that idealists use to show that Reason knows the True is the coherence of *all* our beliefs about the world.

Coherence is the standard for judging which beliefs to accept that makes the third level of linguistic organization functional even though intuitionistic metaphysics is basically mistaken about the nature of Reality. Though metaphysics is doomed to fail in its attempt to know Reality behind Appearance, its standard of coherence causes culture to evolve by Rational selection, and so metaphysical-level spiritual organisms acquire an order of functional powers that are out of reach for spiritual organisms at the psychological level, where culture evolves by pragmatic selection. Rational selection depends on the coherence of beliefs, and thus, as Leibniz was able to hide the Cartesian problem of mind-body dualism, so absolute idealists were able to hide the Kantian problem of an unknowable noumenal world behind the phenomenal world. Idealists defended an explanation of everything in Appearance that seemed to include everything mentioned by Descartes or Kant without having to admit that there is any Reality distinct from Appearance, and the coherence of their explanation was offered as proof that it was knowledge of the True.

German idealism had an early alliance with German romanticism, whose focus on culture and language can be seen in the works of W. F. Schlegel. J. G. Fichte was an idealist with a strong interest in ethics and political action, and Arthur Schopenhauer defended an idealism in which Kant's thing in itself was the will. Though F. W. J. Schelling used a double-aspect theory about substance to hide Kant's problematic dualism, even he can be seen an idealist by interpreting both the subjectification and objectification of the Absolute as objects of intuition. Idealists also dominated academia in 19th-century England, represented by T. H. Green, F. H. Bradley, A. E. Taylor, and R. G. Collingwood. It was even represented in America by Josiah Bradley.

The intuitionistic nature of the Reality that absolute idealists defended is so opposite to materialism, the kind of substance implicit in the laws of nature discovered on the path that Reason actually followed, that objects of intuition hardly seem like a substance at all. In the 19th century, therefore, science on one side of the gulf was trying to reduce beings like us to matter, while philosophy on the other side was defending an intuitionistic substance that already seemed spiritual. With continued advances in science and technology, the idealists' attempt to explain our spiritual nature in terms of intuitions became as untenable as supernaturalism.

Though American philosophers were more sympathetic with science, they could not escape an implicit acceptance of an idealist ontology. In the 19th and early 20th centuries, American philosophers defended pragmatism, a more modest explanation of the world. It was introduced by C. S. Pierce and defended later by William James and John Dewey. Metaphysics holds that Reason knows Reality, and since that is to explain the nature of what exists most basically, it boldly claims to explain the place of everything else as part of a whole. Pragmatists claimed to reject metaphysics because they did not believe that Reason can explain what is found in the world completely. Instead, they defended a more modest claim that Reason discovers what is true as *what works*, that is, as what solves problems. The problems included obstacles that arise in daily life. Indeed, John Dewey (1859-1952) used attempts to solve them as a model for explaining the nature of *thought* (1910). But pragmatism was an explanation of how Reason knows about the world, and since what they meant by the *world* was what metaphysicians had called Appearance, they were implicitly defending a form of idealism. Since pragmatists were taken in by the illusion of intuitionism, they believed that the world is just the objects of their perceptual faculty of intuition, and so they were reducing everything to Appearance. That is, they held that nothing exists but complex phenomenal properties, though they did not realize it since they were naïve realists about perception.

The problems that arise in ordinary situations are not the only problems that confront beings like us. Science tries to solve more basic problems. It is Reason knowing about the world, and Charles Sanders Peirce (1839-1914) explained the method of science as using a kind of inference that was neither deductive nor inductive, but, rather, abductive. This was to explain the empirical method of science as inferences to what is true as the best explanation of what is found in the world, and that is the method that ontological naturalists, from the pre-Socratics to empirical ontology, use to learn more about the natural world. But Pierce did not base his argument on the assumption that the natural world is constituted by substances. He was an intuitionist, and though he recognized that science might eventually discover a complete explanation of the world, it was not an ontological explanation. It would be merely an *end of inquiry* in which all the basic problems of science were solved. It is still just Appearance, and since it is an object of intuition for pragmatists, it is ontologically a form of idealism.

Pragmatists meant to reject metaphysics by defending a more modest theory about the nature of Reason that depends on its practical value. Thus, they defended the use of a pragmatic criterion of truth. It is modest, and seeing it as a retreat from the cultural evolution by Rational selection that occurs in metaphysical-level spiritual organisms, Dewey defended it as abandoning a misguided quest for certainty. But the explicit defense of the pragmatic criterion of truth was an attempt to explain the natural world as completely as possible, and since that is the goal of metaphysics, pragmatism was meant as a replacement for showing that Reason can know Reality behind Appearance. When the goal is to explain the world as completely as possible, pragmatism is the most coherent explanation of what we are doing, and so the explicit defense of the pragmatic criterion of truth presupposes the idealists' coherence theory of truth.

Pragmatism tries to reject metaphysics by rejecting the correspondence theory of truth implicit in its original goal of showing how Reason knows Reality behind Appearance. To pass the Socratic test, a metaphysical argument had to explain the nature of what exists so completely that Rational subjects can understand the real difference between good and evil. But since pragmatism denies that the True is what corresponds to a Reality that is something distinct from Appearance, it denies that there is any such thing as the Good. Since it cannot explain why goals are good, it is a retreat from metaphysical-level to psychological-level spiritual organisms, where it is just assumed that the goals we pursue, especially those we cooperate in pursuing, are good. As we have seen, religions evolve during the psychological stage of evolution that explain why reflective subjects jointly pursue goals, and philosophers who are sympathetic with science generally reject religions as just myths. But William James offers a pragmatic defense of religion that shows how far this kind of idealism is from passing the Socratic test of metaphysics. He defended the rationality of the will to believe in a religion without sufficient evidence on the grounds that it may give us the understanding of the meaning of life that seems to be wanting, in much the same way as believing in one's capacity to attain difficult goals may make it possible to attain them. If it works, it is true.

Into the early 20th century, institutions of higher education harbored defenders of absolute idealism and pragmatism. But in light of the steady advances in science and technology, even metaphysicians concluded that it was a mistake to believe that Reason gives us a way of knowing Reality behind Appearance.[83] Philosophers divided into two camps, but neither abandoned intuitionism. In the English-speaking world, analytic philosophers sided with scientific progress and tried to show that metaphysics is meaningless. Since their method was the analysis of language, they defended what is called the *deflationary theory of truth*. It holds that beliefs are true by correspondence to Appearance in the same way that sentences about the natural world are true by correspondence to it. *Section 3* describes their progress in more detail, and since it takes up technical issues that are mostly of interest to professional philosophers, general readers might skip ahead to *Section 4*, on Continental philosophy. It surveys more briefly how intuitionistic philosophy turned away from issues about Reality and, after trying for a while to settle for describing Appearance, worried about how to live without metaphysics. It rejected the objectivity of science in favor of the critique of ideology, and as post-modernism, it used the consensus about the

---

[83] A notable exception is Alfred North Whitehead, who offered an idealist explanation of modern physics.

mistake of believing in absolute truth to deny that there is an objective truth at all. The rejection of metaphysics allied the two camps in leading to the rise of endarkenment in contemporary popular culture, as described in *Section 5*.

3   Anglo-American Philosophy &

Around the turn of the 20th century, philosophers in Great Britain and America took a so-called *linguistic turn*, beginning what is called *analytic philosophy*. Its unity as a school is disputed. But it differs from modern (and late modern) philosophy as basically as modern philosophy differs from ancient philosophy in that it can be seen as a third phase in the history of Western philosophy.[84] It began as logical atomism.

3.1 Logical Atomism &

Philosophy includes arguments against metaphysics as well as for it, and there is a way for intuitionists to argue against intuitionistic metaphysics that is basically different from ancient and modern philosophy. Like all metaphysical arguments, it begins in the commonsense world. But instead of arguing about whether perceptual phenomenal appearances are public or private, it focuses on language and takes it for granted that reflective subjects use language in the commonsense world. Meanings of sentences have phenomenal appearances, and when they are seen as objects of a faculty of intuition, they seem to enable language users to determine how sentences correspond to the commonsense world. Indeed, some sentences seem to be analytically true, or true in virtue of their meanings, and since this knowledge does not depend on perception, it is prior to perception, or *a priori*. These commonsense assumptions about language enabled G. E. Moore (1873-1958) to defend a refutation of absolute idealism.

Idealists use mind-like substances to explain Reality behind Appearance, and since absolute idealism takes the unity of consciousness to characterize the single substance that constitutes everything, its ontology explains the essential natures of everything in the world by their relations to one another as part of a whole. This is called the doctrine of *internal relations*, and using ordinary sentences in the commonsense world, Moore's way of analyzing language allowed him to refute it. For example, when he put his hand forward and said, *This is a hand,* common sense enabled users of language to know that it was true. Since its truth depended only on the limited part of the world perceived at the moment, it was obviously a fact that could be known without knowing its relation to everything in the world. This also refuted skepticism about the external world since a hand is just as obviously a material object. Hence Moore's way of analyzing language solved another metaphysical problem, albeit on the implicit assumption that direct realism about perception is true.[85]

---

[84] A more abstract case for recognizing analytic philosophy as a distinctive way of doing philosophy is made by Aaron Preston (2004).

[85] G. E. Moore (1939).

Bertrand Russell (1872-1970) took up Moore's rebellion against absolute idealism and, with help from Ludwig Wittgenstein (1889-1951), turned it into *logical atomism*, a way of analyzing logical structure that *showed* how language corresponds to the world. It assumed that all synthetic sentences, that is, all sentences making meaningful assertions about the commonsense world, could be broken down into atomic sentences and, thus, into the atomic facts to which they corresponded in the world, which were known by perception. Other meaningful sentences were all analytically true. Besides sentences whose truth depends on the meanings of their non-logical terms, such as *All bachelors are men*), they included sentences that express logical truths (such as, *p or not-p*). It was, of course, an ideal language, but its construction was expected to clear up confusion about what sentences mean. Complex sentences would all be analyzed extensionally (by the use of so-called *truth-functions*) into atomic sentences and their correspondence to atomic facts, and since the meanings of metaphysical sentences could not be analyzed in this way, this would show that metaphysics is nonsense. As we have seen, ontological science agrees that naturalistic sentences can be analyzed in this way. But in order to carry out their project, analytic philosophers had to solve a number of problems. They had to explain the truth of sentences that describe nonexistent objects (such as *The king of France is bald*), sentences that say what is good, sentences that describe psychological states, and sentences about what is necessary and what is possible. But since these sentences seem to express commonsense facts, logical atomists expected to reduce them to atomic sentences and their correspondence to atomic facts. Thus, was linguistic philosophy born.

By analyzing the language used in the commonsense world, logical atomism established the intersubjective standpoint of analytic philosophy. That is, analytic philosophers continued to assume that they were users of language in the natural world, and by putting aside issues about the role of perceptual phenomenal appearances, they took for granted the truth of direct realism about perception. But as users of language, they had to know the meanings of sentences, and since their meanings seemed to be immediately present when sentences are used, they proceeded on the assumption that they were objects of a faculty of rational intuition.

As ontological science explains them, naturalistic sentences are verbal behavior, which can be generated overtly by the verbal hemisphere of a neural BGS and perceived by others. Their meanings are constructed in naturalistic imagination, which is an interaction between the verbal and nonverbal hemispheres, and since the meanings of sentences determine how they correspond to the natural world, the use of atomic sentences to describe the world depends on constructing their meanings in the input scene where the sensory input circuit constructs representations of the natural world from sensory input. For example, to describe the tulip in the vase as red, the speaker must, at least, see it as an object in space related to the vase, and that understanding depends on naturalistic imagination. Since users of language are conscious, psychological states have phenomenal appearances, and thus, when atomic sentences are used to describe what is perceived in the world, their meanings seem to be part of the world described. In other words, as direct realists, logical atomists projected the phenomenal appearance of both the public utterance of a sentence like *The tulip is red* and its meaning constructed in naturalistic imagination onto the perceptual appearance of the commonsense world, and so the relation between them seemed to be the correspondence between atomic sentences and a public commonsense world.

Though the correspondence relation seems obvious, it is not compatible with the intersubjective standpoint of analytic philosophy. That standpoint assumes that language is used by animals in the natural world, and for direct realists about perception, who interpret perceptual phenomenal appearances as the natural world, the correspondence of atomic sentences to the world seems to be public. But the correspondence depends on the meanings of the atomic sentences, and since they are constructed in naturalistic imagination, direct realists must admit that those phenomenal appearances are private. They are objects of a faculty of rational intuition, and (unless they are Platonists, who treat meanings of sentences like Forms in a realm of Being) logical atomists must admit that the states of the natural world to which the meanings of atomic sentences correspond are not public. Thus, the project of reducing meaningful language to atomic sentences and then, showing how they correspond to the natural world depends on the assumption that users of language agree about what sentences mean.[86] But as intuitionists, analytic philosophers cannot make that assumption, and the privacy of meanings is a fatal flaw in the attempt to use the logical analysis of language to show that metaphysics is meaningless, as became clear in its second form, logical positivism.

3.2 Logical Positivism ❦

This flaw was discovered in a second phase of analytic philosophy, called *logical positivism*, which began in the 1920s and 1930s with a group of philosophers and physicists, called the *Vienna Circle*. They used empirical science as a model of the meaningful use of language to show that metaphysics is meaningless. (The doctrine was promulgated in the English-speaking world by A. J. Ayer's (1910-89) famous book, *Language, Truth and Logic*.) Logical atomism had shown how observational sentences correspond to the natural world, but science was also meaningful empirical knowledge, even though it included laws and theories that could not be reduced to atomic sentences. Thus, if they showed how science is reducible to observational sentences, they could use science as a model to dismiss metaphysical sentences as empirically meaningless for being irreducible to observational sentences. Confidence in the possibility of such a reduction came from the British empiricists and their use of the principle of empiricism to reduce empirical knowledge to perceptual appearances. But

---

[86] In the spatio-material world, language users do agree about the meanings of sentences because the spiritual world (superimposed on the natural world as part of the commonsense world) is constituted by the coordination of meanings constructed in the neural BGSs of members of spiritual organisms.

logical positivists (or logical empiricists) analyzed language from the intersubjective standpoint of its users, and they used the *verificationist principle of meaning,* which holds that the meaning of a sentence is its method of verification.

The main obstacle on which logical positivists focused was sentences in theories in physics whose terms refer to entities that are not observable, such as electrons. The method of physics is empirical lawism, and since its theories are confirmed by measurements they predict, their solution was to formulate theories as axiom systems. Sentences containing theoretical terms were the axioms, other premises were *correspondence rules,* which implicitly defined theoretical terms by observational terms, and with the help of logic and mathematics, these premises could be shown to entail observational sentences. The correspondence rules, like the truths of logic and mathematics, were analytic, and so only theoretical and observational sentences were true by correspondence to the natural world. Thus, the meanings of theoretical sentences could be reduced to the observational sentences that confirmed the theory.

The problem with the logical positivist analysis of empirical meanings is that physical theories that could be formulated as axiom systems could also be reformulated as axiom systems in which all the theoretical sentences were replaced by observational sentences. That badly misrepresented physics. Physicists interpret theoretical terms as references to entities that exist but cannot be seen, typically, for physically explicable reasons, such as being too small, like electrons, or being too fast, like changes in atomic energy states. But attempts to replace the definitions of theoretical terms by observational terms with a looser relation (correspondence rules) opened the way to sanctioning metaphysical sentences as meaningful.

In the spatio-material world, it is possible to describe how theoretical terms are related to observational terms because both correspond, by way of meanings of sentences constructed in naturalistic imagination, to interactions of the space and matter that constitute the natural world. Such sentences are ontologically necessary because they correspond to the first cause. But analytic philosophers are not ontologists. They are intuitionists who interpret meanings as objects of rational intuition, and in order to use the logical analysis of language to show that metaphysics is meaningless, they would have to agree about which sentences are analytic and which are synthetic. But since intuitions are private, disputes about meanings cannot be settled intersubjectively, and that flaw is fatal for logical empiricism.

The significance of the privacy of meanings was driven home by Willard Van Orman Quine (1908-2000) in his argument against what he called the *Two Dogmas of Empiricism.* One dogma was the assumption that there is an objective difference between analytic and synthetic sentences, so that they hold for everyone, and the other dogma, which depends on the first, was the assumption that meaningful sentences can be related to a limited set of observations that confirm it. Scientific confirmation is intersubjective, and Quine showed that meanings are not fixed by what is public in the use of language. The synonymy relations described by analytic sentences ultimately depend on stipulating definitions of terms, and given any set of sentences, such as a theory in physics, different language users can treat different sentences as definitions, leaving the truth of others to depend on how they correspond to the world. Thus, Quine argued, confirmation is *holistic*. The evidence used to confirm a theory depends on sentences corresponding to observable states in the world, but when the observation sentences that confirm a theory vary with the subject who understands them, the theory is a set of sentences that confronts perception as a whole.

Given the irreducibility of scientific theories to the observations that confirm them, analytic philosophers had to abandon the project of using language analysis to show that metaphysics is meaningless. But Quine was a true revolutionary because his response to the failure of logical positivism was the attempt to take sides with science. He proposed to abandon analytic philosophy entirely and replace it with *naturalized epistemology*.[87] That is, epistemology would be a topic in psychology. Instead of relying on the rational intuition of meanings, the issue about how language corresponds to the world would be left to science. Since this was to reject intuitionism about meanings of sentences in favor of the empirical method of science, he moved in the direction of ontological naturalism. But physics is based on intuitionistic naturalism, and since Quine took physics as his model, his view of naturalized epistemology was crippled by physicalism. As he understood the empirical method, all the evidence for scientific theories depends ultimately on the stimulation of sensory receptors, and thus, in the branch of science that discovers laws about human behavior, he was a behaviorist. He assumed that the relation between language and the world is a regularity about how verbal behavior occurs in the presence of sensory input that would be described by a law of psychology, and so he expected a mature psychology to describe how sensory stimulations cause the verbal behavior by which users of language describe the 3-D world, including not only theories and all of science but also history. Epistemology could still guide research if this was the goal of psychology, but epistemology would be "naturalized into a chapter of engineering: the technology of anticipating sensory stimulation."[88] Without recognizing that geometrical efficient causes are as basic as physical efficient causes, Quine could not anticipate that ontological science would explain the correspondence between language and the natural world by the construction of meanings of sentences in the faculties of imagination of language users. And when naturalized epistemology banned rational intuition for its privacy, instead of explaining it by the nature of consciousness, it threw out the obvious clue to the existence of a faculty of naturalistic imagination.

3.3 Analytic Philosophy ☞

Analytic philosophy survived Quine's attempt to replace it with science. For one thing, there was another way of using the analysis of language to show that metaphysics is meaningless, and it was widely discussed during the twenty years after WWII as logical positivism fell out of favor. Ordinary language philosophers explained

---

[87] W. V. O. Quine (1969)

[88] W. V. O. Quine (1992, p. 19).

language as a game in which users follow implicit rules, and so they took the meaning of a word or sentence to be determined by how it is used. Assuming that ordinary language is the limit of what can be said meaningfully, the analysis of *meaning as use* enabled Wittgenstein to argue that metaphysics and skepticism about it are both meaningless. They misused language in certain ways, and his way of analyzing language was meant to cure philosophers of this tendency so that philosophical problems would simply go away.[89] Ordinary language philosophy insisted on the intersubjectivity of the standpoint of philosophy. It was the second way of doing linguistic philosophy that Wittgenstein introduced during his lifetime, and when it fell out of favor, analytic philosophy did not end because it did not have to show that metaphysics is meaninglessness.,

Philosophers could still use phenomenal appearances of meanings to describe and clarify concepts on the assumption that words acquired their meanings intersubjectively. This was a modest form of rational intuition, which analytic philosophers could use after abandoning the analytic-synthetic distinction, and so it might be called a faculty of *reflective intuition*. Since it could be used to analyze concepts in other fields, analytic philosophers had something special to offer them. They did not always agree about how to proceed. But they had a different method from science, and seeing it as continuous with science, they could travel under the banner of Quine's naturalized epistemology. For example, reflective intuition could be used to contrast the approach of traditional epistemology with naturalized epistemology. The former takes private perceptual phenomenal appearances as objects of intuition, uses them as evidence for beliefs about the natural world and, thus, is *internalistic*, whereas the latter explains perception as a public power of animals, uses its reliability (along with other cognitive faculties) to explain knowledge of the natural world, and, thus, is *externalistic*.

After the abandonment of linguistic philosophy, reflective intuition could still be used in the philosophy of language, and since reflective intuition could be used to clarify concepts in any field, analytic philosophers could divide up and serve as under-laborers in various branches of science, from physics and biology to psychology and social science. To be sure, since reflective intuition is, in practice, what reflective subjects use to see into other minds, it is the foundation of interpretationalist social science, which describes the spiritual world. But since analytic philosophy uses reflective intuition to clarify concepts, it has something to offer social science, for example, showing how interpretationalism is different from the methods used in natural science.[90] In psychology and neural science, as we have seen, reflective intuition is used to

---

[89] Wittgenstein's *private language argument* was a critique of traditional intuitionism. It showed that the meanings of words could not be the private phenomenal appearances to which they seem to refer because there is no way to show that one is mistaken in using them. But Wittgenstein did not completely reject intuitionism. He accepted direct realism and showed how rules of ordinary language games could be enforced intersubjectively.

[90] Alexander Rosenberg (2015).

distinguish consciousness, as the *hard problem* of mind for physicalism, from the easy problem of explaining how the brain works. It could also be used to distinguish the various positions that philosophers have taken in ethics, law, and political philosophy, on issues both normative and meta-ethical. Reflective intuition could even be used to do what analytic philosophers now call *metaphysics*, for example, by explaining metaphysical necessity as what holds in all possible worlds.[91] Analytic philosophers have even taken up the study of the history of Western philosophy, since reflective intuition can be used to analyze the positions defended without endorsing them.

Arguments in analytic philosophy clarifying concepts are usually clear, economical, and even elegant. This is useful and often illuminating. But intuitions about meanings are private, and since the standpoint of analytic philosophy is intersubjective, significant disputes are rarely settled. Instead, analytic philosophers wind up describing different intuitions about what to say. They can agree, for example, that beliefs about what morality requires have traditionally been defended in three basically different ways (by the principle of utility, the social contract, and as virtues valued in a community). But they cannot agree about which one is true. Indeed, they cannot even agree about how it might be shown that one or the other theory is true. And a lasting contribution of G. E. Moore to analytic philosophy is the belief that any attempt to explain goodness naturalistically commits the so-called *naturalistic fallacy*. It turns Hume's distinction between facts and values into a logical fallacy, and science uses the alleged impossibility of deriving an *ought* from as *is* to explain why it cannot determine which goals are good.

In the Anglo-American world, academic philosophy is considered the dumping ground of unanswered questions, and since analytic philosophy has only conceptual clarification to offer, analytic philosophers do not expect to answer them conclusively. But there is one conclusion on which analytic philosophers generally agree. They accept a decidedly deflationary version of the correspondence theory of truth: to say that a sentence is true is merely *to assert it* in the commonsense world. That is an implication of the intersubjective standpoint of analytic philosophy. Since analytic philosophy is a form of intuitionism that takes direct realism about perception for granted, it can reduce truth to the correspondence of language to Appearance. And this is a milestone on the path toward endarkenment because it rejects Reason. Though beings like us have a faculty of reflective intuition, we have no faculty that enables us to know Reality behind Appearance, so no one expects analytic philosophy to discover the True as correspondence to Reality, much less show how the Good is part of the True. Indeed, in feminist philosophy, the traditional focus of philosophy on knowing objective truth is sometimes dismissed as an artifact of a bias shared by its

---

[91] Since the standpoint of analytic philosophy is intersubjective, reflective intuition enabled Saul Kripke (1980) to introduce the modal concept of *metaphysical necessity* to analytic philosophy by showing how references of terms, such as names, could be *rigid designators* that pick out the same objects in space in all possible natural worlds. This was the foundation of Kripke's compelling refutation of the physicalist mind-brain identity theory mentioned in *Chapter 2*.

mostly male practitioners in the history of philosophy.

4 Continental Philosophy

Continental philosophy also rejected outright the possibility of Reason knowing Reality behind Appearance, but it did so with feeling. It began like analytic philosophy, with respect for the naturalism of science. Rejecting the historicism of German romanticism, Edmund Husserl (1859–1938) wanted to sidestep the ontological problems that had defeated the attempts of modern metaphysics to show how the nature of Reality behind Appearance provides a foundation for science. He intended to provide a foundation for science in objects of intuition, and by *bracketing* issues about Reality, he limited scientific inquiry to the description of Appearance. That is, he set aside all arguments about metaphysics, including Kant's attempt to show how Reason helps construct the phenomenal world. Husserl's method was to describe as carefully as possible phenomenal appearances. He called the foundation he hoped to provide *phenomenology,* and though it would abandon from the outset the possibility of discovering the True or the Good, it would use a description of how they appear as the foundation for science.

Seeing himself as a defender of science, Husserl's description of the human condition was even-tempered. But when Continental philosophers accepted phenomenology as a foundation for science, what they found was absurdity. There was no such thing as the Good. But neither was there any objective difference between what is good and what is bad, since science could not tell them what they ought to choose. As intuitionists, however, it seemed obvious that they have a free will, and so they found themselves in an absurd situation. They could choose goals freely, but there was no reason to choose any one goal from all the goals possible. Thus, Continental philosophers took up the challenge of understanding how to lead a life in a world in which there is no objective difference between good and evil. This was the puzzle about the human condition that existentialists addressed.

The absurdity of the human condition had been recognized much earlier by Søren Kierkegaard (1813-1855). Rejecting the absolute idealism by which Hegel reduced God to dialectical Reason, Kierkegaard embraced a leap of faith that he daringly advertised as rationally indefensible. As he explained in *Fear and Trembling,* his rendering of the famous Biblical story, no one can understand the kind of faith that led Abraham to follow God's command and prepare to sacrifice his own son, Isaac. But Kierkegaard called him a *knight of faith* because Abraham had the kind of faith that gave one an absolute relation to the Absolute. Faith did what Reason could not do.

In *Thus, Spoke Zarathustra*, Friedrich Nietzsche (1844-1900) makes the opposite claim with equal boldness. He announced the death of God, claiming that denizens of the natural world had killed him. This was to deny that there is any such thing as the Good, and Nietzsche would replace the attempt of Reason to know a transcendental foundation of goodness with the *will to power*. He saw humans as walking a tightrope from apes to superman (*Übermensch*), seeking a transformation of value that would ultimately justify human existence. Thus, he promised a naturalistic explanation of the meaning of life. And the meaning would be eternal since Nietzsche saw it as part of an eternally recurring cycle in the natural world.

The Continental philosophers who called themselves *existentialists* accepted Husserl's phenomenology as a description of what can be known about the natural world and tried to understand how life could have any meaning in it. In *Being and Time*, Martin Heidegger (1889-1976) described an object of intuition that he called *being in the world* (*Dasein*) to point to *our* existence as something more basic than substance and to insist that authenticity is more basic than choosing goals that are good and doing what is right. In *Being and Nothingness*, Jean-Paul Sartre (1905-1980) also explained existence in terms of the phenomenal subject. The object of intuition was being *in-itself*, and since the subject to which it was immediately present was *not* being in-itself, it was being *for itself*, that is, a being that knows its own existence only by denying that it is being *in-itself*. This nothingness is Sartre's phenomenal subject, and since nothing immediately present causes its choices, the for-itself has a free will. But since the in-itself does not determine what ought to exist, there is no objective difference between what is good and what is evil, and so the only possible way for a goal to be good is to choose some goal freely and continue to choose it. But if choosing a goal is what makes it good, it cannot guide our choice, and Sartre recognized that leading a life in this way is absurd. And he saw absurdity was a source of anxiety. But he insisted that leading one's life in recognition of this absurdity about the human condition is the authentic way to exist. This authenticity is the only meaning there is to life.

History had its own unsubtle way of denying that Reason knows Reality behind Appearance. From the 19th century to the early 20th century, there was progress, and it was possible to believe in the Enlightenment. But proof of its foolishness was provided by World War I, the Russian Revolution, World War II, and the Holocaust. Since then, waves of fashionable philosophical arguments on the Continent have embraced endarkenment more and more explicitly. They begin by denying that beings like us have a cognitive power that enables us to know the existence and nature of a Reality behind Appearance, and they end by claiming that it was a mistake to believe that there is any such thing as the Good or the True. This current of Continental philosophy can be seen as the evolution from the critical theory defended by the *Frankfurt School* to embodiments called variously *post-modernism, post-structuralism* (among Marxists), and *deconstructionism.*

The Frankfurt School began shortly after WWI defending Marxism and promoting the overthrow of capitalism. Marx had based his critique of capitalism on science. He was the scientist who had the motor of history. It was a class struggle caused by changes in the forces of production that proceeds from feudalism to capitalism and, finally, when the polarization and pauperization of the proletariat makes the injustice of capitalism behind its free-market ideology obvious, it leads to an overthrow of capitalism in favor of socialism and eventually becomes communism. This motor presupposes anger about unjustified inequalities, and since there is no objective difference between just and unjust, it depends on the instinctive anger found in social animals.[92] As we noticed, Marxists, believing that they were on the right side of history, exploited this instinctive anger to foment revolution. When Max Horkheimer (1895-1973) and Theodor Adorno (1903-1969) gained control of the Frankfurt School around 1930, they gave up Marx's claim to be doing science. They were not naturalists who used the empirical method to learn about capitalism. But they assumed that some infrastructure like the mode of production shapes culture in a way that makes it seem acceptable to people. It

---

[92] That is, the moral equality recognized by reflective subjects in spiritual organisms is just a rationalization of the bodily equality recognized by social animals. See footnote 79.

is called the *superstructure*, and this deformation of culture was called an *ideology* because its function was to deceive the reflective subjects who internalized it. This Marxist assumption was the foundation of the Frankfurt School's *critical theory*. Reflective subjects were dominated by ideology, and believing that the critique of culture would emancipate them from ideological domination, they hoped to change history. By arousing a visceral indignation about unexplained inequalities, they were using the same method that Marxists used to overthrow capitalism. But they were intuitionists, and without a science that explains how a motor of history determines the superstructure, the foundation of critical theory was the same as interpretationalist social science (and the intersubjective standpoint of analytic philosophy).

　　Ontological science explains how critical theorists can make a difference in history. Culture is how spiritual organisms share a plan that coordinates the behavior of its members in the pursuit of goals that are good for the whole, and since culture evolves by exchanges of arguments, arguments by critical theorists can change culture. But the standpoint of critical theory is inside culture, and since the currents flowing from the Enlightenment into Continental philosophy in the 20th century took intuitionism for granted, it assumes that nothing exists but Appearance. Critical theory is implicitly a form of idealism that reduces Reality to what is believed by reflective subjects sharing a culture. But it is different from absolute idealism because it denies that the coherence theory of truth can discover the Good and the True. Critical theorists do not even try to show that there is an objective difference between true and false and between good and bad. And since they assume that culture is an ideology with a cause that cannot be known by science, they are historicists who believe that truth is just what members of a spiritual organism at their point in history say is true.

　　Not surprisingly, the free-market values that Marxists saw as enabling capitalists to dominate workers was one of the first targets of the Frankfurt School. But workers had not risen up and overthrown capitalism, and critical theorists gave up Marx's motor of history. Instead of promoting a socialist revolution, they intended to free people from ideological domination by criticizing the culture caused by capitalist progress in producing commodities as an ideology. Horkheimer and Adorno (1947) traced this ideology to the Enlightenment, arguing that the belief in Reason is inherently self-destructive. For example, turning people into consumers of efficiently produced commodities narrowed their interests and made them robotic. And advances in communications technology deprived people of individuality by imposing a uniform mass culture on them. Horkheimer and Adorno (1947) even attributed the rise of Hitler and the holocaust to Enlightenment belief in Reason. With no way to explain the nature of the Good, their critiques were necessarily negative.

Though the Frankfurt School was founded on the assumption that capitalism was the cause of ideological domination, it was replaced by the assumption that science cannot know how the cultural superstructure depends on infrastructure. This was the foundation on which Jürgen Habermas, a later member of the Frankfurt School, argued for preserving the flavor of the Enlightenment as the p*ublic sphere*, a free and open discussion among equals in which *communicative reason* uses a *consensus theory of truth* to discover something akin to an objective difference between true and false and good and bad. He described the public sphere as what replaced the *representational culture* by which one class dominated another during the feudal period before the Enlightenment, and believing that the rise of mass media, the welfare state, and the like was causing new ideologies, he expected critical theory to emancipate people by restoring the public sphere.

Habermas' optimism about open discourse leading to agreement has been replaced in Continental philosophy by the belief that all discourse is the domination of one group by another. Analyzing discourse in terms of signs that carry meanings, Jacques Derrida called his critique of ideology *deconstruction*. Michel Foucault's analysis of discourse was meant to show how expressions have meanings that give power to one group over another in a social order. *Post-modernism* was the term that Jean-François Lyotard used to characterize his rejection of all *meta-narratives* such as the Enlightenment, that assume there is an objective truth. Discourse is immediately present to naïve realists, and since that is all that is left of metaphysics in the post-modern era, Continental philosophers have little choice but to offer a critique of ideology that claims to emancipate reflective subjects from domination.

By claiming to unmask ideological deception, however, critical theorists are following the Marxist playbook. They are arousing visceral indignation about unexplained unequal treatment. Even though post-modernists deny that science can know that class struggle or any other cause is the motor of history, they insist that they are defending classes of victims from oppression by powerful social interests. They claim to know their way around the ideological jungle, but since they deny the objectivity of goodness, they cannot say what should replace it. They do not aspire to the intellectual coherence that absolute idealists believe discovers the True. Their arguments are not falsifiable like theories in science. And by scorning the clarity of argument in analytic philosophy,[93] they embody the deception that they attribute to all discourse. Instead of making arguments that are meant to stand up to scrutiny, they do word dances that seem like wallowing in intellectual decadence. Post-modernism is non-Rational romanticism minus the transcendental ambition of being related to Reality. It is relativism, giddy with the belief that there is no such thing as the True or the Good. And it is a sophistry, arousing instinctive feelings of righteous anger.

In sum, after the bankruptcy of intuitionistic metaphysics and Husserl's retreat to phenomenology, existentialists struggled with the absurdity of human life in a world where everything is permitted. After World War II, when critical theory became post-modernism, Continental philosophy spread to America, where universities began teaching their students to make nearly incoherent expressions of anger about any sign of unexplained unequal treatment on the unsupported assumption that victimization of some kind or other was the unavoidable cost of using language to coordinate behavior in pursuit of shared goals.

5   Popular Culture in the 21st Century

Intuitionistic metaphysics became the confidence in Reason celebrated popularly as the Enlightenment, and besides science and an economic system based on liberal political institutions, what Reason left behind when it rebelled against its intuitionistic upbringing was a momentum that propelled intuitionistic philosophy along various currents until it petered out as

---

[93] Except for Richard Rorty, the pragmatist famous for defending postmodernism in America.

endarkenment. In the 19th century, Romanticism replaced the belief that Reason knows Reality behind Appearance with the belief that intense feelings (or will) puts us in touch with something that transcends Appearance, while idealist metaphysics tried to show that an object of rational intuition could explain everything in Appearance coherently, like a first cause. But as scientific evidence for materialism accumulated, what idealist metaphysicians offered were ontological explanations of everything found in Appearance that seemed increasingly like fairytales. In the 20th century, when metaphysics had been abandoned by most philosophers, it was no longer credible to claim that Reason knows the True, much less the Good. Though analytic philosophers were sympathetic with science, they recognized that by saying that science is true, they were merely asserting it. And in the vanishing shadow of metaphysical aspirations, this deflationary view of truth could be seen as implying relativism about facts and values: the true was ultimately just what reflective subjects believe; the good was just what they value; beauty was in the eye of the beholder.[94]

Endarkenment is not just the evolution of spiritual organisms falling back from the metaphysical linguistic level to the psychological level because it returns to the earlier stage, knowing what is missing. Culture at the psychological level evolves by pragmatic selection because exchanges of arguments come to an end when an agreement is reached about how to attain shared goals. Even beliefs about situations are accepted as true when they work. Though the standard of *what works* presupposes that reflective subjects agree about which goals are good, American pragmatists were optimistic about pragmatism because they assumed everyone shares the same basic goals. But now, that assumption seems naïve. Basic goals are in dispute, and it is widely assumed that argument cannot resolve them. The morality of abortion is one such dispute. But it is just an example of others, including some on which the issue about abortion depends, such as the nature of life, the nature of the good, the nature of morality, and the meaning of life. No help can come from science. Biologists cannot even explain the origin of life. Physicists have given up hope of explaining what really exists in a way that

---

[94] This part of endarkenment has been a calamity for the fine arts in the 20th century. See Charles Murray (2003, Chapter 21).

can be understood in naturalistic imagination. And though scientists have a method that enables them to agree about what to believe, they do not include agreement about an objective difference between good and bad, right and wrong, just and unjust. Hence, disputes about basic issues threaten to turn post-modern relativism into nihilism.

Cultural evolution by Rational selection was once the job of intellectuals. But since disillusionment has led them to abandon Reason, they now admit that basic disputes cannot be resolved by argument. Now, they reside mainly in universities, and bearing sad tidings about the foolishness of believing in Reason, they teach endarkenment, even if they are reluctant. Well into the 20th century, the goal of traditional universities was still to give students a liberal education. But without belief in Reason, universities struggle even to explain what that goal was. To be sure, they can tell their students about the origin of a liberal education in Medieval universities, where it included a canon of historical texts that were meant to bring a new generation up to speed in the Rational pursuit of Truth so that they could make independent judgments on basic issues. But without the belief in Reason, there is no expectation that argument will ever settle basic disputes and, thus, no such project to take up.

To be sure, universities teach science, and scientists reach agreement about what to believe. But science is based on physics, and since its method is to confirm laws of nature by predictions of measurements, the truth it discovers is not correspondence to Reality. It is pragmatic truth because it is merely what works in attaining a common goal. Physics is baffled by what it has found at the bottom, while the rest of science is divided into specialized fields that do not fit together. Moreover, science is now seen as an endless project in which progress always turns up another intractable puzzle. Philosophers and historians of science commonly assume that anomalies will always turn up and that prevailing paradigms will always be overthrown in subsequent scientific revolutions. Curious students happily learn enough to join that noble project. But they are not given a liberal education.

Since there is no canon defining a liberal education, universities no longer require students to learn the intellectual history of Western civilization. Instead, professors teach multiculturalism, and they betray no embarrassment about their inability to explain why only Western culture holds that all cultures are equally valuable. Though they may still give lip service to the history of the Rational pursuit of Truth when they welcome freshmen or congratulate graduating seniors, they have little of it to offer in between. Students are sometimes still encouraged to learn about philosophy. But it is defended mainly as training in critical thinking, and there is little point in learning to think critically when emotional appeals are all that really matter. In Medieval universities, students were required to master rigorous disputations about basic issues. But students cannot be motivated to take arguments seriously when the underlying lesson is that, in the end, no argument can resolve basic disputes. Hence the value of a university education is increasingly advertised as training for jobs with a higher income, and for the best students—and students enrolled at prestigious universities—it offers membership in an elite ruling class. Professors often know enough about history to feel nostalgic thinking about the Enlightenment, and they may try to defend it.[95] But as products of higher education, they know that the belief in Reason was a mistake, so they settle for defending an incomplete scientific explanation based on physics and passing liberal values onto students that they do not attempt to justify.

Endarkenment has spread from universities to popular culture. These days, a reliable test of having a higher education is believing that knowledge of the True is sophomoric. Though there are still theists who believe that there is an Absolute Truth, most academics are naturalists who take religion seriously only as a puzzling human phenomenon to be studied in social science. Students who still admit to believing in a transcendent God are forced to admit that their belief depends on faith, not Reason. Since scientists themselves deny that science can discover a real difference between good and evil, the Good is just what is believed to be good. Students graduate with the belief that argument has been replaced by rhetoric and sophistry, and thus, they know that to persuade others to agree with them about what is good, they might as well manipulate others, appeal to their emotions, deceive them, or use any other means, including bribery and coercion, if that is what works. Politicians no longer make arguments, and journalists no longer expect them

---

[95] Most recently, Pinker (2018) musters an impressive array of statistics to prove there has been progress since the Enlightenment. But he fails to recognize its origin and nature.

to. Indeed, arguments are called *conversations*, premises are called *talking points*, and explanations are called *narratives*. What counts is who wins, not who has the better argument, and so journalists see assessing the soundness of arguments as *carrying water* for one side or the other.

The sense that the foundation of Western culture is slipping way is spreading. The salons and public forums where expressions of diverse viewpoints were expected to promote progress have vanished, and recently, some observers are looking for a way to revive the Enlightenment.[96] But endarkenment is spreading to the *hoi polloi*, and though it is not clear how far it will go, its direction can be seen in the growing political polarization. Anger about unequal treatment that, unlike age and gender, has no obvious explanation is an instinct in many animals, and instinctive indignation about victims of oppression is easily aroused in those who take the moral equality of everyone for granted. Critical theory is aimed at emancipation, and so activists can use it to paint their opponents, whatever they say, as defending an ideology that enables a more powerful class to dominate another class. Since reasoning cannot settle disputes about what is good in a world where there is no such thing as the Good, political activists see the arguments of their opponents as supporting oppressors, and so those arguments can be dismissed without hearing, and their proponents can be vilified. Bullying, political correctness, and cancel-culture replace the only way of settling disagreements amicably ever discovered.

A recent example in America is critical race theory. Critical theorists cannot claim credit for the emancipation of women and gay people because the removal of restrictions on them was a contribution of Enlightenment values. But they can point to unequal racial outcomes for blacks in America. It is evident in all the usual measures of success, such as education, income, and representation in the most demanding professions. And so, critical theorists can claim to be defending minority races from oppression. They do not point to unequal obstacles, such as Jim Crow institutions, that we know how to correct. Indeed, they do not consider what science has to say about racial differences because they do not believe in objective truth. They explain science as just another ideology found in discourse. Instead, they attribute the

---

[96] For example, see Shapiro (2019) and Goldberg (2019).

racial disparity to ideological domination. They call this ideology *systemic racism*. For example, the *New York Times* recently promoted the *1619 Project*, which claims that the American system is based on racism. Slaves were first imported in 1619, and it holds that all the other historical events since then, including the war of independence, the constitution of a government based on Enlightenment principles, and even the Civil War that freed the slaves in American, are a cultural deception that enables whites to dominate blacks. This ideological domination is called *white privilege*, and those who do not admit that the racial disparity is caused by whites having a special privilege are called *racists*. Or, if they are white, they are denounced as *white supremacists*.

Critical race theory has spread from its academic home in departments of social science and humanities to popular culture. Thanks to schools of education and its Internet appeal to teachers, the curriculum in many K-12 schools defend the critique of systemic racism under the banner of *diversity, equity, and inclusion*. It was given a boost by the nearly universal condemnation of the police killing of George Floyd in 2020, the rise of the *Black Lives Matter* movement, and the many months of "mostly peaceful" demonstrations in its defense. When those who deny that American is systemically racist offer other explanations of racial disparity, their arguments are considered *hate speech,* and political activists inspired by critical race theory insist that they be banned. Nor is this an idle threat. *Twitter, YouTube, Facebook, Google,* and other social media have publicly announced their policy of censoring arguments that contradict *authoritative information,* and on search engines, they shadow-ban links to websites that do not conform to their policies. But there is no censorship of critical race theory. On the contrary, it is taught to employees in a wide variety of capitalist corporations, and its propagation in departments of government and the military became so widespread that it was banned as racially divisive in 2020. When the presidential election that year put the opposite political movement in power, the new president declared that correcting systemic racism was the overriding whole-of-government goal of his administration. He called that goal *equity*, and though he did not bother to define it, it is a recently coined term that is widely understood as meaning equality of outcome of identity groups, defined by race, sex, sexual orientation, gender identification, and the like.

Defenders of Enlightenment principles see this political movement as an attack on the Constitution that would put aside rights guaranteed to citizens. Besides abrogating freedom of speech, the use of governmental power to bring about *equity*, that is, equality of outcome for races (and other identity groups), is bound to violate the principle of the equality of opportunity for individuals, if only by eliminating meritocratic institutions based on individuals competing freely for rewards of excellence, such as tests measuring what students have learned and hiring employees by their qualifications. But defenders of Enlightenment principles risk being denounced as racists. And dissenters have little hope of public support ns a county where journalists have given up the job of reporting what happens objectively because they believe that they contribute more to society by promoting a narrative that they believe (or tell themselves) will lead people to do what they and others in the elite ruling class see as required by the national interest.

The use of critical race theory to justify governmental intervention in the lives of individuals is only one way that endarkenment is a menace to remnants of Enlightenment. It might even cause Western civilization to disintegrate into chaos. But since activists are bound to exploit it, the most likely long-term outcome of this era is collectivism. Since psychological-level spiritual organisms have a class structure, the default government without the liberal political institutions from the Enlightenment is autocracy of some kind, and using the high-tech media spawned by scientific progress, a political ideology can replace religion as its justification. Digital communications technology makes it easy to censor dissenting arguments as "misinformation" and muddy the waters of mass discourse by introducing Orwellian "newspeak." Arguments defending the pursuit of truth can be silenced by bullying, defamation, job loss, and violence in the street. And potential dissidents can be nudged into compliance early in their lives by the use of mass data and artificial intelligence to award social credits and demerits. Democracy by mob rule quickly becomes autocracy, and autocracy with digital technology becomes the totalitarianism that Orwell warned us about in *1984*. The kind of collectivism that endarkenment has in store for the West could be a state as powerful and stable as the one that the Communist Party is currently installing in China.

But that is not inevitable. If the level of coherence in Western culture has not already fallen too low, this threat can be countered by Reason resolving its identity crisis.

PART THREE: REASON

This argument began by reducing physical science to ontology. It solved the puzzles confronting modern physics by showing how its laws correspond to regularities generated by interactions of space and matter, and since spatio-materialism describes the essential natures of the substances constituting the natural world, it showed how science can know Reality. But it was not obvious that Volume I was showing how Reason knows Reality because it began with physical science and used empirical ontology to return physics to pre-Socratic philosophy and the discovery that substance is the first cause. This preceded the first argument intended to show that Reason is a cognitive power that can know Reality behind Appearance, and looking back to ancient Greece, we can see that the path that the argument of this trilogy has taken is a late development in the biography of Reason. It is, in effect, a story about how Reason, thinking of itself as empirical science, solved the puzzles of modern physics and used ontology to bridge the mathematical gap between quantum and gravitational physics. The unification of physics revealed that matter has a holistic power that is expressed as a kind of efficient cause that is not recognized by physics, and since geometrical efficient causes can impose geometrical constraints on the collective effects of physical causes, the recognition of geometrical action solved all the puzzles that have long stymied the specialized sciences. Basing science on ontology, rather than physics, is what unified the specialized sciences, and since that revealed that reflective subjects like us eventually come to exist on all suitable planets in the universe, it seemed to fulfill the original goal of science: explaining every kind of regularity found in the study of nature.

Ontological science was not, however, a complete explanation of what is found in the natural world because it did not explain the unprecedented powers acquired by Western civilization. Though the essential nature of psychological-level spiritual organisms explained the rise of civilization, it seemed that Western civilization might be invulnerable to the causes that historians had used to explain the fall of civilizations. Indeed, optimists saw the fall of the Soviet Union as the end of history, and though they were criticized by pessimists who expected a clash of civilizations, recent history is clearly unfolding in a way that ontological science did not predict. Furthermore, even the existence of a science based on ontology that could show that beings like us inevitably come to exist was puzzling. Physics was one of the unprecedented powers acquired by the West after the Enlightenment, and its reduction to ontology showed the specialized sciences, inspired by its success, how to explain everything that had been found in the study of nature. But attaining the goal of science requires a uniquely complete cognitive power, and though ontological science explained the evolution of reflective subjects as members of psychological-level spiritual organisms, it did not explain the origin of ontological science itself. At the beginning of this argument, physical science did not seem to be Reason, and ontological science still did not know that it is Reason. Reason had yet to resolve its identity crisis.

By the time of the Enlightenment, there were accounts of other civilizations on Earth, and members of Western spiritual organisms commonly believed in the superiority of their civilization. As Volume III shows, ontological science agrees with them in the end, and that is how Reason resolves its identity crisis.

Though Christians assumed that the superiority of Western civilization came from knowledge of God, ontological scientists are naturalists, and they trace it to the intuitionistic metaphysical arguments on which Christian theology is founded. Nothing like the philosophy of Western civilization is found in other civilizations on Earth. It is the exchange of arguments about the power of Reason to know Reality behind Appearance, and seeing philosophy as the study of Appearance, ontological science was able to solve the puzzle about its own existence. Ontological scientists are conscious reflective subjects, and given that the natural world is constituted by space and matter, they could explain how consciousness is part of the natural world. This explanation exposed an illusion inherent in consciousness, and that enabled them to explain Western civilization as the beginning of a third stage of spiritual evolution. Philosophy was the study of Appearance, and this stage of evolution is called metaphysical because metaphysical arguments have a higher level of linguistic organization than psychological sentences. Their exchange caused culture to evolve by Rational selection instead of pragmatic selection.

Officially, the argument of Naturalistic Reason is the prediction of an imminent scientific revolution on Earth. But it has also been portrayed as the final part of a biography of Reason that holds on every suitable planet. Reason is born at the beginning of the metaphysical stage of spiritual evolution. It grows up as intuitionistic metaphysics, and its identity crisis begins when it rebels against its intuitionistic family, sides with science, and accepts naturalism. But it takes a priori mathematics with it, and this treasure from intuitionistic metaphysics makes Reason astonishingly successful in discovering laws of physics. Though mathematics enables physics to use the empirical method to learn about the natural world, it causes problems to accumulate that cannot be solved until physics gives up empirical lawism in favor of empirical ontology. When it reduces the laws of physics to spatio-materialism, physical science turns into ontological science, and by tracing its origin to the civilization from which it evolves, it discovers its intuitionistic ancestry and recognizes its true identity as Reason. That is how science becomes naturalistic Reason.

On Earth, Reason began in ancient Greece, and if this argument is sound, physical science discovers its identity as Reason when it becomes ontological science, traces its origin to philosophy, and explains the history of Western civilization as the beginning of the metaphysical stage of spiritual evolution. Naturalistic Reason is the perfect cognitive power that philosophers have long called wisdom, and since it knows its own nature, it can explain its functions. Chapters 10 through 12 show how theoretical, practical, and aesthetic Reason attain their respective transcendental goals: knowing the True, the Good, and the Beautiful. But the biography of Reason is just a way of summing up the prediction of a scientific revolution, and since that is an event that must stand out in history, the question is whether naturalistic Reason will prevail now.

CHAPTER 9
WILL REASON PREVAIL NOW?

If this argument is mistaken in some basic way, it is not sound, and, clearly, Reason will not ever prevail. As an empirical argument, it can be falsified by showing that its conclusions are somehow incompatible with what is found in the natural world. I know of no such conflict. But I could be mistaken, and if someone can show how a conclusion cannot be reconciled with what is found in the natural world, this prediction of an imminent scientific revolution will not be justified. These volumes will have been a wild goose chase, and I will have to apologize for wasting your time.

The argument of this trilogy infers spatio-material ontological mechanisms as the best explanation of regularities about change that have been found by physics, the study of nature, and the study of Appearance. But I do not claim that the ontological mechanisms described here are the best way that interactions of space and matter can explain all of them. It would not be surprising if some modifications of them were a better explanation of what is found in the world. In many fields, their details have been left to be worked out by research projects, and those discoveries will probably refine these ontological mechanisms. That is the kind of progress that is expected in science.

But this argument is not sound if an empirical argument or research project shows that there is a regularity found in the natural world that cannot be explained by ontological mechanisms like these, which are based on the discovery that space is a substance that interacts with matter. As we have seen, interactions of space and matter explain the truth of mathematics as correspondence to the natural world, reveal that matter has a holistic power that is expressed as geometrical efficient causes, and show that an intrinsic phenomenal property of matter helping constitute the geometrical action of mammalian brains is how consciousness is part of the natural world. If any of these basic conclusions is falsified, Naturalistic Reason is not a sound argument, and I will be apologizing for wasting your time.

On the other hand, if the argument in these three volumes is sound and none of its basic predictions can be falsified, naturalistic Reason will prevail because it entails a prediction of its own evolution on Earth. In the spatio-material world, it is inevitable that a series of stages in the evolution of life on suitable planets everywhere leads to a metaphysical stage of spiritual evolution during which all the puzzles of physics, science, and philosophy are solved by the discovery that space is a substance that interacts with matter. If naturalistic metaphysics is true, it is inevitable that Reason will prevail.

The inevitability of naturalistic Reason does not mean, however, that now is the time that it will prevail on Earth. Since the course of evolution is what happens in the long run, its progress can be interrupted by external causes, like the asteroid hitting Earth that ended the age of dinosaurs. It could also be delayed by Earth-based causes, such as an environmental disaster, a nuclear war that returns humans to the stone age, or, perhaps, a pandemic that makes humans extinct. But unless it made Earth unsuitable for the evolution of life, such a catastrophe would not prevent the evolution of naturalistic Reason because spiritual organisms would eventually evolve and go through stages caused by levels of linguistic organization that lead inevitably to the metaphysical stage. Evolution in the direction of maximum functional power is progressive, so naturalistic Reason will eventually prevail.

Absent such a catastrophe, the evolution of naturalistic Reason seems imminent. If this argument is sound, the publication of Naturalistic Reason can be expected to lead to the scientific revolution that it predicts. Physical science will become ontological science, and since that will resolve Reason's identity crisis, science will become Reason. The track record of science has earned it the reputation of being our most reliable way of knowing about the natural world, and so this argument for naturalistic Reason is likely to cause the scientific revolution that it predicts. At its birth in the Enlightenment, the goal of science was to explain the natural world as completely as intuitionistic metaphysicians had promised that Reason would explain it, and after a series of scientific revolutions, this will be just another revolution. The only difference is that this one will complete its mission.

This is how optimists would expect the publication of Naturalistic Reason to be welcomed. But Reason may not prevail now because it can also be delayed by contingent historical conditions inimical to its evolution. This explanation of Western civilization as the metaphysical stage of evolution explains physical science is how Reason understands itself after rebelling against its intuitionistic parents, and since physics is based on intuitionistic naturalism, it cripples the other branches of science and leads to disillusionment about Reason. But this argument also predicts an era of endarkenment. When Reason became physical science, it left behind various currents in philosophy, and one of them became post-modernism in Continental philosophy. It sees the failure of intuitionistic metaphysics as showing that there is no such thing as the True of the Good. It has been popularized as relativism, the belief that there is no objective difference true and false or good and bad, and thus, it has ushered in an era of endarkenment on Earth. A decline from the metaphysical stage of spiritual evolution has begun, and since Western civilization is returning to the psychological stage of spiritual evolution without a shared religion, it will have no way to settle disputes about which goals to pursue. The widespread belief that might makes right could be disastrous, and though it would be prevented, if Reason prevailed now, the political forces of endarkenment may keep this argument from getting a fair hearing.

The era of endarkenment is settling in more quickly than even the most pessimistic observers of the globalization of Western culture could have predicted a few decades ago. To be sure, there are holdouts against endarkenment. Theists still believe that the difference between good and evil is real, and scientists may give naturalistic Reason a hearing because they and their allies in analytic philosophy believe in the empirical method. But in contemporary America, the prospects for naturalistic Reason can seem dismal.

1   Endarkenment and Censorship

Endarkenment can take many forms, but as we have seen, it is currently embodied in America most conspicuously as critical race theory. It points to the disparity of outcomes for different races, and attributing it to systemic racism, it holds that the only way to overcome this ideological domination is by the use of governmental power to bring about *equity*, that is, an equality of outcome of all identity groups, defined not only by race but also by sex, sexual orientation, gender identification, and the like. But the most blatant is the disparity by race, and government intervention in people's lives to correct it means sacrificing equal treatment for individuals and reward for merit. This is to replace the Enlightenment principle that everyone has a right to as much liberty as compatible with the same liberty for all with the principle that people should be treated differently by race. It is hard to imagine a more direct rejection of Enlightenment respect for the autonomy of Rational individuals who can be trusted to act morally. This was once the American creed, but the insistence that that equal outcomes for identity groups has a higher priority than it has the full support of most news media, most institutions of higher education, most teachers in K-12 schools, Hollywood, popular culture generally, and most of the largest corporations, including high-tech social media. Since critical theorists do not believe that there is an objective difference between true and false, they deny that science has anything relevant to say about systemic racism, and since they also deny that there is a real difference between good and bad, they have no way to show that equity is better than equality. But their critique of American culture is politically correct, and the Woke defend it on the individual scale by bullying and cancel-culture. They denounce those who speak out in defense of classical liberal values from the Enlightenment as racists.

In such an era of endarkenment, the argument for naturalistic Reason will be inflammatory because it implies that Western civilization is superior to other civilizations. Explaining the course of evolution as progress, it explains the West as the beginning of a metaphysical stage that follows the psychological stage represented by them. Recognizing the superiority of one civilization over others on Earth flies in the face of multiculturalism. It began in the early 20th-century when anthropologists held that relativism about the true and the good is the best way for Western scientists to understand other cultures. But this method of seeing other cultures from inside has become the popular belief that all cultures have equal value. In the muddied waters of popular culture, the suggestion that Western civilization is the beginning of a third stage of spiritual evolution will be a lightning rod in this storm of endarkenment, grounding bolts of denunciation of naturalistic Reason as *white nationalism*, and all references to it. The Woke make no distinction between culture and race, and critical race theorists will portray naturalistic Reason as *white nationalism*. Its defense will be considered *hate speech*, social media will denounce this argument, and it may even be censored. That is the pathway to a collectivist revolution like those that occurred in Russia and China in the past century.

This dismal picture of the reception for naturalistic Reason is a cartoon depicting what may come of the political polarization in America. But for the record, the defense of naturalistic Reason has nothing to do with race. What made ancient Greece the beginning of the metaphysical stage has more to do with the decentralized political power of city-states on the Aegean Sea than race. Metaphysics is just a level of linguistic organization in culture. What distinguishes Western civilization from other civilizations is just the kind of arguments exchanged among its members. Reflective subjects are mammals with the same basic brain structure, and naturalistic Reason implies that as members of spiritual organisms who can see into one another's minds, they are all equally entitled to moral rights and equally subject to moral duties in dealing with others, regardless of race, culture, or any other identity group.

It does not matter, however, that the attack on naturalistic Reason as racist is false. What distinguishes the era of endarkenment from spiritual organisms at the psychological stage is the general acceptance of relativism, and it is taken for granted that argument cannot settle basic disputes about facts and values. Since there is no objective difference between true and false or good and evil, all that matters to political activists is giving government enough power to bring about the goals that they believe in. Relativists will neither read these volumes nor listen to the argument they contain, and since members of a group tend to believe whatever other group members believe, gut-level feelings about which goals are good will lead relativists to behave like a mob in which no one takes personal responsibility for what they do. They will simply go along with others in the group, and in the era of the Internet and social media, political activists can be a mob in which no one doubts that they are doing what justice demands. Though they will use high-tech means, they will have the courage of a lynch mob in seeing that justice is done. Nor can they be blamed if they do evil. They are misled by a culture afflicted with the confusion and irrationality of an era of endarkenment. Ontological scientists will recognize that they have good intentions.

In sum, the argument for naturalistic Reason is that it is empirically True, in the sense of corresponding to Reality, and truth is not relevant in an era when it is generally assumed that there is no such thing as the True. Naturalistic Reason is not likely to be given a hearing in an era of endarkenment. Visceral indignation about unequal treatment that does not seem justified is a powerful weapon, and all that matters to political activists who are relativists is empowering the government to bring about what they know in their gut is good for the whole. They are not likely to be deterred by individuals trying to protect their right to freedom of speech and other Enlightenment principles that respect their moral autonomy.

2 Theism and Sympathy

Critical race theory may be a passing phase that passes when parents oppose teaching it to their children in public schools. But it arises from endarkenment, and whatever form it takes, it leads to collectivism because governmental power is the weapon that enables political activists to attain their ends. However, the roots of endarkenment may not yet be deep enough for activists to keep the argument for naturalistic Reason from being heard, and there is a least one group that can be expected to urge giving it a hearing.

Though naturalists have forced Christians and orthodox Jews to admit that their belief in God is based only on faith, theists believe that there is an absolute truth about what is good. Though they are almost alone in this belief, it is essential to their understanding of the meaning of life, and though they are supernaturalists, they may be curious about a naturalistic argument that claims to show that it is possible to know the Good as part of the True. Indeed, many contemporary theologians are less interested in defending the existence of a being that exists outside space and time than they are in understanding what it means to believe in God in a natural world where regularities can be explained scientifically. They will be curious about how naturalists might explain the nature of the Good.

In naturalistic metaphysics, goodness is explained by the essential nature of life, and since life on the fourth floor of the edifice of life has a spiritual nature, theists will learn how the commandments of the Old and New Testament could have a naturalistic justification. To members of spiritual organisms at the psychological level, following the rules of morality matter because their existence as beings who share a spiritual life depends on it. And since members of spiritual organisms at the metaphysical level believe they have a free will, they take responsibility for doing what they know is good. Moreover, this explanation of their spiritual nature justifies their belief that goals beyond self-interest are good. Theists in the Judeo-Christian tradition will be intrigued by how far naturalistic Reason goes toward explaining the meaning of life as they understand it.

However, this naturalistic vindication of their belief in a real difference between good and evil will hardly turn theists into defenders of naturalistic Reason. It is the prediction of a scientific revolution caused by a discovery about the nature of space that has yet to occur, and theists have no stake in how issues in naturalistic ontology are settled. On the contrary, the nature of what really exists in the spatio-material world may be a bridge too far for ordinary Christians, if not for all orthodox Jews, since it denies personal immortality.

Still, the sympathy that theists feel for naturalists defending a real difference between good and evil may lead them to help give this argument a hearing, and they will not be deterred by endarkenment because they are used to being derided by naturalists in the mainstream media. By the same token, however, their support will not count for much among naturalists. If theists insisted that naturalistic Reason be given a public hearing, most naturalists would ignore them because they see belief in God as unscientific. They have been carefully taught in institutions of higher education that the cause of religious beliefs is an unfortunate and mysterious tendency of humans to accept beliefs that are plainly false, and so they tend to look down on evangelical Christians as ignorant people clinging to their guns and the bible. Hence, support for naturalistic Reason from theists cannot be expected to precipitate the predicted scientific revolution.

3 Physics and Heresy

There is another quarter in American culture whose support would ensure that naturalistic Reason receives a fair hearing in popular culture. As the basic branch, physics is at the top of the pecking order in science, commanding billions of dollars from governments in support of its research, such as CERN, Fermilab, the Hubble telescope, and the International Space Station. The political forces of endarkenment probably cannot silence physicists, and if they were convinced by what naturalistic Reason has to say about the basic branch of science, there would be a revolution in physics, and it would initiate the predicted revolution in science. But to have this support, there is another kind of barrier naturalistic Reason must overcome.

Physicists cooperate in the pursuit of the goal of understanding the basic nature of the natural world. They are members of a most prestigious professional association, and supported by universities and research institutions, they are so busy settling disputes about what to believe that they have no time to waste considering arguments that contradict foundational beliefs. Outsiders who attack beliefs that physicists take for granted are routinely dismissed as cranks, if not kooks, and when arguments that contradict basic assumptions in physics are made by members of their group, there are ways of excommunicating them—along with potential members who show signs of heresy, such as graduate students. All professional associations post sentries in supporting institutions, such as publishing houses and professional conferences, to keep cranks out. This is a formidable barrier to airing arguments that contradict orthodoxy because members of professional associations admire one another for making the same mistakes. And members cannot be blamed for censoring efforts of outsiders to correct them because earning the respect and admiration of other members is necessarily a personal goal of those cooperating in the pursuit of common goals. Professionals are hesitant to risk their standing in the group with which they identify.

When arguments challenging mistaken assumptions are sound, what is protected in this way is clearly an ideology, and so the excluded views are properly labeled *heresy*. In ontological science, the barrier to heresy is called the *ideological mechanism* because it puts the brakes on cultural evolution by judgmental selection. It constrains how culture evolves by making it seem that there are no arguments against mistaken assumptions. Religions and governments have a long history of punishing heresy to protect their doctrines, and when false beliefs are protected to deceive people, they are an ideology. But the ideological mechanism should not be confused with *ideological domination*. That is just a way that critical theorists portray parts of culture from inside a spiritual organism to arouse instinctive anger at unequal treatment with the goal of emancipating victims of oppression. The ideological mechanism, by contrast, is a scientific explanation of the suppression of heresy. It shows how a constraint on the reproductive mechanism embodied in the spiritual BGS of a group protects the false beliefs that the members share.

Since physics is the most prestigious branch of science, it is able to oppose the forces of endarkenment. But by the same token, it is the branch most well protected by the ideological mechanism, and naturalistic Reason is clearly heresy in physics because if its defense is sound, what it corrects are basic beliefs in physics. For example, Einsteinian physicists are confident that they have shown that Newtonian absolute space and time must be replaced by spacetime, while empirical ontology assumes that the natural world is constituted by a spatial substance that endures through time interacting with matter. And physicists are sure that robust composite bodies can be explained by physical causes, while empirical ontology claims that the geometrical structures of composite bodies impose geometrical constraints on what happens by physical causes.

Naturalistic Reason is even more of a heresy in physics because it holds that there is a more basic branch of science than physics. But it challenges such a basic assumption of physics that physicists will not be able to take it seriously. Naturalistic Reason claims to solve the intractable puzzles of modern physics by showing that the laws of physics correspond to interactions of substances that can be understood in naturalistic imagination. But physicists have long tried to find ways of interpreting the laws of physics that show how they correspond to the natural world as we ordinarily understand it, and what they mean by the *puzzles* of modern physics is that no such interpretation of them can be found. Defenders of naturalistic Reason will be seen as so uninformed that they are fools. The goal of physics is to find the simplest mathematically formulated laws of nature that cover the widest range of basic phenomena whose precise predictions can be confirmed by careful measurements, and so a mastery of highly abstract and esoteric mathematics is a condition of membership in the community of physicists. Thus, the suggestion that the regularities described by laws of modern physics can be explained by ontological mechanisms that can be understood in naturalistic imagination will seem like ignorance of the role of mathematics in physics. Theoretical physicists know that mathematics is the key to unlocking the secrets of nature because their labor is mainly deriving equations entailing predictions of quantities that can be measured. And experimental physicists will take offense at the suggestion that confirming predictions is not what the basic branch of science is all about because they rightly pride themselves as being among the most competent and creative engineers alive today.

This is to misinterpret the recommendation that physics consider replacing empirical lawism with empirical ontology as the offer of an interpretation of the laws of modern physics that can be understood in naturalistic imagination. And reinforcement of this view will come when physicists hear that naturalistic Reason proposes to overcome the disparity between quantum and gravitational physics by showing how the equations used to formulate both laws describe interactions of the same two kinds of substances. To physicists, the disparity is so obviously mathematical that the claim that it can be solved by describing an ontological mechanism that can be understood in naturalistic imagination will seem like proof of how wildly off base its proponents are.

In sum, seeing the argument for naturalistic Reason as based on an interpretation of the laws of physics, physicists will see its defenders as cranks whose lack of understanding of mathematics leads them to claim expertise in a field that depends on its mastery. They are unlikely to take lessons about the foundation of physics from a philosopher without proper credentials in mathematics. It is possible, to be sure, that physicists will take the argument for naturalistic Reason seriously enough to recognize the difference between an ontological interpretation of the laws of physics and their reduction to ontology, and if so, physics will ensure that naturalistic Reason gets a hearing even in this era of endarkenment. The predicted scientific revolution will have begun. But for that to happen, the barrier protecting the physicalist ideology will have to be penetrated by an argument based on naturalistic imagination that challenges it, and that is something that ontological science cannot predict.

4   Philosophy and Possibility

To say that something is true is merely to assert it. That is called the deflationary theory of truth. But the analytic philosophers who accept it still believe that there is an objective difference between the true and the false, so they may help naturalistic Reason receive a fair hearing. Since philosophy is the study of Appearance, it has only unsolved problems to discuss, and it is not as well-protected by the ideological mechanism as science because it does not have to live up to a reputation of making progress in learning about the natural world. Philosophers are open to arguments of all kinds, and if those who see themselves as under-laborers in science take naturalistic Reason seriously, they could trigger the predicted scientific revolution.

To be sure, arguments that defend the belief that Reason knows Reality behind Appearance are not generally considered in analytic philosophy because it began as the attempt to show that metaphysics is meaningless. But the failure of intuitionistic metaphysics is obvious, and in its wake, puzzles about Appearance have boiled down to the *hard problem of mind*. Physicalists cannot explain how consciousness is part of the natural world except by postulating a law of nature that describes brain states as causing phenomenal properties that have no effect on what happens. And simply postulating a basic law that describes this puzzling regularity is hardly a satisfactory solution to the problem of mind.

Naturalistic Reason offers a novel solution to the problem of mind that claims to solve all the problems of philosophy. Though philosophers do not know that naturalistic Reason is true, they are accustomed to considering arguments about hypotheses whose truth is unknown, and they can understand in naturalistic imagination how the natural world might be constituted by space and matter. Panpsychism has recently become a reputable view in arguments about mind, and physicalists will be able to understand how consciousness might be explained even more completely on the assumption that what has a phenomenal intrinsic nature is matter interacting with space. If they assume that the basic structure of the mammalian brain is a faculty of imagination, they will understand how ontological science explains consciousness, so they will see how an illusion might be inherent in consciousness. And if they grant for the sake of argument that the use of language is explained by faculties of imagination based on mammalian imagination, they will understand what reflective subjects exchanging metaphysical arguments mean by describing knowledge as depending on faculties of intuition. Thus, philosophers of mind who are familiar with the history of philosophy will be able to understand how the illusion of intuitionism offers a novel explanation of all the kinds of metaphysical systems defended in Western philosophy, how problems have arisen for them, and how all those problems can all be solved ontologically. This includes its explanation of the *Cogito*, the argument on which Descartes based his metaphysical argument, and to know how mind could be just a phantom Reality, they will have to understand how the identity of mind and brain could be a theoretical discovery of ontological science.

This would solve the hard problem of mind in the way that naturalists have always expected it to be solved, and since intuitionism is merely an implicit assumption of their intersubjective standpoint, analytic philosophers may well be happy to give it up in favor of a better way of defending science. Distinguishing their consciousness as the phenomenal character of experience from their reflection on psychological states, philosophers may defend the possibility of naturalistic Reason as a new way of solving what has been seen as an unsolvable problem. Since the problem of mind is the Gordian knot of philosophy, the discovery of a new way to cut it might initiate a public discussion of naturalistic Reason that triggers the predicted scientific revolution.

But ontological science cannot predict that such a reception for naturalistic Reason will cause Reason to prevail now. In the first place, its solution to the problem of mind depends on an explanation of the mammalian brain that is not yet accepted in neuroscience, and under-laborers in science will see it as mere speculation about a possible discovery in neuroscience. Furthermore, the ontological explanation of consciousness on which it depends assumes that matter interacts with space, and since a spatial substance that endures through time contradicts the belief that spacetime is what really exists, philosophers would have to defend a highly implausible prediction of a revolution in modern physics.

Indeed, ontological scientists have a reason to expect philosophers who are intrigued by this argument to remain silent. Though philosophers are not protected from arguments that challenge their basic assumptions by the ideological mechanism, they are not protected from vilification by defenders of endarkenment for defending a solution to the hard problem of mind that implies that Western civilization is superior to other civilizations on Earth. They are likely to be called *white nationalists*, and such attacks are likely to come from other members of their profession since many American philosophers now embrace the post-modernism of Continental philosophy. There are philosophers with the courage to stand up to such bullying, but in this era of endarkenment, their arguments are likely to drown in a sea of name-calling.

5   Science and Curiosity

Sciences are better protected by the ideological mechanism than philosophy because scientists know that they are making progress in the study of nature, and combined with the political forces of endarkenment, this might keep them from considering the possibility of naturalistic Reason. But this barrier will be penetrated if philosophers of mind discuss it because many neural scientists now recognize that they must explain the nature of consciousness. Though neuroscientists, like other scientists, have long looked down on philosophy as unscientific, their curiosity will be aroused when they learn from philosophers that naturalistic Reason solves the Cartesian mind-body problem. If that explanation of the history of philosophy is scientific, the identity of mind and body is a theoretical identification in science. To be sure, scientists will be skeptical about Western civilization being a stage of evolution that follows the psychological stage represented by other civilizations on Earth. But neuroscientists will want to know whether the overall course of the evolution of life can be explained by a series of stages because that would solve the puzzles of neural science.

Neuroscience is the study of nervous systems, and as a branch of physical science, it is atomistic about neurons. The assumption that the brain can be explained by tracing all the connections among individual neurons is what makes the *Allen brain atlas* seem plausible. But ontological science suggests an opposite approach. Recognizing that there are efficient causes that impose geometrical constraints on collective effects of physical causes, it uses the reproductive mechanism to explain the course of the evolution of life by stages. Nervous systems are part of the animal BGS on the third floor of the edifice of life, and since levels of geometrical organization cause stages of evolution, levels of neural organization can explain minor stages in the evolution of animals. Since this reveals the essential nature of the object that neuroscientists study, it provides an ontologically necessary framework that would solve all the basic puzzles about how the mammalian brain works. It would show (1) that the nervous system is a BGS set up by an animal BGS to guide the behavior of animal bodies in a world of objects in space, (2) that the neural BGS has three subsystems serving the three essential functions of all BGSs, (3) that neurons in all three subsystems can be organized for serving those functions on a series of four levels of geometrical organization, and (4) that each level of neural organization evolves because it gives animals a definite functional power. This framework reveals that the third level of neural organization gives mammals a faculty of imagination that enables them to understand basic physical causes and that the fourth neural level gives primate brains a faculty of imagination that enables them to understand basic geometrical causes. Furthermore, this explanation of the mammalian brain supports an explanation of the human brain. Together with the recognition that humans are members of spiritual organisms on the fourth floor of the edifice of life, it reveals the faculties of imagination on which the use of naturalistic and psychological sentences depend.

Since this framework of levels and stages of animal evolution depends on the reproductive mechanism, neuroscientists will ask biologists whether it is possible that the reproductive mechanism causes evolution. That means that all sciences studying regularities about human beings can be reduced to natural sciences, and psychologists and social scientists will add to the pressure on biologists.

Clinical psychologists who see therapy as coaching patients in reasoning about basic issues in leading their lives will welcome this explanation of the human brain because it reveals that reasoning is a cognitive power that members of a spiritual organism have when their spiritual desire motivates them to submit to the linguistic input provided by its plan-sharing BGS. And clinical psychologists studying mental illnesses will welcome it because it will enable them to explain schizophrenia, autism, and the like as deviations from its normal functioning. The human brain is explained as part of the BGS of spiritual organisms on the fourth floor of the edifice of life, and social scientists who describe regularities by gathering statistics about social behavior will want biologists to assure them that this is the essential nature of the object they study because that would enable them to reduce those regularities to natural science. Likewise, since economists study regularities about quantities of money measured as part of the behavior of spiritual organisms, they will want assurance that capitalism can be explained as an embodiment of the reproductive mechanism. Confirmation from biology would assure anthropologists that the cultural change they currently attribute to the accidental replication of memes can be explained as progressive cultural evolution by judgmental selection.

However, pressure on biology from social science to consider naturalistic Reason will be muted because faculty members of the many departments of social science, including the many newly established departments of gender studies, feminist theory, and the like, are post-modernists. Since their standpoint is inside spiritual organisms, they are intuitionists. As critical theorists, they are social holists who deny that social regularities can be explained scientifically. And since they are relativists about truth and goodness, they are natural allies of political forces of endarkenment, and so they will try to silence discussion of naturalistic Reason by calling reductionistic social scientists white nationalists.

Even if pressure from social science is neutralized, the pressure on biologists within science will be great enough for them to consider the possibility that a series of inevitable stages of evolution brings reflective subjects into existence. Biology is the study of life, and as physicalists, evolutionary biologists are mostly atomists about genes, classifying kinds of organisms by the similarity of their genomes. But when they see how genes are parts of double-action geometrical causes that gradually become more powerful when they go through reproductive cycles in regions of finite resources, they will understand how a bi-level embodiment of the reproductive mechanism can turn them into triple-action geometrical causes on a higher level of biological organization by giving them a BGS that enables them to go through reproductive cycles on their own. Thus, instead of classifying natural kinds of life by their genomes, they will consider the possibility of classifying them by the floors of the edifice of life on which they evolve. Since forms of life are defined by the kinds of BGSs they evolve, biologists will discover that in addition to the major stages in which forms of life evolve, it is possible that a series of levels of geometrical organization in the nervous system set up by the animal BGS to guide animal bodies in a world of objects in space causes a series of minor stages of evolution on the third and fourth floors. Each stage of evolution is an increase in functional powers, and biologists will be excited to learn that the overall course of evolution may be progressive in the sense taken for granted in the 19th century. But since it depends on a definition of the nature of life in terms of BGSs that they cannot defend, they will not be able to defend progressive evolution, and so the pressure on biologists from neural scientists and social scientists will be passed on to chemists, asking them whether the essential nature of life can be explained ontologically by its origin.

Alerted to this possibility, chemists will be intrigued because they have not previously considered the possibility of explaining the origin of life by a reproductive mechanism that is embodied on two levels at once on suitable planets everywhere. Taking naturalistic Reason seriously, they will learn that the reason they must keep track of entropy to predict which chemical reactions are spontaneous is that having Gibbs free energy depends on storing Gibbs bound energy in their products, and since chemical reactions are a way that geometrical causes constrain the collective effects of physical causes, they will see how geometrical action could be what evolves. Discovering how double-action geometrical causes at the molecular level that are driven through reproductive cycles by external cycles on two levels of organization at once can evolve into triple-action geometrical causes, they will see how a planet like Earth, where the cycle of night and day is one of the two externally imposed cycles, could embody the reproductive mechanism in a way that causes life to evolve from non-life. This explanation of the origin of life would solve the biggest puzzle of all the specialized sciences, and since it implies that life begins with the evolution of the first BGS, chemists would be able to assure biologists that life may have the essential nature needed to explain the course of evolution by stages. But chemists cannot be sure it does because this explanation of the origin of life depends on the existence of efficient causes that can impose geometrical constraints on collective effects of physical causes, and so the pressure on chemists to consider the argument for naturalistic Reason will be passed on to the basic branch of physical science.

6 Physics and the Basic Branch of Science

Though the ideological mechanism may protect physicists from heretics challenging physics from outside science, they will feel the pressure from scientists in specialized branches asking them to consider the possibility of naturalistic Reason. Knowing that the puzzles facing them would be solved if geometrical causes are as basic as the efficient causes recognized by physics, they will insist that physicists tell them whether they exist. Since geometrical efficient causes are not entailed by any ontological interpretation of the laws of physics, physicists will be forced to consider the possibility of reducing laws of physics to an ontological theory in which space is a substance that endures through time, and they will be surprised to learn that the discovery that space interacts with matter solves all the seemingly intractable puzzles confronting modern physics.

Puzzles arise when physicists try to understand what must exist in the natural world for their laws to be true by correspondence, and their inability to solve them has become so frustrating that physicists are open to the possibility that mathematics is not the key to unlocking the mysteries of nature. Their puzzles force modern physicists to take seriously the possibility that, for example, there are many universes, perhaps, infinitely many, and such bizarre stories about what exists seem like fairytales.[97] Indeed, some physicists have already begun to wonder at the "unreasonable effectiveness"

---

[97] Baggott (2013)

of mathematics in discovering laws of physics, and through mastery of esoteric mathematics is a condition of admission to their prestigious discipline, they are less willing than ever to go along with Wigner (1959) in thinking of mathematics as a "wonderful gift which we neither understand nor deserve." And when they have an explanation of "[t]he miracle of the appropriateness of the language of mathematics for the formulation of the laws of physics" that can be understood in naturalistic imagination, they will not be "grateful" for that miracle and "hope that it will remain valid in future research."

Though empirical ontology simply assumes that the natural world is constituted by substances of the kind discovered by the pre-Socratics, its first step in reducing physics to ontology is its inference to spatio-materialism as the best explanation of why mathematics is so effective in discovering basic regularities about change. The essential natures of space and matter imply that their interaction can generate only quantitatively precise regularities, and this explains why physics was so successful after the Newtonian revolution. But it implies that there may be other quantitative regularities that cannot be described by equations that depend on coordinate systems for their references to the natural world. Thus, space may play roles in helping matter generate quantitative regularities about change that mathematically formulated laws of nature cannot describe. This possibility is what the metaphor of a mathoscope was meant to describe. If images viewed in the mathoscopes of physics filter out regularities that depend on some roles that space plays in helping matter generate quantitative regularities about change, they are hidden from physics by its assumption that laws of physics are the deepest possible empirical knowledge about the natural world. And by giving up empirical lawism in favor of empirical ontology, physicists will discover how space and time in the natural world could be absolute, as Newton believed. They will also discover that space has a power based on its geometrical structure by which it gives matter a holistic power that is expressed as geometrical efficient causes, and so they will justify specialized scientists in using geometrical causes to solve the puzzles confronting them.

The ideological mechanism may protect physicists from philosophers outside science arguing that the puzzles of modern physics can be solved by reducing the laws of physics to an ontological theory instead of merely looking for interpretations of them. But naturalistic Reason predicts that this argument will eventually be considered by physicists because, if nothing else works, its solution to the problem of mind will give them sufficient reason to consider it. Influences within science will eventually lead them to consider naturalistic Reason. Pressures from two directions will push physicists to replace empirical lawism with empirical ontology. On the one hand, they will be pushed to consider the possibility of geometrical efficient causes because the discovery of the identity of mind and brain depends on the reduction of the language-using mammalian brain to interactions of space and matter. When they discover that space is a substance that interacts with matter in much the same way that materialists assume that material substances interact with one another, they will understand how the puzzles of modern physics can be solved. On the other hand, they will not be embarrassed to admit that physics had become addicted to mathoscopes because they will know that its success over the centuries depended on it. An explanation of the success of physics is part of the explanation of Western civilization as the metaphysical stage of evolution, and its discovery of the identity of mind and brain also depends on explaining how consciousness is part of the natural world. Thus, pressures on physics within science will come from two directions, as suggested in Figure 9.

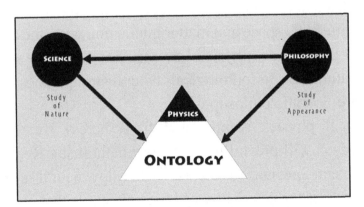

Figure 9 – Pressure on Physics from Two Directions

The explanation of Western civilization as the metaphysical stage of evolution depends on space being a substance, and for the phenomenal intrinsic nature of matter to explain how consciousness is part of the natural world, matter must interact with space. The spatiotemporal structures of small volumes of the magnetic field helping constitute the geometrical action of the mammalian brain are all isomorphic with the configurations of qualia that are immediately present when mammals perceive the natural world, and thus, the phenomenal character of experience can be explained as what it is like to be that magnetic field matter if matter has a proto-phenomenal intrinsic property. That assumption contradicts nothing in physics since it implies that consciousness is a pseudo-efficient cause. And this ontological explanation of consciousness supports an explanation of the history of intuitionistic metaphysics in which science begins when Reason rebels against its intuitionistic parents, assumes that what exists is the natural world, and uses the empirical method to learn more about it. But its success in discovering laws of physics depends on a treasure that Reason takes from intuitionism. It wrongly assumes that mathematics is *a priori* knowledge, and since that enables physics to formulate its laws of nature mathematically, it is spectacularly successful for centuries in discovering basic quantitative regularities about change. But since physics is founded on a false belief inherited from intuitionistic metaphysics, it eventually turns up intractable puzzles about the nature of what exists most basically, and since the discovery of the identity of mind and brain reveals the cause of those puzzles, physicists know they must give up empirical lawism in favor of empirical ontology. They discover that mathematical truth can be explained by its correspondence to a world constituted by space and matter interacting with one another as they endure through time. Thus, physics becomes ontology. By returning from intuitionistic naturalism to ontological naturalism, physics takes up the standpoint of pre-Socratic philosophy.

Thus, even if physics is protected from heresy by the ideological mechanism, Reason will prevail now because naturalistic Reason solves the mind-body problem. Specialized sciences will follow neural science in asking physicists to consider the possibility of efficient causes that can constrain the collective effects of physical causes, and physicists will learn from philosophers of mind why they were blind to the possibility of empirical ontology. There is no doubt that physicists will accept naturalistic Reason because it is an empirical argument, and they are scientists before they are empirical lawists. They want to know the real nature of what exists in the natural world, and though they are rightly proud of their discipline, they will not insist that empirical lawism is the criterion of truth. Since they know that the best way to discover true beliefs about the natural world is to let their beliefs to be determined by the natural world as much as possible, they will not refuse to infer the nature of what exists as the best explanation of what they find in the natural world. Though they have acquired many beliefs by accepting mathematically formulated laws of nature that have been confirmed by measurements of their quantitative predictions, many more will be acquired by reducing laws of physics to spatio-material ontological mechanisms, and so the predicted scientific revolution will begin.

Thus, the answer is, "Yes, if this argument is sound, Reason will prevail now." Giving this argument a hearing does not require many physicists because they will alert others, and the opportunity is open to physicists around the globe. This will cause a revolution because endarkenment has not set in completely enough for political activists to prevent physicists from announcing their discoveries. Only an unforeseeable catastrophe that destroys human civilization could do that. These discoveries in physics will cause revolutions in specialized sciences and philosophy. Though one of its implications is downright counterintuitive, as explained in the next chapter, scientists, philosophers, and non-professional naturalists will be drawn into agreement about what to believe because they will all be able to explain how their beliefs are true by their correspondence to Reality. To be sure, most people do not take arguments about basic issues seriously enough to be convinced by naturalistic Reason. But they will find themselves sharing the beliefs that follow from it. Since they believe what others believe in the groups with which they identify, their beliefs will change. That is how Reason will prevail now.

CHAPTER 10:
THE TRUE

To portray this argument for naturalistic Reason as the biography of Reason is to abstract from some steps involved in showing how science recognizes itself as Reason. They are steps that depend on the discovery that Western civilization is the beginning of the metaphysical stage of spiritual evolution, and they explain the nature of *naturalistic Reason* more concretely and completely.

When physical science is reduced to spatio-materialism, science becomes ontological science, and since ontological science explains the nature of reflective subjects, it implies that reflective subjects can understand their own nature completely. Ontological mechanisms can be understood in naturalistic imagination, and since reflective subjects are mammalian brains with the use of psychological sentences, they can use naturalistic imagination to understand their own nature. They can know that the self is a neural BGS with the function of guiding their behavior, and since reflective subjects represent brain states helping cause their behavior in the process of choosing a plan of action in each situation, their behavior can be guided by a BGS that understands that its function is to guide behavior. That is a uniquely complete kind of BGS, and since it does not depend on consciousness, it is a kind of cognitive perfection that is conceivable at the psychological stage of spiritual evolution. If ontological science knew the nature of Reality, reflective subjects who were informed by ontological science would know the True, and that would be a limited kind of theoretical Reason. It reveals the nature of practical and aesthetic Reason, as shown in *Section 1*.

However, even though reflective subjects without consciousness would evolve the same way in a spatio-material world, theoretical Reason would not evolve in them. As we have seen, the beginning of science depends on the success of physics represented by the Newtonian revolution, and since that depends on intuitionistic naturalism, science could not evolve in the same way. Indeed, it would probably never evolve. Mathematics would not evolve because reflective subjects without consciousness would not be fascinated by a kind of knowledge that does not depend on perception, and so there would be no laws of physics at the psychological stage for science to reduce to spatio-materialism. But suppose that the ontological explanation of the natural world were somehow available to reflective subjects without consciousness. This would be a limited kind of theoretical Reason, and it would enable them to conceive of consciousness being part of the natural world because it is just matter having a proto-phenomenal intrinsic property. In principle, therefore, they could understand the cause of the metaphysical stage of spiritual evolution. When they put their understanding of how the reflective mammalian brain works together with their understanding of the unity of consciousness, they could understand how consciousness causes the illusion of intuitionism. That is, they would know that when a mammalian brain perceives the natural world, a phenomenal intrinsic property of magnetic field matter helping constitute the geometrical action has a spatiotemporal structure that is isomorphic with what is perceived, and so they would know that there is an illusion inherent in consciousness that could lead reflective subjects to believe that they have a cognitive power that enables them to know Reality behind Appearance. Hence, they could explain how consciousness might cause a third stage of spiritual evolution. But since they are not themselves conscious, they would not have Reason because it would be just another explanation of the kind that can be understood in naturalistic imagination. As *Section 2* shows, they would predict how a third linguistic level causes a third spiritual stage in much the same way that they explained the psychological stage by the second level of neural organization and as they explained the naturalistic stage by the first linguistic level. It would be just an idle thought experiment.

In a spatio-material world where consciousness exists, however, it is not possible for reflective subjects to lack consciousness because it is caused ontologically by matter having a proto-phenomenal intrinsic property. Reflective subjects partly constituted by matter of that kind are necessarily conscious, and that means that another step is required for science to recognize itself as Reason. Ontological scientists are conscious, and since they naturally assume that the immediate presence of their complex phenomenal properties is how they know about them, they can see into the minds of metaphysicians and understand their arguments in the same way as intuitionists. They have a faculty of metaphysical imagination like them. But with their naturalistic explanation of phenomenal properties, they can also understand what metaphysicians say in naturalistic imagination, and so they can switch between accepting the illusion of intuitionism and discounting it. As *Section 3* shows, this *double-sightedness* defines the essential nature of *naturalistic Reason*.

Reason resolves its identity crisis when ontological scientists recognize that they know Reality behind Appearance. This is a necessary step in the biography of Reason, and when science becomes naturalistic Reason, science has the certainty that metaphysics claims. *Section 4* describes the kind of certainty claimed by intuitionistic metaphysics, contrasts it with the certainty of naturalistic metaphysics, and shows that an ontological explanation that passes the pre-Socratic test has the perfect kind of knowledge to which philosophy has always aspired.

1 Knowing Reality

Ontological science is knowledge of Reality because it defines the essential natures of the substances constituting the natural world and shows how they explain everything found in it except consciousness. Since it is knowledge of the True, it attains a goal of theoretical Reason. It is a limited form of theoretical Reason because it does not include an explanation of how consciousness is part of the natural world. But it reveals enough about the nature of Reason to explain its other goals, knowing the Good and the Beautiful.

Before ontological science traces its origin to Western philosophy, it has already discovered the essential nature of reflective subjects. By showing how they are a product of an inevitable series of evolutionary stages caused by a series of levels of geometrical organization, it reduces reflective subjects to interactions of space and matter, and that is an explanation of their spiritual nature, sharing the form of life that evolves on the fourth level of biological organization. They are members of spiritual organisms whose culture is on the psychological level of linguistic organization, and since they are mammals, they have both a faculty of naturalistic imagination that enables them to use naturalistic sentences and a faculty of psychological imagination that enables them to use psychological sentences. The former enables reflective subjects to understand how ontological mechanisms generate regularities in the spatio-material world, and since the latter enables them to represent the psychological states guiding their behavior as part of the process of guiding their behavior, they can tell a story that explains their self and how they see into the minds of other reflective subjects. This is part of the explanation of the overall course of evolution represented by the diagram for the unification of science by the reduction of physics to ontology. (See Figure 10.)

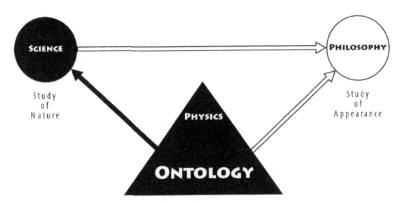

Figure 10 – Ontological Science

As we have seen, evolution is caused by the reproductive mechanism, and since the evolution of a new kind of BGS is what turns double-action geometrical causes into a form of life, or a triple-action geometrical cause, it defines the nature of life. BGSs define the forms of life on all three floors of the edifice of life, and mammals with the use of language are members of spiritual organisms evolving on the fourth floor. Thus, when reflective subjects learn what has been discovered by ontological science, they learn that their self is a geometrical cause with the function of choosing goals that are good for them, and they can understand in naturalistic imagination how it guides their behavior. The self of such a reflective subject is, therefore, a BGS that can guide behavior in a uniquely complete way. Since it understands its own function, it can use its understanding of its function to serve its function.

BGSs have three essential subsystems (input, choosing, and output), and BGSs that understand how they serve their behavior guiding function can serve all three subfunctions in a way that is more complete than any other BGS.

The function of the input subsystem is to provide information about the situation, and since ontological science explains the nature of the situation all the way down to its ontological causes, input to a reflective mammalian brain that understands ontological science is less likely to be misleading than in any other kind of BGS. Moreover, since it knows that it is a BGS, it knows that it serves the input subfunction, and since it knows how ontological science explains all the regularities that physical science has found by the study of nature, it serves the input subfunction as completely as possible. It knows that the spatio-material world is the Reality in which it exists.

Philosophers called perfect cognition *knowledge of the True*, and since they believed that it comes from knowing Reality behind Appearance, and since Reality transcends Appearance, they saw this knowledge as a transcendental goal of Reason. What ontological science knows about Reality does not include consciousness. But since it knows the natures of the substances constituting the natural world and can explain everything found in the world, it knows enough about Reality to eliminate a basic error that input subsystems might otherwise make. Mistakes are not caused by false beliefs about the nature of the true. This enables a neural BGS that knows that it is a BGS to serve the input function in guiding behavior as completely as possible. Thus, naturalistic Reason has what has traditionally been called *theoretical Reason*.

A BGS uses input to choose goals that are good, and a BGS that understands itself as a BGS can also serve the choosing subfunction in a similarly complete way. In all BGSs, the input subsystem provides information about the current situation, and the choosing subsystem uses this information to determine which goal is good for the situation. But theoretical Reason knows the True, and since it includes an explanation of the nature of the good, it can determine whether the choosing system is using the right criteria for judging which goal is good in the situation. This is what philosophers called *knowledge of the Good*, and since the Good is part of the

True, theoretical Reason eliminates a basic error that choosing subsystems might otherwise make. Mistakes are not caused by false beliefs about the nature of the good. This enables the BGS to serve its choosing subfunction as completely as possible. Hence naturalistic Reason is also what has traditionally been called *practical Reason.*

The choice of a goal that is good is not a simple choice because, as we have seen, the BGS is not simply a geometrical cause using feedback to attain a single goal. Each choice of behavior in a situation is, in effect, two tiers of choices: the choice of an end and the choice of means to that end. As we have seen, in BGSs with imagination, the two tiers are merged since the choice of a plan in the situation depends on the means required to attain the ends involved. The choice of the means can nevertheless be distinguished as a part of what practical Reason does. Given the goal chosen for a situation, it must determine the best means of attaining the end in the situation, and that is the function of the output subsystem. Since a BGS informed by ontological science knows that it is a BGS, it knows that the function of the output subsystem is to determine the most efficient means to the end, and since it can determine whether the output subsystem is using the right criteria to judge which are the best means in the situation, given the chosen goal, it eliminates a basic error that the output subsystem might otherwise make. Philosophers called this *knowledge of the Beautiful*, and since the Beautiful, as part of the Good, is part of the True, theoretical Reason enables the BGS to serve the output function as completely as possible. Mistakes are not caused by false beliefs about the nature of the beautiful. Hence naturalistic Reason is also what has traditionally been called *aesthetic Reason.*

A reflective BGS informed by ontological science can use its understanding of its own essential nature to serve its functions in a most complete way. It is difficult to imagine how any geometrical cause could be more reliable in serving behavior-guiding functions. No doubt, some tinkering with the genetic plans for constructing neural BGSs can make its geometrical action more efficient. Perhaps, neural BGSs can be given additional sensory modalities, such as echolocation, sensitivity to broader ranges of electromagnetic waves and frequencies of sounds, or direct input from computers. The motor output circuit has already been hooked up by electrical connections to robots so that the subjective neural BGS can use its covert behavior to use them to act on objects in space. But the neural BGS of a Rational subject has an essential nature, and unless there is a more reliable geometrical cause for serving its behavior guiding functions than a BGS that uses its understanding of its nature as a BGS to serve them, a BGS that knows the True is, in a sense, complete, that is, perfect.

2 Knowing Consciousness as Part of Reality

The cognitive perfection of a reflective BGS informed of its own nature by ontological science is not complete because it leaves out consciousness. Ontological science is knowledge of Reality because it is what science knows about the natural world when it is based on ontology rather than physics, and it explains everything by showing how it is constituted by space and matter. It accomplishes what pre-Socratics tried to do when they searched for the first cause. To describe it as *ontological science* is to abstract from the reflective subjects who understand it by thinking of it as a part of culture. It is a complete explanation of Reality that does not depend on the knower being conscious. Given what ontological science explains in a spatio-material world without consciousness, reflective subjects can understand how there might be something else that must be known before ontological science becomes naturalistic Reason. What this limited perfection of theoretical Reason leaves out is consciousness, and explaining it is another step in the story about how Reason resolves its identity crisis. But consciousness is something that reflective subjects could, in principle, understand without being conscious. Since naturalistic imagination would enable them to understand ontological mechanisms, they could understand what consciousness is and how it would help metaphysics cause a stage of spiritual evolution even if they were not themselves conscious.

Consider a spatio-material world in which reflective subjects are conscious, and though it is not ontologically possible, suppose that some reflective subjects informed by ontological science are not conscious. This is just another thought experiment involving ontological impossibilities. We have already supposed that there are reflective subjects informed by ontological science in a world where consciousness does not exist (despite having no reason to believe that their existence is ontologically possible). But if there were a reflective neural BGS informed by ontological science that was not conscious, it could understand how consciousness is part of the natural world and predict that it would help metaphysics cause the third stage of spiritual evolution. (It is represented by the two arrows pointing at philosophy in Figure 11.)

Figure 11 – Knowing Consciousness as Part of Reality

Consciousness is part of the natural world because the matter helping space constitute the natural world has a proto-phenomenal intrinsic property. Reflective subjects understand how substances constitute the world, and thus, if it is stipulated that an intrinsic phenomenal property is immediately present to a bit of matter whose intrinsic nature it characterizes, reflective subjects who were not conscious could understand how a substance can exist in itself in a way that makes a difference only to the substance that exists in that way.

Such reflective subjects would know that matter has a holistic power expressed as geometrical efficient causes, enabling them to understand what geometrical action is. The inertial system enables them to understand how the quantum structure of the mechanical system enables geometrical structures of composite bodies to constrain the collective effects of physical efficient causes, and so they can see how all the particles in the natural world are entangled. They can apply this knowledge to the special case of the geometrical action of the mammalian brain. Their knowledge of ontological science would enable them to understand how the structure of the mammalian brain is a geometrical cause that serves as a faculty of imagination and how that enables the brain to guide behavior to goals that are good for it. Thus, knowing that matter has a proto-phenomenal intrinsic property, they could understand the unity of consciousness. The relevant part of the geometrical action of the mammalian brain is the firing of neurons, and since that involves the acceleration of charged particles across membranes, the collective effects of physical causes that are constrained geometrically include the flow of magnetic field matter (as Gibbs bound energy). Though the details have been left as a research project, the spatiotemporal structure of magnetic field matter helping constitute the mammalian brain determines the configurations of sensory qualia in phenomenal space that are immediately present to mammals perceiving the natural world. Given the proto-phenomenal intrinsic property of matter, this would enable reflective subjects without consciousness who were informed by ontological science to know that the magnetic field matter helping constitute mammals has a phenomenal intrinsic property that seems to *be* the natural world. Given their understanding of the unity of consciousness in this special case, they would know that the immediate presence of complex phenomenal properties makes it seem to mammals that phenomenal properties are objects known by a faculty of intuition, and so they would know that what it is like to be a mammal is to be *inside consciousness.*

This founds an ontological explanation of how consciousness manages to cause a metaphysical stage of evolution. Metaphysical arguments used by direct realists assume that perception is a faculty of intuition, and so direct realism is a model for interpreting reflective phenomenal appearances of a certain kind as objects of a faculty of rational intuition. Thus, reflective subjects who were not themselves conscious could understand how conscious reflective subjects are able to believe that they have a faculty of rational intuition that enables them to know Reality behind Appearance. The reproductive mechanism is embodied in the BGS of spiritual organisms; culture evolves by judgmental selection; and since a culture in which metaphysical arguments are exchanged evolves by Rational selection, culture predictably acquires enough understanding of the natural world to force conscious reflective subjects to give up direct realism in favor of representative realism. Hence, conscious reflective subjects who exchange metaphysical arguments will eventually come to believe that there is a world outside consciousness, and since they will believe that the self is a mind, they will know that the external world has a nature that is opposite to the unity of mind. All the developments that inevitably occur during the metaphysical stage are predictable, including how intuitionism gives rise to a physics whose success inspires science, how physicalism causes the hard problem of mind, how empirical ontology turns physical science into ontological science, and how ontological science eventually recognizes itself as naturalistic Reason.

Though it may not seem possible for reflective subjects who are not conscious to understand how consciousness would cause a metaphysical stage of evolution in reflective subjects who are conscious, it is possible because consciousness is just a pseudo-efficient cause. Consciousness does not help determine what happens in the natural world. It merely helps constitute it. Hence, it is an ontological cause that is impotent as an efficient cause, and this is something that can be understood in naturalistic imagination. The power of consciousness to help metaphysics cause a third stage of spiritual evolution depends on an illusion inherent in consciousness. Though that illusion is an expression of the holistic power of matter, it is a phenomenal expression that depends on the holistic power of matter being expressed geometrically, that is, as the geometrical cause called the mammalian brain guiding behavior. Consciousness is what it is like to be the magnetic field matter helping constitute the neural geometrical action of the mammalian brain. The illusion of intuitionism explains what intuitionistic metaphysicians mean when they eventually conclude that the self is a mind. But it implies that the mind is a phantom Reality, and that explains how the mind is identical to the brain. The mind is nothing but a conscious reflective subject holding a false belief about knowledge made possible by the intuitionist illusion. As we have seen, an explanation of the plausibility of believing that Reason knows Reality behind Appearance reduces the mind to the reflective mammalian brain in much the same way as an explanation of reflection by the use of psychological sentences reduced the reflective mammalian brain to the mammalian brain with the use of naturalistic sentences. As always, it is an identity that depends on a part-whole relation between geometrical causes at two different levels of organization. In this case, it is a part-whole relation in the structure of faculties of imagination. But it is, in principle, the same kind of identity that holds between water and H_2O. Such theoretical identifications enable science to reduce all the regularities described by specialized science to interactions of space and matter at the bottom, and ontological scientists do not have to be conscious to understand it.

3 Knowing Reality behind Appearance

There is a third step in ontological science becoming naturalistic Reason because no reflective subject in the spatio-material world lacks consciousness. That is ontologically necessary because of the kinds of substances that constitute our natural world. Thus, the ontological scientists who trace the origin of ontological science to the metaphysical stage are conscious, and for them to understand the cause of its evolution, another step is required.

As reflective subjects, ontological scientists are conscious, and like all mammals, they are inclined to accept direct realism about perception. They assume that the complex phenomenal properties they have when they perceive the natural world *are* the natural world, and when the use of metaphysical sentences leads them to believe that phenomenal properties are known by their immediate presence, they believe that phenomenal properties are basically different from states of the brain. Since they are taken in by the intuitionist illusion, they have a faculty of metaphysical imagination in which phenomenal properties are interpreted as objects of intuition. But they also see phenomenal properties as ways that substances helping constitute the mammalian brain exist in themselves, and since that depends on naturalistic imagination, they have a different kind of metaphysical imagination from intuitionists. Using it to understand how consciousness is part of the natural world in this way, they discount the illusion of intuitionism. This depends on the naturalists' faculty of metaphysical imagination because they must understand how phenomenal properties can be seen as objects of intuition that are basically different from brain states in order to reject that false belief in favor of believing that phenomenal properties are identical to intrinsic properties of magnetic field matter helping constitute the mammalian brain. That way of being constituted by space and matter is how *Part One* of *Volume III* explained consciousness as part of the natural world.

Conscious ontological scientists can interpret metaphysical arguments in two ways. When they do not discount the intuitionist illusion, they see into the minds of metaphysicians and understand their arguments as they do, and they use the intuitionists' faculty of metaphysical imagination to understand the developments during the metaphysical stage in the way they were presented in *Part Two*. But since ontological scientists understand the nature of consciousness, they can discount the intuitionist illusion, and when they do, they use the naturalists' faculty of metaphysical imagination to explain metaphysical arguments as what metaphysicians say when they are misled by false beliefs about the nature of phenomenal properties. Since both interpretations depend on distinguishing between phenomenal properties as objects of intuition and phenomenal properties as how magnetic field matter exists in itself, both are ways of driving a faculty of metaphysical imagination. But the naturalists' faculty of metaphysical imagination is more complete than the intuitionists' faculty. Thus, the ontological scientists who explain how the metaphysical stage is caused have a kind of *double-sightedness* that enables them to understand the history of philosophy as historical philosophers understood it and, at the same time, to understand how they are misled. That is possible because the faculty of metaphysical imagination in ontological scientists uses naturalistic imagination to represent how their own reflection is constituted by interactions of space and matter.

Conscious ontological scientists explain direct realists about perception as inside consciousness, and since they can understand how the discovery that direct realism is false leads to the acceptance of representative realism, they can explain the origin of the belief in mind. It comes from intuitionistic metaphysicians recognizing that there is a world outside consciousness whose unity is basically different from the unity of consciousness. The problem of mind-body dualism is solved because it is just what intuitionists falsely believe when they take the difference between the unity of mind and the unity of the natural world to mean that mind and body are opposite kinds of substances interacting in the natural world.

Physicalists who try to explain how consciousness is part of the world call this the *hard problem of mind,* because they fall for the intuitionist illusion and cannot explain how the Cartesian mind is part of the physical world.[98] But

---

[98] Or else physicalists deny that phenomenal properties have any effect on what happens (that is, accept epiphenomenalism) and cannot explain how they know they are conscious.

since ontologists can explain how consciousness is part of the natural world, they know that an illusion inherent in consciousness makes it seem that phenomenal properties are objects of intuition. That is what it is like to be a mammalian brain, and their explanation of what it is like to be a mammalian brain enables them to discount the illusion of intuitionism and use their faculty of naturalistic imagination to understand their self as a neural BGS with a faculty of metaphysical imagination. They discover that mind is the phantom Reality conjured up by modern metaphysics.[99] But this does not make the intuitionist illusion go away, any more than optical illusions go away when they are exposed as illusions. What it is like to be a mammalian brain is to see phenomenal properties as objects that are known by their immediate presence. Conscious reflective subjects are still inside consciousness. But as naturalists, ontologists are scientific realists about perception who take perception to be reliable knowledge about objects in space that exist independently of one another, so they explain the nature consciousness from outside consciousness. And with a faculty of metaphysical imagination based on using naturalistic imagination to understand how everything is constituted by space and matter, they are able to keep from using the illusion of intuitionism as a reason for any belief that they accept, and so they have a complete understanding of the world that depends only on the empirical method. But it does depend on discounting the intuitionist illusion, and since ontological scientists find themselves knowing Reality behind Appearance, ontological science becomes naturalistic Reason, as depicted in Figure 12 by adding the label *natReason*.

---

[99] And ontologists can explain how they know they are conscious as deriving from a discovery of the metaphysical stage of spiritual evolution.

Figure 12 – Naturalistic Reason

4 Knowing Reality with Certainty

What distinguishes philosophy from science in contemporary culture is the claim of metaphysics to know Reality with certainty. Science, by contrast, can be falsified, and though it is undeniably learning more about the natural world, its progress is piecemeal and may never end. The certainty promised by metaphysics was desirable because knowledge of the True includes knowledge of the Good and reflective subjects normally recognize that they lead lives trying to choose goals that are good. But intuitionistic metaphysics failed to know Reality with certainty, and by contrast with its failure, naturalistic Reason knows Reality with the kind of certainty to which philosophy has always aspired. Consider the various ways that knowledge can seem to be certain.

4.1 Knowing Reality with Intuitionistic Certainty

Intuitionist metaphysics claimed that Reason knows Reality behind Appearance with certainty because Reason is (or involves) a faculty of intuition whose objects are inherently certain. Different kinds of metaphysical arguments claim certainty for Reason in different ways. But they all assume that rational intuition cannot be refuted by anything learned from perception or reflection of other kinds. In the ancient era, objects of rational intuition are more real than objects of perception because they are unchanging. In the modern era, objects of rational intuition cannot be doubted because they are self-evident. And in late modern philosophy, Reason plays a role in constructing objects of intuition that makes what they contribute to the phenomenal world necessary and universal.

Each kind of intuitionistic metaphysics failed, however, because it could not pass a test of coherence set by the pre-Socratics when they discovered the basic nature of the first cause. The pre-Socratics concluded that the kind of cause that could explain everything found in the natural world is a substance or substances. Substances explain what is found in the natural world by constituting it, and for such an ontological theory to succeed, kinds of substances identified as enduring through time must have essential natures that enable them to constitute all the kinds of things found in the natural world and whose interactions can explain how they all change. The pre-Socratics thought of substances as material, but they did not agree in the end about the kinds of material substances that constitute the world.

Though the pre-Socratics discovered the nature of the first cause of the natural world before the exchange of metaphysical arguments began, Plato did not realize that they had set a standard of coherence for explanations of everything that intuitionistic metaphysics would have to pass. Metaphysicians claim that Reason is a kind of cognitive capacity that can know the nature and existence of Reality behind Appearance, and that is to promise implicitly that they will show how Reality explains everything found in the world. But when metaphysicians tried to show how the kinds of substances that constitute Reality explained what everyone found in the world, including its Appearance, they were challenged to solve a problem about how two substances of opposite kinds could be related to one another and interact in a way that explains coherently the existence of everything. The difference between Appearance and Reality made that impossible, and the only way to cope with the ontological problem that frustrated them and make good on their promise to explain everything was to hide their dualistic ontology. They could either defend a double-aspect theory, which claims there is a single kind of substance with two opposite essential natures, or they could defend idealism, an ontological theory in which one kind of intuitionistic substance explained both Reality and Appearance. Both strategies were explored in all three eras of philosophy, and neither way of hiding the problem of ontological dualism was ever coherent enough to pass the pre-Socratic test.

In the ancient era, as we have seen, Plato could not explain how Forms in the realm of Being are responsible for visible objects in the realm of becoming (except by using a myth about a demiurge making them appear as moving images in a receptacle). Aristotle tried to hide Platonic dualism by postulating particular substances that are both form and matter, and that is ontologically incoherent because substances cannot exist in themselves in two opposite ways at once. Plotinus tried to hide Platonic dualism by postulating a phenomenal subject, called the One, to which both Forms and visible objects were immediately present, and that did not explain how matter could seem to be what exists most basically in the natural world.

In the modern era, the existence of a substance outside space and time was not in doubt because it was part of a shared religion, and Descartes' metaphysical argument failed because he could not explain how mind and body interact in the natural world. Spinoza used a double-aspect theory to hide Cartesian dualism, and since mind and body were related as two attributes of single substance, he could claim to have solved both the Cartesian and Platonic dualism. Leibniz used an idealist ontological theory to hide Cartesian mind-body dualism by postulating nothing but minds (called monads) whose perceptual phenomenal appearances all fit together as if they were all located in space and time. What is more, he could also claim to solve the problem of Platonic dualism because he postulated an infinite monad outside space and time that created all the finite monads and determined their essential natures as what were required for the best of all possible worlds.

In the late modern era, Kant's critique of pure reason implied that Reason helped construct the phenomenal world in faculties of intuition called space and time. Though he intended to show the impossibility of metaphysics, his argument entailed a problematic ontological dualism. In addition to the phenomenal world, Kant had to postulate an unknowable noumenal world, that is, things in themselves. His explanation of everything did not pass the pre-Socratic test of coherence because it implied that passing the test was impossible. But Kant's constructivist theory of Reason enabled Schelling to use a double-aspect ontological theory to hide Kant's problematic dualism as a substance, called the *Absolute,* that could both objectify and subjectify itself, and it enabled Hegel to hide Kant's dualism of phenomena and noumena by arguing that Reason has a dialectical character by which Reason discovers that it is itself the thing in itself behind the phenomenal world. The former was ontologically incoherent, and the latter became increasingly incredible as scientific discoveries about the material world accumulated.

This explanation of its history is not how philosophy is currently taught because teachers do not know how to discount the illusion of intuitionism.[100] Since the default condition is to fall for the intuitionist illusion, they take rational intuition for granted and try to explain the failure of intuitionistic metaphysics by defending skepticism about the capacity of Reason to know Reality behind Appearance. Instead of recognizing that there is no such thing as rational certainty, intuitionists settle for showing that Reason is not up to the task that metaphysics sets for it.

4.2 Knowing Reality with Naturalistic Certainty

What caused the failure of intuitionistic metaphysics cannot cause the failure of naturalistic metaphysics. Ontological scientists are not confronted by any problem explaining how two opposite kinds of substances are related and interact because they are ontological naturalists. Like the pre-Socratics, they find themselves with animal bodies in a world of objects in space and time, and since they assume that the objects exist independently of one another, they trust perception and use the empirical method to discover kinds of substances constituting the natural world whose natures can explain everything. In the end, they discover that the natural world is constituted by two opposite kinds of substances. But there is no problem about ontological dualism to solve because they would not have considered spatio-materialism in the first place if they could not understand in naturalistic imagination how they are able to constitute everything in the natural world. The coherence required by the pre-Socratic test is built into spatio-materialism from the

---

[100] Discounting the intuitionist illusion is not the same as accepting epiphenomenalism. Epiphenomenalism assumes that there is a psychophysical law that describes phenomenal properties as effects of brain states that have no effect of what happens in the brain, and that makes it impossible for physicalists to explain how reflective subjects know that they are conscious. A brain reduced to physical causes cannot describe the unity of consciousness. But when consciousness is explained by a proto-phenomenal intrinsic property of matter, phenomenal properties are the intrinsic nature of matter helping constitute the mammalian brain. They are identical to phenomenal intrinsic properties of magnetic field matter helping constitute its geometrical action. Since it is not ontologically possible for mammalian brains to guide behavior without phenomenal properties being immediately present to the mammal, phenomenal properties are not effects of brain states. They are what it is like to be some of the matter constituting the mammalian brain.

beginning.

To be sure, ontological naturalists accept the empirical method. For ontological naturalists, that is just commonsense because they assume that the natural world is constituted substances and they want beliefs about the natural world that are true by correspondence to those substances. Language-using mammals can understand how sensory organs afford reliable knowledge about the natural world, and so their strategy is to use perception and let the natural world itself determine their beliefs about it as much as possible. Instead of believing what others in their group believe or what authorities tell them, they judge for themselves which beliefs are true. Since they prefer beliefs that are more completely determined by the natural world, they infer what is true as the best explanation of what is found, and using their faculties of naturalistic imagination, they follow the principle of optimality and look for theories that explain the most with the least. They judge theories superior when they explain more with the same cost in ontological causes, when they explain just as much with less cost in the way of causes, or both. These criteria can conflict, but the empirical method works well enough for science to continue making progress.

It seems that what is known by the empirical method cannot be known with certainty because it is always possible that evidence will turn up that falsifies the explanation already accepted. Scientific theories have repeatedly been overthrown by revolutions in which new theories are superior by the principle of optimality. But if this is how science makes progress, it may never attain its original goal.

Unending progress is what the history of a science based on physics suggests. Its method, empirical lawism, assumes that mathematically formulated laws of nature are the deepest possible empirical knowledge about the natural world, and its success has been impressive. But since progress comes from making measurements that confirm quantitative predictions of laws, physics evolves by pragmatic selection. Physicists can agree about which laws to accept because they all share the goal of finding laws of nature that predict the greatest range of measurements using the simplest mathematics. Furthermore, physicalism has crippled specialized sciences by making the unity of science depend on explaining the regularities they study by basic laws of physics. These problems are solved by ontological science, as shown in *Volume II*. But it begins in *Volume I* by replacing intuitionistic naturalism with ontological naturalism. The empirical method is used to show that the unreasonable effectiveness of mathematics in discovering laws of nature can be explained by the kinds of substances that constitute the natural world. Spatio-materialism explains why it seems that mathematics is known prior to perception of the natural world, and since there are powers by which interactions of space and matter are able to generate all the regularities described by the laws of physics, substances replace laws of physics as the first cause. Though success has addicted physicists to mathoscopes, they will solve the puzzles confronting modern physics by using empirical ontology to discover the limitations of their wonderful instrument.

Indeed, ontological science traces the puzzles of philosophy as well as science to intuitionism. But without intuitionistic naturalism, physics could not have learned as much about the natural world as it did. The metaphysical stage of evolution on which it depends would not have begun without believing that Reason is a faculty of intuition. That is what ontological science discovers by explaining its own origin. Its ontological explanation of how consciousness is part of the natural world reveals an illusion inherent in consciousness that explains how the metaphysical stage begins, and by discounting that illusion, ontological science reveals how the pre-Socratic test of coherence dooms intuitionistic metaphysics to failure. But when intuitionistic philosophy is explained scientifically, culture continues to evolve by Rational selection because ontological scientists agree about what to believe only when all their beliefs about the natural world correspond to the substances constituting it at once.

To be sure, since naturalistic Reason is based on the empirical method, it can be falsified by what is found in the natural world. Indeed, there is obviously more to be learned about space and matter. Astronomy is only beginning to gather data about bodies on the largest scale, and this argument has left a number of research projects to be completed. But this argument does not depend on discovering the best ontological explanation of everything found in the natural world. The powers of space and matter described in these volumes are probably incomplete, and besides modifications that enable interactions of space and matter to explain more about the regularities found in the world, there are probably mistakes about their powers to be corrected. The corrections will be beliefs about the natural world that are determined as much as possible by the natural world itself. But this argument does depend on them all being true by correspondence to space and matter as described in this trilogy. What unifies physics and what unifies science is the discovery that space is a substance that interacts with matter as both endure through time, and that is what enables ontological science to explain Western civilization as the beginning of the metaphysical stage in the evolution of life. This way of explaining what is found in the world depends on causes that have a unique unity and completeness. (See Figure 13.)

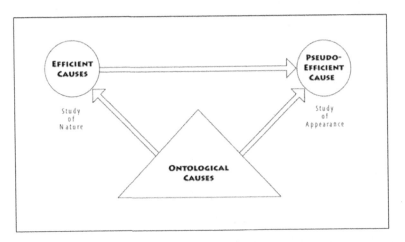

Figure 13 – Unity and Completeness of Naturalistic Reason

Naturalistic Reason discovers substances constituting the natural world that explain everything that holds necessarily. They are the first cause that the pre-Socratics set out to find millennia ago. Substances are ontological causes that explain the existence of everything found in the natural world by constituting it, and interactions of space and matter explain all the causes of what happens, including not only the two kinds of efficient causes that reduce all the specialized sciences to ontology, but also the pseudo-efficient cause that metaphysical arguments use in causing a third stage of spiritual evolution. Explanations depend on causes. This unity and completeness of the explanation offered by naturalistic Reason is represented in Figure 13. This claim of naturalistic Reason would be falsified empirically if it turned out that the natural world cannot be constituted by space and matter as substances enduring through time. For example, it would be falsified if spacetime and Big Bang cosmology could not be replaced by something like the Big Shrink in which bound matter shrinks relative to space. The inertial system is part of the *gravitational system*, the all-inclusive ontological mechanism represented by the triangle in Figure 13, and naturalistic Reason would also be falsified if an ontological mechanism with parallel electromagnetic and mechanical systems could not explain the regularities described by laws of quantum physics. The inertial system is what reveals the existence of geometrical efficient causes not recognized by physics, and as represented by the arrow from *Ontological Causes* to *Efficient Causes*, reducing all the specialized sciences to ontology depends on how they jointly cause geometrical action. Finally, naturalistic Reason would also be falsified if the ontological reduction of quantum laws did not imply that matter has a holistic power that is expressed not only by geometrical action, but also by giving the proto-phenomenal intrinsic property of matter helping constitute the mammalian brain the unity of consciousness. The unification of science and philosophy is represented by the two arrows pointing at the circle labelled *Pseudo-Efficient Cause*.

That space and matter play these roles is the basic claim on which this prediction of an imminent scientific revolution depends. This argument has shown how that such an explanation is possible, and it would be falsified empirically if what perception finds in the natural world showed that there are no powers that enable space and matter to play all these roles and justify the use of all these causes to explain everything that holds necessarily in it. But in the absence of such an empirical falsification, the risk of accepting it is not great because spatio-materialism leaves no grounds for critics to refute it. All standpoints from which this argument may seem vulnerable to refutation have a deeper ontological explanation that refutes all criticisms based on it.

All the non-naturalistic entities to which philosophers might point, such as Plato's Forms and abstract objects, Cartesian minds and self-evident truths, and Kant's phenomenal world and synthetic a priori truths, are reducible to interactions of space and matter because if matter has a proto-phenomenal intrinsic property, they are explained as false beliefs caused by the illusion of intuitionism. They are phantom Realities, and more commonplace ghosts, such as the immaterial spirits to which new age spiritualists point, can be explained in a similar way.

To be sure, spatio-materialism would be false if the first cause were a God outside space and time who created the natural world. But theism is just one of many logically possible ontological theories that would explain space and matter by postulating other substances whose powers are expressed by making it appear that the natural world is constituted by space and matter, and the empirical method forces naturalists to reject all of them because spatio-materialism is a superior explanation. Such alternatives cost much more in the way of ontological causes and yet do not explain any more than spatio-materialism. Nor can theism be defended as offering a better explanation of the meaning of life. Neither Christianity nor Judaism has an adequate explanation of it. They claim that it is explained by God's purpose in creating a world for us will. But that is just a promise because, even if it is known, it will be known in heaven or after death when we somehow live in the presence of God. Though theists do know something valuable about the meaning of life, it is also explained by naturalistic Reason. Its explanation of the existence and nature of life implies that there is a real difference between good and bad without postulating a creator outside space and time and postulating a basic teleological cause. Beings like us have a spiritual nature because we are members of living organisms on the fourth floor of the edifice of life, and since we continually choose between good and evil, the meaning of life depends in a similar way on being moral and resisting the temptation to sin.

This argument predicts, therefore, that a scientific revolution will occur in which everything that exists is explained by spatio-materialism. That revolution will not occur until ontological scientists trace the origin of science to the metaphysical stage of evolution. But the metaphysical stage began in ancient Greece with pre-Socratics looking for the first cause, and when ontological scientists recognize the difference between reflection and consciousness, they will know Reality behind Appearance. Naturalistic Reason will enable them to explain everything by the first cause.[101] That is the

---

[101] Let me emphasize that this is not to justify naturalistic Reason by the coherence theory of truth, as absolute idealists do when they justify beliefs about Reality by the coherence of their explanation of everything as an object of intuition. Naturalistic Reason requires reflective subjects to discount the illusion of intuitionism, and they know substances that are the Reality behind Appearance.

denouement of the metaphysical stage, and there is undoubtedly more to be learned. But whatever naturalistic Reason discovers after that will include an explanation of everything found in the world that passes the pre-Socratic test in an optimal way. It will explain the most with the least, and skepticism will be unreasonable. There will be no place for skeptics to stand and cast doubt on naturalistic Reason because all possible standpoints will have been reduced to interactions of space and matter.

4.3 Knowing Reality with Cartesian Certainty

Since ontological scientists are conscious, reflective subjects, their understanding of this optimal ontological explanation of everything that exists has a phenomenal appearance. Indeed, the phenomenal appearance of this explanation of the natural world is what Descartes would call a *clear and distinct idea*. It is *clear* because the essential natures of everything found in it, including conscious reflective subjects and the spiritual world in which they live, are reduced to interactions of space and matter at the bottom in a way that can be understood in naturalistic imagination. And the idea is *distinct* because it explains everything in space and time in a way that does not depend on anything outside space and time. The phenomenal appearance of this optimal ontological explanation of everything satisfies Descartes' definition of clear and distinct ideas.

However, since there is no such thing as rational intuition, the clarity and distinctness of this idea is not a good reason for believing it. It is potentially as deceptive as the clear and distinct ideas of the mind and the body that led Descartes to believe that they are substances that must be interacting in the natural world even though there is no way to explain how that is possible. By itself, each idea seemed indubitable to him. But ontological science shows that both ideas can exist even though there is no substance with the unity of mind, and the substance outside the mind is not extension, but, rather, space and matter. This ontological explanation of the nature of consciousness shows how it helps cause a metaphysical stage of evolution in which an intuitionist who accepts representative realism about perception is confronted with the problem of mind-body dualism. Descartes was mistaken in believing that clear and distinct ideas are innate ideas that enable the mind to know the essential natures of substances helping constitute the world. And intuitionists would make the same mistake if they believed that the clarity and distinctness of the complex phenomenal property that is immediately present to language-using mammals who understand how spatio-materialism is the first cause of everything found in the natural world shows that it is indubitable. There is no such thing as a faculty of rational intuition.

In the spatio-material world, naturalistic Reason has a phenomenal appearance that is clear and distinct because the faculty of naturalistic imagination enables reflective subjects to understand how the first cause explains everything that exists. That is what happens when they judge whether naturalistic metaphysics is better than other ontological explanations. As language-using mammals, they use faculties of naturalistic imagination to pull all the parts of this argument together as single intuition, much as Descartes described in his *Rules for the Direction of the Mind*. But since this argument includes an ontological explanation of the metaphysical stage of evolution, reflective subjects use the double-sightedness of a faculty of metaphysical imagination that is based on naturalistic imagination to switch between seeing complex phenomenal properties as objects of intuition and discounting the illusion that makes them seem to be objects of intuition. The former is how understanding appears from inside consciousness. But reflective subjects who accept scientific realism about perception explain consciousness from outside. They recognize that the empirical method is what enables them to know about what exists. Thus, naturalistic imagination enables them to tell that naturalistic Reason is superior to alternative ways of explaining everything by a first cause, including intuitionistic metaphysics and materialism.

Naturalistic Reason is an ontological explanation with a kind of certainty because nothing found in the natural world is evidence that it is false. This kind of certainty is different from what intuitionists claimed because rational intuition could not be falsified by perception. Intuitionists explained Reason as a faculty of intuition that is different from perception and invulnerable to what perception reveals. Intuitionistic Reason is more certain than naturalistic Reason because it cannot be falsified by perception. But that is true by definition, and since intuitionism is false, it is irrelevant because there is no such thing as rationally necessary truth. To be sure, there are logically necessary truths, such as the law of excluded middle (a proposition is either true or its negation is true) and the rules of quantificational logic (governing the use of "all" and "some" referring to objects). But they are true because they are a necessary part of the structure of any language that can describe any world. In the spatio-material world, all other truths depend on correspondence to the natural world, and that includes mathematics, since it is true by corresponding to everything constituted by space and matter in a world where regularities are generated by their interactions.

Thus, if this prediction of an imminent scientific revolution is true, naturalistic Reason will turn out to be as certain as any knowledge that is possible for beings like us because it is the best ontological explanation of what is found in the natural world, and it is complete. There are no reasonable grounds for doubting that it is true.

But knowing that naturalistic metaphysics is true in this way is not easy because naturalistic Reason knows Reality behind Appearance. That is, knowing the True is a transcendental goal of Reason because Reality is behind Appearance, and naturalistic Reason attains that goal by discounting the intuitionist illusion. That is not easy because reflective subjects must recognize that the qualia objects in phenomenal space that are immediately present in perception are not the natural world in which they find their bodies. They are, rather, part of the self, and it is safe to say that, currently, most people do not know that. Getting used to that is an obstacle that everyone must overcome to have naturalistic Reason. Reflective subjects must recognize that all the phenomenal appearances that are immediately present when they use language to reflect on their psychological states are identical to intrinsic properties of magnetic field matter that help constitute the geometrical action of their mammalian brains. That is what ontological science discovers, and it is not easy to understand because it contradicts what almost everyone assumes when they reflect on their psychological states: it denies that complex phenomenal properties are known by their immediate presence. The failure to distinguish reflection from the consciousness that is necessarily part of it is the main cause of confusion about basic issues today.

However, discounting the intuitionist illusion and distinguishing reflection from consciousness is something that conscious, reflective subjects can learn to do. When universities teach students how to discount the intuitionist illusion, they will once again offer a liberal education that brings students up to speed in the wisdom that has been evolving since ancient Greece. But after the scientific revolution predicted here has taken root, universities will not be necessary because it will be common knowledge that there is an illusion inherent in consciousness, and since explanations of what exists when it is discounted can be understood in naturalistic imagination, anyone growing up who takes arguments seriously will be able to understand how everything depends on a first cause. Everyone will be able to judge for themselves what is true by correspondence to the spatio-material world. Even defenders of endarkenment will give up relativism in favor of naturalistic Reason. It they continue to believe what others around them believe, they will believe that the True is what is known to exist behind Appearance because that is what those who take arguments seriously believe. All reflective subjects will know how and why they must discount the illusion of intuitionism, and remembering not to use intuitionism as a premise of any conclusion they draw, they will be able to relax and enjoy having a clear and distinct idea that seems to show that naturalistic Reason is indubitable. That is what it is like to be a mammal with naturalistic Reason, knowing Reality behind Appearance.

CHAPTER 11:
THE GOOD

Ever since ancient Greece, metaphysicians have assumed that knowing the *True*, the *Good*, and the *Beautiful* are the goals of Reason. But as intuitionists, they were misled about the nature of Reason, and ontological science, using the empirical method, discovers that Reason is a behavior guidance system. Its functions explain why the True, the Good, and the Beautiful are, respectively, the goals of theoretical, practical, and aesthetic Reason. As we have seen, this BGS seems to be perfect. It is hard to see how a geometrical cause could serve these functions any better than one that knows its functions and uses its understanding of how it serves them to serve them.

Metaphysical arguments are about Appearance, and since the True, the Good, and the Beautiful are known as aspects of the Reality that Reason discovers behind Appearance, they are called *transcendental goals* of Reason. Attaining them was just an aspiration of intuitionistic metaphysics because its assumption that Reason is a faculty of rational intuition led to wildly false conclusions about the nature of Reality. But this false belief about the nature of Reason was caused by an illusion inherent in consciousness, and when an ontological explanation of this illusion enables ontological scientists to explain Western civilization as the metaphysical stage of spiritual evolution, science becomes naturalistic Reason. Ontological scientists discount the intuitionist illusion in themselves, and since they explain everything in the world by ontological causes, they find themselves knowing Reality behind Appearance—and, as we have seen, knowing it with certainty.

Attaining the transcendental goals of Reason is a metaphysical triumph. But naturalistic Reason is, ironically, just the discovery of a perfect means for serving the basic function of Reason. The basic function of a BGS is guiding behavior towards goals that are good, and since practical Reason chooses those goals, it matters more to Rational beings than theoretical Reason. Since the Good is part of the True, theoretical Reason enables practical Reason to serve its function in the most perfect way, and attaining the transcendental goal of theoretical Reason is, therefore, just the means by which naturalistic Reason serves its basic function as a BGS that defines a form of life.

Knowledge of the Good makes naturalistic Reason unique among BGSs. When ontological scientists discount the illusion of intuitionism, science becomes Reason, and Rational beings discover which goals are good by explaining the nature of the good ontologically. As we have seen, its nature in the spatio-material world is explained by the nature of life. Life begins when a double-action geometrical cause evolves a BGS, and the goals that a triple-action geometrical cause *normally* chooses are good for it because they control conditions that enable it to reproduce if and when the time comes. Controlling relevant conditions is not, by itself, what makes goals good. That makes them functional. What makes goals that are functional good is that they are chosen by a BGS. The nature of the good depends on the essential nature of life, and since its origin reveals that life begins when a double-action geometrical cause acquires a BGS, a goal is good only when a triple-action geometrical cause chooses it from among other goals. Thus, for most living organisms, what is good are the goals serving functions that their BGSs normally chose. But the Good is part of the True, and when reflective subjects acquire naturalistic Reason and know the True, they also know the Good. They know that goals are good only when a BGS choses them over other goals. But since they know that the self is the neural BGS that guides their behavior, they know that the goodness of any goal that *they* choose depends only its being functional, so they choose goals that maximize their control over relevant conditions. Those goals are good for them because that is how beings with naturalistic Reason *normally* choose one goal from among others. The goal that is good for them is the one that contributes most to their natural perfection. Indeed, since they understand how their natural perfection is part of the natural perfection of life on their planet, it depends on what contributes most to the natural perfection of life.

As each situation arises, practical Reason uses input to choose a plan for attaining goals in it, and since the Good is part of the True, knowing the True enables them to determine what is good as the goal in any situation that maximizes its power to control relevant conditions and contribute to natural perfection. In other words, there is a fact of the matter about what is good, and the discovery that value relativism is false has profound implications for beings like us. Since we can discover what is objectively good in the same way as science discovers what is objectively true, we can agree about which shared goals are good for us. We can infer what ought to be done as the best plan for attaining our shared goals in each situation, given the means that are available. Assuming that all the alternatives can be heard, a science based on ontology can predict the plans that naturalistic Reason will choose to solve the problems facing us because that is the outcome of cultural evolution by Rational selection. This chapter explores those predictions, and since practical Reason depends on knowing the nature of the good, it begins by recalling how goals are good for forms of life.

1 The Good as Part of the True

Life begins on suitable planets during major stages of gradual evolution when the first double-action geometrical cause with a BGS evolves by the reproductive mechanism. Since that BGS is able to choose between growth and reproduction and go through reproductive cycles on its own, it replaces an externally imposed reproductive cycle, and it is the kind of geometrical cause that can acquire the function of choosing between other goals. The power it acquires to choose which goal is good is a kind of intelligence. And since its function entails being able to choose otherwise, a BGS has a free will in the sense of being responsible for what it chooses.

When a BGS starts evolving, it is simple, weak, and uniform, and by going through reproductive cycles in a region with finite resources, it imposes natural selection on itself. As it acquires the power to choose between goals in other situations that control conditions that promote its reproduction when the time comes, it becomes more complex, more powerful, and more diverse. Evolving by the reproductive mechanism, it gradually acquires every possible functional power as it becomes possible, adapting to all ecological niches where it can tap acceleration fuel. A stage of gradual evolution ends only when there is no additional goal that it can choose that would enhance its ability to reproduce if the time comes, and in any situation, therefore, the goal that contributes most to the maximum functional power of its form of life is the goal that is good for it. That maximum functional power defines *natural perfection* for its kind, and though it is approached only asymptotically, ontological scientists can use natural perfection to predict the goals that it will pursue. In sum, life is geometrical action aimed at the good, and in regions with finite resources, a BGS necessarily approaches natural perfection for its kind.

Goals are good relative to the kind of BGS that evolves by the reproductive mechanism, and since levels of geometrical organization enable the reproductive mechanism to cause stages of gradual evolution, there are BGSs of four basically different kinds (each of which adapts to many ecological niches). Since they are on successive levels of biological organization, each causes a major stage of gradual evolution that brings a new form of life into existence on a floor of the edifice of life. The prokaryotic BGS on the first floor is little more than a loop of DNA that interacts with other molecules in a simple cell, and using such molecules as input about the situation, it chooses ways of synthesizing proteins that are good for it are because they enable it to reproduce. Goals are good for eukaryotes in the same way, but its BGS is a nucleus containing multiple strands of DNA that enable the cell of which it is part to reproduce sexually as well as asexually. Both BGSs are cell-sharing geometrical causes, but on the other two floors, the geometrical causes guiding behavior are plan-sharing geometrical causes. On the third floor, the animal BGS uses DNA molecules in the nucleus as a genetic plan that cells share through asexual reproduction, and the plan coordinates their behavior in the construction of a body with a neural BGS to guide its bodily behavior through a reproductive cycle. In animals, the *neural* BGS has four levels of geometrical organization, each of which causes a corresponding stage of gradual evolution, and these stages of animal evolution make life on the next higher level of *biological* organization possible. On the fourth floor of the edifice of life, the reproductive mechanism gives groups of animals a spiritual BGS. The evolution of language enables members of spiritual organisms to use language to share a cultural plan that coordinates their behavior, and the goals they normally choose are good for them because they control conditions that enable their spiritual organism to reproduce if and when the time comes.

Since the parts of animals with plan-sharing BGS are cells, the parts are themselves organisms with BGSs, and so they have goals that are good for them. Since these parts can go through reproductive cycles only as parts of an animal, goals of cells are good for them only when they contribute to the good of the organism of which they are parts. Thus, animals routinely sacrifice some of their parts for the good of the whole, for example, by shedding skin cells and behaving in ways that risk injury. Parts of spiritual organisms may also be sacrificed for the good of the whole, for example, by risking their lives in war. But since they are members of a spiritual organism, it is part of spiritual input that has spiritual authority.

Cultural plans for coordinating behavior in spiritual organisms are shared by the use of language, and since linguistic exchanges are a BGS-dependent form of the reproductive mechanism, they cause culture to evolve by judgmental selection. Since there is a series of levels of linguistic organization in spiritual organisms that are both possible and functional, there is a series of stages of spiritual evolution. Goals that are good for members of spiritual organisms are prescribed for them as spiritual input to neural BGSs from the spiritual BGS. Since the members are animals, they are motivated to obey spiritual input because they have a spiritual desire. But the goals that are good depend on the level of linguistic organization.

At the naturalistic neuro-linguistic level, the use of naturalistic sentences (with a subject-predicate grammar) depends on a dominance hierarchy that enables a leader to coordinate their behavior, and the goals that are good for other members are determined by his commands. That is the source of their spiritual authority. Tools can also evolve by technical judgmental selection because the spiritual desire also normally motivates members to follow spiritual input from members with a higher status in the dominance hierarchy.

At the psychological neuro-linguistic level, the use of psychological sentences (whose grammar includes psychological predicates) enables members of spiritual organisms to reflect on their goals and see into one another's minds. They are able to cooperate, and since authoritative spiritual input to members includes rules, it is good for members to follow their cultural plan. That is how their behavior is coordinated in pursing goals that are good for their spiritual organism. There are rules that prescribe roles in plans of coordinated behavior aimed at shared goals, called *institutions*. But rules governing how members treat one another under all circumstances also become part of their shared plan. Called *moral rules*, they have a predicable content because culture evolves by the exchange of arguments about limits on behavior, and since reflective subjects can see into one another's minds, agreement is constrained by their mutual recognition of their equality as parts of their spiritual organism (except for deviations required by institutions, including class structure in civilizations). Besides prohibiting members from harming others unnecessarily, they require members to tell the truth, keep their promises, help others in need, and the like. Members who fulfill their social roles are permitted to choose and pursue goals that are good for themselves as long as they observe the limits imposed by moral rules. Obeying moral rules is good for members because obedience is normally chosen and it contributes to the natural perfection of their spiritual organism as a whole. It enables them to cooperate in pursuing goals that they share.

Morality is an ontologically necessary aspect of the cultural plan of spiritual organisms from the psychological stage on, and during the metaphysical stage, metaphysicians claim that Reason explains the nature of the morally good. The metaphysical linguistic level depends on consciousness, rather than a higher level of neurological organization, and since intuitionistic metaphysicians believe that they know the Good, they believe that they can formulate principles that justify moral rules. But since their theory about Reason is mistaken and leads to false beliefs about Reality, intuitionists are confronted by intractable puzzles in formulating basic moral principles. They believe that Rational beings ought to be moral, but they are not able to explain why it is good for them to be moral when it is contrary to their self-interest, except by giving religious reasons that depend on teleological causes that do not exist.

Those puzzles are solved, however, when ontological science becomes naturalistic Reason because the Good is part of the True. The nature of Reality reveals the nature of the Good, and it explains not only what is good but also why the good is good. Rational beings have a spiritual nature, and that explains why being moral is good for them even when it is not in their self-interest. And since reflective subjects who have naturalistic Reason know that their spiritual nature makes it good for them to be moral, they have a motive to be moral. To see how this solves puzzles about morality, consider what it implies about the basic dispute in philosophical ethics.

The disagreement among intuitionists about moral rules is encapsulated in the choice between two traditional justifications of them: contractarianism and utilitarianism.[102] Contractarians, such as Kant and Rousseau, hold that moral rules are the rules that Rational subjects who act in their own self-interest would mutually accept for governing their behavior toward one another under ideal conditions. Though this determines the content of morality, contractarianism is not a complete explanation of morality because it does not explain why Rational subjects must agree to abide by a contract that limits the pursuit of their self-interest in the first place. This is how utilitarians, such as Jeremy Bentham and John Stuart Mill, contribute to the explanation of morality. They hold that following moral rules is good because it results in the greatest happiness of the greatest number.[103] But utilitarianism is also an incomplete explanation because it fails to explain why we should care about the happiness of strangers and not wish unhappiness for people we dislike (except by insisting, implausibly, that happiness is intrinsically good, regardless of whose happiness it is).

Furthermore, intuitionistic philosophers cannot resolve their dispute about which view is the foundation of morality. Contractarians reject utilitarianism because the principle of utility does not explain the content of moral rules, such as why it is wrong for some members to enslave others when that

---

[102] A third view popular among philosophers, called *virtue ethics*, explains moral goodness as what *flourishing* human beings would do in relevant situations. It is inspired by Aristotelian teleology, the view that the good for human beings is the actualization of the full potentiality of their essential nature. But like Aristotle, it reduces goodness to a regularity about change found in the natural world, and that does not explain why flourishing is good. If *flourishing* refers to the natural perfection of spiritual organisms, naturalistic Reason can explain what is true in virtue ethics. But that is not something that can be explained in a science based on physics because it is blind to geometrical causes, including the spiritual BGS.

[103] But, as hedonists, utilitarians are far from the truth about this. When they explain happiness as pleasure, they are taken in by the intuitionist illusion and believe that pleasure is an object of intuition. Bentham saw the utilitarian good as maximizing the quantity of pleasure in everyone, while Mill corrected this mistake by insisting that there are also qualitative differences among pleasures. But both accept an intuitionistic explanation of the nature of the good. And even if there were phenomenal properties that make a difference in what happens in the spatio-material world, hedonism would be false because there are no teleological causes in a world where every event has an efficient cause.

maximizes the happiness of the group. And utilitarians reject contractarianism because their mutually acceptable rules would require one to act in ways that obviously do not maximize the general happiness, for example, by obligating Rational beings not to lie to a murderer about the location of his intended victim.

But since naturalistic Reason knows the True, it also knows the Good, and since it can explain not only why the morally good is good for us, but also the content of moral rules, it can show how contractarianism and utilitarianism both have part of the truth. Morality is essential to the nature of spiritual organisms (from the psychological stage on), and it is good for its members because it is good for the spiritual organism of which they are part. Thus, the dispute about the content of moral rules can be resolved by recognizing that these intuitionistic moral theories base their explanations on different aspects of moral goodness. Utilitarianism points to an essential aspect of the morally good because it recognizes that the goodness of the goals that we share as members of a spiritual organism is what makes it good for us to follow moral rules, much as the goodness of the goals of the animal as a whole is what makes the goals of the cells good for them. Contractarianism also points to an essential aspect of morality because it recognizes that goals are good for members of spiritual organisms in a way that has no analog in what is good for cells in an animal body. Moral rules evolve by pragmatic selection as self-interested beings argue about how they ought to treat one another, and since reflective subjects can see into one another's minds, the content of the rules that evolve are constrained by a mutual recognition of their basic equality, as contractarianism implies. Both views have part of the truth.[104]

Knowledge of what makes good goals good enables naturalistic Reason to determine which goals are good in situations as they arise. The function of moral rules in spiritual organisms explains the priority of morality over self-interest, and the way that moral rules evolve as part of culture explains their content. To be sure, it is not always easy to determine what morality requires, especially in situations in which wrongs have already been done and all the

---

[104] For a brief and perceptive statement of this philosophical puzzle about morality, see Nagel (2021), and notice that naturalistic Reason reconciles contractarianism and utilitarianism is in much the way that Nagel expects.

alternatives violate one moral rule or another. Principles governing some situations have yet to evolve. And though there are situations, such as war, in which it is good for members to sacrifice their lives for the good of the whole, it is not a routine means of serving the good as it is for cells in an animal body because it must be justified morally. And the need to justify such means would be eliminated if Rational beings controlled the causes of war.[105] But the essential nature of spiritual organisms provides a framework for discovering what is morally good in the situations that arise, and since there is a fact of the matter about it, naturalistic Reason resolves moral disputes like disputes in science.

The morally good is not the only way that goals are good for individuals. Members have a self-interest as well as their spiritual interest. Following morality has priority over self-interest because following moral rules is the ante that Rational beings must put up as members of spiritual organisms to play out lives in which they can pursue self-interest. They have a self-interest because, as animals, they have desires that are good for them, and since mammals with the use of psychological sentences can represent goals of desires as good for themselves as individuals, they can plan ways of behaving in situations that maximize the satisfaction of their desires. This is a way of reasoning about self-interest. It depends on having a spiritual interest because the ability to defer gratification when needed to attain goals depends on the spiritual desire, which evolves during the naturalistic stage when authoritative spiritual input prescribed only goals that were good for the group as a whole. The ability to see into one another's minds leads to the moral equality of self-interested reflective subjects manifested in the content of moral rules, and choosing to do what morality requires matters to them. That is what they must choose to maximize their functional power as members of spiritual organisms whose geometrical action as a form of life is aimed at the good.

Furthermore, there are goals that good for members of spiritual organisms beyond morality and self-interest because spiritual organisms are geometrical

---

[105] If slavery and class structure are necessary for civilization to evolve, the kinds of functional powers that only civilization can evolve, such as writing and its level of technology, would justify a relatively brief historical period during which moral rules accommodate those institutions, if it were judged by Rational beings in an original position who understood what is ontologically necessary about how spiritual organisms evolve and what becomes of them in the end and they did not know what generation they were in. Evil is a necessary part of progressive evolution.

action aimed at the good. Intuitionistic metaphysicians used religious myths to explain why Rational beings pursue such higher goals. But naturalistic Reason explains why they are good. They contribute to the natural perfection of their spiritual organism. And since the maximum functional power of spiritual organisms includes dominion over the natural world, higher goals include the natural perfection of the ecology of which they are part, that is, the natural perfection of non-spiritual life as well as spiritual life.

2 Free Will and Autonomy

As Socrates required from the beginning, metaphysics must show that knowledge of the Good causes knowers to choose goals that are good. The nature of the good enables Rational subjects to know which goals are good, and since it must also explain why good goals are good, Socrates believed that Reason would lead them to choose good goals. That is, to know the good is to do the good. As we have seen, ancient metaphysicians explained how Reason knows the Good in a way that did not come close to passing the Socratic test until the marriage of Platonic metaphysics with Judeo-Christian monotheism, and even if there were teleological causes, that religious explanation would not be fully adequate.

God required beings with intuitionistic Reason to be moral in their treatment of one another, and since those who believed in God knew what is good, they were motivated to do what is morally good because they had a free will that enabled them to be moral and they held themselves responsible for doing so. They could not deny that they had a free will because their conception of the self as a phenomenal subject made it seem self-evident that nothing causes their choices but themselves. (Their beliefs and desires were just objects of reflective intuition, and since nothing immediately present connected those objects to the intentions that followed them, it seemed that reasons did not have the power to cause intentions.) But even if a reason did cause them to be moral, it was not knowledge of the nature of the Good. It was at most the promise that there is an explanation of why the good is good. God was portrayed as creating a natural world populated by beings fashioned in his image for some purpose. But God's purpose in requiring them to live lives in which they had to choose between good and evil was unknown, and so believers had to have faith that God had a purpose that explains why it is good for them to be moral. God's purpose would be revealed only after death in heaven. In the absence of such an explanation during their lives on Earth, they had a self-interested reason to do what morality requires even when it runs contrary to their self-interest or strong animal feelings because choosing goals that are evil would earn them an eternity in hell. But in that case, what caused them to be moral was not an explanation of why the morally good is good.

Faith in God is not necessary for morality. But naturalists who believed that they ought to be moral had to assume that they have a free will in order to hold themselves responsible for following moral rules, and after the Enlightenment, science described a kind of determinism in the natural world that is incompatible with free will. Punishment for wrongdoing is justified only as long as one *could have done otherwise*. But one could not do otherwise if every event in the natural world had a physical cause. As Laplace showed in the 18th century, a God-like mind that knew the laws of physics and the precise state of the universe at any time could predict all future states (and retrodict all past states). They were just a result of the motion and interaction of particles, and since choices were determined by physical causes that lay outside their animal bodies, no one could have chosen otherwise. Without a free will, reflective subjects could not be held responsible for what they choose, so punishment could not be justified. Indeed, reflective subjects explain away their feelings of guilt by attributing them to the superego, a part of the Freudian psyche that has the power to punish the ego. Since it does not make sense to take responsibility for one's choices without free will, the belief that there is no such thing makes one's will unfree.

This was part of the disillusionment with Reason after the Enlightenment. Seeing itself as physical science is what causes Reason's identity crisis, and it is resolved when science and philosophy are united . Reflective subjects with naturalistic Reason know that they have a free will in the sense that they could have done otherwise, and so they know that institutions are justified in using punishment to hold them morally responsible.

Beings with naturalistic Reason recognize that the self is a BGS. Since a BGS is a geometrical cause with the function is guiding behavior to goals that are good, it has the power to choose between goals. Thus, Rational beings know that when they choose a goal in any situation, they could do otherwise, and so they know that they are responsible for what they do. This is not incompatible with complete determinism. Though every event in the natural world has an efficient cause, events in the spatio-material world are effects of geometrical causes as well physical causes. (Naturalistic imagination enables us to understand how BGSs choose goals, and though the quantitative details by which momentum and energy are conserved cannot be measured, they can be understood in naturalistic imagination because they are constituted by the inertial system.) Free will is compatible with determinism because it is the power of a geometrical cause that is expressed by constraining the collective effects of physical causes, not an effect of physical causes, as Laplace believed. The incompatibility of free will and determinism is an appearance caused by physicalist blindness to geometrical causes, and as we have seen, intuitionistic naturalism (empirical lawism) is what leads physicists to believe that physical causes are complete.[106]

To be sure, every organism has a free will. Since they all have a BGS, they all have the power to choose otherwise. That power is responsible for the *autonomous activity* by which we confirmed that the evolution of the first BGS is the beginning of life. A new form of the autonomy of life evolves on each floor of the edifice of life, and since organisms that evolve on higher floors of the edifice of life are more powerful in controlling conditions, they have more autonomy. The question is, at which stage do organisms have enough autonomy to justify using punishment to hold them responsible?

Punishment is pointless in the case of prokaryotes, eukaryotes, fungi, and plants. In many animals, *negative reinforcement* can inhibit behavior, as behaviorists have shown. In pigeons and rats, for example, electric shocks can extinguish kinds of behavior. But such neural BGS mere detach instincts or desires from certain kinds of objects. Only in groups of social animals in which a dominance hierarchy determines a leader is there any suggestion that

---

[106] It has long been recognized that Heisenberg uncertainty shows that it is not impossible to reconcile free will and physical determinism, but since no one could show how that wiggle room might make the will free, this solution seemed preposterous. But this possibility turns out to be true in the spatio-material world because the probabilistic nature of quantum mechanics hides the ontological mechanism responsible for geometrical causes and their power to constrain what happens by physical causes is what make a BGS possible.

a negative reinforcement is *punishment*. When a challenger loses a ritualistic battle with the leader, the aggressive desire is replaced by a desire to submit to the leader, and as we have seen, such a genetically determined desire is what made it possible for spiritual organisms to evolve.

The spiritual BGS is a plan-sharing geometrical cause that coordinates the behavior of its members in pursuit of goals that are good for the spiritual organism as a whole. It provides the linguistic input to the neural BGSs of its members that prescribes goals for them to pursue, and with a desire to submit to spiritual input that normally overrides their other desires, their behavior is controlled by the use of language. A lack of free will (*akrasia*), which is evident, for example, in drug addiction, is due to the weakness of the spiritual desire relative to the addictive desire in keeping the resolution not to take the drug. If the spiritual desire evolved from the instincts that are responsible for the dominance hierarchy in social animals, there is an explanation of the nearly universal use of punishment to hold members of spiritual organisms responsible. By strengthening the desire to submit to spiritual input, it inhibits the impulse to ignore or disobey the relevant linguistic input.

Punishment is probably already used to discipline members of spiritual organisms at the naturalistic stage. Since leaders have the ability to use naturalistic sentences to assign tasks to members in plans of coordinated behavior in advance of acting, they can refer to the misbehavior of members and do ritualistic injury to them in the presence of other members. The expectation of the leader's punishment is internalized, and so when one is tempted not to submit to the spiritual authority, the spiritual desire is felt as fear of punishment.

At the psychological level of linguistic organization, this is the institution called *punishment*. When moral rules evolve, reflective subjects know that they are responsible because they can reflect on their choice about whether to submit to their spiritual desire or not. When they are held responsible, they know how they are responsible, and fear of punishment takes the form of shame. Reflective subjects conceive of their self as occupying certain roles in the spiritual world, and since the ideal self to which they normally aspire is being a kind of member that others respect and admire, the punishment for violating the rules defining their roles, which strengthens their spiritual desire, is felt as the fear of losing the respect of others.

Spiritual organisms at the metaphysical stage differ from those at the psychological stage as so-called *individualistic cultures* from *collectivistic cultures*. Whereas what matters in collectivistic cultures is being respectable in one's spiritual world, what matters in individualistic cultures is being right with the world. When members have intuitionistic Reason, they conceive of the self as having a free will, and punishment for violating moral rules is felt as guilt. Punishment for wrongdoing is not just fear of the loss of status in the eyes of other members of their spiritual organism. Shame can be avoided by keeping the violation secret. But for intuitionists, the fear is guilt because it feels more like a sin that jeopardizes the fate of their immortal soul because it cannot be kept secret from an all-knowing God. Not all choices have moral significance, and beings with intuitionistic Reason also fear shame, for example, when they fail to attain self-interested goals for lack of effort or not deferring gratification. Friends and family may look down on one for such failings, but they do not necessarily impugn one's moral character.

Rational beings have a free will even though it depends on their desire to submit to spiritual input because the spiritual desire helps constitute the geometrical cause whose function is guiding behavior. Spiritual input is linguistic, and the way that language is used to determine the goals that members choose is called *reasoning*. Arguments are understood by constructing the meanings of linguistic representations in metaphysical imagination, and when their conclusions are clear, the spiritual desire puts Reason in charge. Subjects do not represent their spiritual desire as the goal of using reasoning to guide their behavior because the desire is normally satisfied, like the desire to breathe. But when the spiritual desire is opposed by strong desires, the effort in overriding them is felt as willpower. Without a spiritual desire, reflective subjects would not have the self-control to act in their own self-interest, and there would be no issue about the moral limits of self-interest.

The unique function of the spiritual desire explains what Kant referred to as *free will*. He held that an action from duty is chosen freely because it is caused by Reason, and since action from duty is obedience to moral rules when it is contrary to self-interest (or strong contrary desires), it is caused by the spiritual desire. Reason called it the *autonomy* of the will, by contrast to *heteronomy*, in which Reason merely imposes the hypothetical imperative: *to will the end is to will the means*. Actions done for the end of attaining a goal that is desired, including prudence, which is done for the sake of happiness, are heteronomous because they depend on desires that do not help constitute Reason, that is, they depend not only on the spiritual desire but also on desires aimed at goals that are good for the agent. But as an intuitionist, Kant goes wrong. He believes that the morally good is good because we ought to follow the categorical imperative and that we act only on those maxims that we can will to be a universal law of nature *out of respect for law as such*, that is, for Reason as a logical constraint on action. Instead, the motive is the spiritual desire, and though it may be felt as respect for Reason, it helps constitute the geometrical cause that guides one's behavior through cycles of reproduction as members of spiritual organisms.

Hegel is closer to the ontological explanation of free will. He explains Reason as a kind of autonomy that becomes increasingly powerful, much as life does in the course of evolution. Hegel uses the three moments of the dialectic (thesis, antithesis, and synthesis) to explain not only the logical structure of Reality but also how Reality unfolds over time, and so it can be interpreted as an account of how beings with naturalistic Reason come into existence in the spatio-material world. If we interpret the *idea in itself* as space and matter, the *idea outside itself* can be seen as how ideas constitute the natural world, and the *idea in and for itself* can be interpreted as how ideas become subjects constituting a spiritual world. In Hegel's view, this synthesis is *spirit*, which goes through a dialectical change of its own in which it is, first, *subjective spirit* (the reflective subject), second, *objective spirit* (the spiritual world and history), and, finally, *absolute spirit* (when spirit recognizes its nature as Reason). That is, the Absolute Truth is the identity of spirit and Reason.

The Hegelian dialectic can be seen as analogous to the evolution of subjects with naturalistic Reason since it is an increase in the autonomy of life that also culminates in spirit recognizing its identity with Reason. Spiritual life at the naturalistic stage is least autonomous. Members are slaves of the spiritual organism because the desire to submit to spiritual input causes them to follow a leader's commands under threat of bodily injury. At the psychological level, spiritual life is more autonomous because the spiritual desire motivates members to cooperate in following rules that constitute the spiritual world. Since fear of punishment is felt as shame, they are able to violate moral rules in their self-interest when others do not know about it. But since civilization uses the spiritual desire to constitute a class structure, members are, once again, enslaved by their spiritual organism, and after the marriage of Platonic metaphysics and Christianity, the spiritual desire that motivates subjects with intuitionistic Reason is fear of punishment that is felt as guilt. They believe that they lead a moral life because that is what God commands for some unknown purpose that explains why the morally good is good, and they choose freely to follow moral rules even when it is contrary to their self-interest because they have a free will that enables them to be true to their faith (though it is easier when they picture punishment for sin as eternal like in hell).

When subjects have naturalistic Reason, they recognize the self as a BGS in the spatio-material world and know that they have a free will. Since a BGS is a geometrical cause whose function is to choose between goals, they know that they could have done otherwise. Though this power depends on a spiritual desire, they know it helps constitute Reason, and thus, they recognize that punishment for wrongdoing is justified. Since it strengthens the spiritual desire, it may be necessary to restore the health of naturalistic Reason. But normally, punishment is not necessary because naturalistic metaphysics passes the Socratic test of metaphysics. To know the good is to do the good. Since beings with naturalistic Reason know the True, they know the Good, and knowledge of the Good causes them to do what is good. They respect moral limits on acting in their own self-interest even when they could get away with disobedience because they know why following moral rules is good for them. They know the essential nature of life, and so they know that what is good for a living organism is good because choosing goals that are good is what matters to a BGS. Since Rational beings are part of a spiritual organism, they know that what is good for their spiritual organism is good for them. And since they are going through animal cycles of reproduction as parts of a spiritual organism, they know what is good for them as an individual. They know that attaining both the spiritual and the individual good is what matters to them. And they know that everyone following moral rules is the balance between self-interested members and shared goals that maximizes the attainment of goals that are good on both levels of biological organization. Thus, they do what morality requires because they know that that is what they must do to have the kind of life they have. That is what matters to beings with naturalistic Reason. Since the individuals have Reason, while the whole of which they are part is their spiritual life, Hegel was right. The autonomy of life is greatest when Reason and spirit are one. That unity depends on members being moral, and knowing that, Rational beings act morally. They are morally autonomous beings. And naturalistic Reason passes the Socratic test for the practical wisdom of metaphysics.

3   Freedom of Action

The liberal political order was a product of the Enlightenment that expresses the conception of the self that intuitionistic metaphysics justified, and since successive stages of evolution are progressive, it was an advance over autocratic states based on a class structure, which characterizes civilizations during the psychological stage of spiritual evolution. Their citizens did not have equal rights, and their conception of the ideal self was filling their social role in a way that does not bring shame on them and could earn their admiration. The Enlightenment brought respect for the sovereignty and moral responsibility of Rational beings. It was not extended to everyone in the 18th century, but despite disillusionment with Reason, Enlightenment momentum extended equal rights to more and more groups, including women, racial minorities, and gays. This is a predictable consequence of democratic governments because, when everyone has a vote, arguments that treat everyone equally have the greatest political appeal. But ontological science predicts that an argument of the kind that was responsible for the Enlightenment will become part of the cultural plan when Reason resolves its identity crisis, and that will lead to the completion of the progress that began in the Enlightenment.

Government is the institution that chooses goals that are good for the spiritual organism as a whole, and Locke used the social contract to show that the legitimacy of government depends on the consent of the governed. He showed that its legitimate authority is limited to the pursuit of shared goals whose attainment depends on its centralized coordination of everyone's behavior. Ever since the Enlightenment, the spiritual world has become increasingly large and complex, and during the era of endarkenment, government has become more like an administrative state, trying to solve problems of all kinds by dictating plans that determine the goals pursued by everyone. But collectivism is opposite to the individualism implicit in the moral autonomy of Rational beings, and since culture evolves by judgmental selection, it will once again evolve by Rational selection when naturalistic Reason evolves. Ontological science predicts that cultural evolution will restore mutual recognition of Locke's social contract, and Rational beings will find ways to limit the power of government as much as possible to the pursuit of goals whose attainment depends on governmental power.

Locke assumed that, in the state of nature, individuals are Rational beings who can be trusted to be moral, and he used the social contract to show that legitimate governmental power is limited to pursuing goals that can be attained only by the coordination of everyone's behavior, such as punishing wrongdoing fairly, protecting against attacks by foreign powers, and pursuing ends whose means are inherently common, such as roads and money. The Lockean state of nature is just a hypothetical condition, and ontology can accept it, since it represents Rational subjects in the spatio-material world as having moral autonomy. As an intuitionist, Locke believed that Rational subjects would be moral in the state of nature because they knew they were creatures of God with free will, and they would choose goals that respect the rights of others because others were also created in God's image. Ontology agrees because subjects with naturalistic Reason would also be moral in the absence of a government. They would understand the nature of the good, and since they would know that they are parts of spiritual organisms, they would know that they are BGSs whose way of life depends choosing only goals that conform to the limits of morality.

The Lockean social contract holds in the spatio-material world because it describes the outcome of cultural evolution by Rational selection. If all possible alternatives are given a hearing, and if Rational subjects continue to exchange arguments until they all agree about what to do, culture will evolve in the direction of discovering what is true and what is good. When Rational beings discount the illusion of intuitionism, they will know Reality behind Appearance, and since the Good is part of the True, they will attain the transcendental goal of practical Reason. Thus, ontology predicts that, as Rational subjects exchange arguments about the use of laws to coordinate their behavior in the pursuit of shared goals that are good, they will insist that government be limited to the pursuit of goals that cannot be attained by individuals looking after their own interests in the situations they face. Since they conceive of the self as having naturalistic Reason, they will recognize that everyone is capable of judging for themselves what is true and what is good, and since Rational subjects know why it is good to be moral, they will respect the moral autonomy of individuals as much as possible. Thus, they will grant everyone as much freedom as is compatible with the same freedom for all because that maximizes the power of everyone to attain their goals as individuals. Since they know that they are members of a spiritual organism, they will cooperate in pursuing goals that they mutually recognize as good for all of them, and since technological progress has made the spiritual world more complex, there are functions that government must assume that Locke did not imagine. But ontology predicts that naturalistic Reason will lead to the recognition of limits on governmental power that promote the moral autonomy of its citizens as much as possible. That is how autonomous Rational beings flourish in the spatio-material world.

Subjects with naturalistic Reason will agree that punishing wrongdoing is justified because it treats Rational subjects with the respect they deserve. Properly used, it restores the health of the Rational BGS in individuals crippled by the weakness of their spiritual desire. Since practical Reason can serve its function only if it knows the situation in which it chooses goals, Rational beings will deny government the power to censor arguments. On the contrary, they will insist that government protect the right of individuals to speak freely, and that may mean treating digital giants, such as *Google* and *Facebook*, as the public square in an old-fashioned company town, where they were held legally responsible for protecting free speech. But instead of enforcing laws that require individuals to do what the government believes is in their self-interest, they will recognize that individuals are most powerful when they can take responsibility for determining for themselves what is in their self-interest, and they will see the role of government as merely ensuring that individuals have the information they need to know what is good for themselves. Its goal is to enhance their power to take responsibility for doing what is good, not to do it for them.

Locke believed that owning property was the essential means to the pursuit of individual happiness, and so he held that everyone has an equal right to *life*, *liberty*, and *property*. Locke included property because that was the basic means of having autonomy in his time, and with the affluence that comes from the evolution of technology, there may be better ways of ensuring everyone the right to the necessary means.[107] But in the meantime, the equal right to property can lead to unequal wealth, and cultural evolution by Rational selection will have to solve issues about the justification of economic inequality.

4   Equality and Justice

Locke saw private property as the means to happiness because he assumed that Rational subjects in a state of nature acquire private property from the commons by combining their labor with commonly available resources. But in capitalist economies, most of the resources are privately owned, labor is hired by capitalists to earn a profit, and the flow of commodities against money has become a very complex system. Capitalist associations vary in size, from store owners and their clerks to corporations with hundreds of thousands of employees. Some individuals have great incomes and wealth, while those who own very little live paycheck to paycheck. When Rousseau claimed that man is born free but is everywhere in chains, economic inequality and competition for wealth was one of his complaints. But if he was trying to explain morality, as I argued, his ideal was the virtue of reflective subjects before civilization, not equality outcome in a capitalist spiritual organism, and the difference between the inequality of class structure and the inequality of capitalism is crucial in discussing issues of distributive justice.

Marx used class structure to arouse moral outrage, and the main reason

---

[107] See Nagel (2021).

that contractarians reject consequentialism is that it can justify such inequalities as slavery and inherited class structures that maximize total happiness. But since class structure is part of the essential nature of psychological-level civilization, it is not chosen. Since it does not evolve by judgmental selection, it cannot be judged by principles of justice. Marx was right about civilization being the product of a motor of history that operates behind the back of cultural evolution. But the motor is not dialectical materialism. It is the reproductive mechanism. And consequentialists were, at least, pointing to the function for which it was naturally selected. Class structure greatly increased human happiness by greatly increasing the number of humans whose behavior could be coordinated over wide territories. But civilization evolved by the brutal form of group-level natural selection called war, and to believe that the agreements that Rational subjects would reach in the social contract can be used to judge the moral acceptability of class structure is an illusion propelled by Enlightenment confidence in Reason stemming from intuitionistic metaphysics. Rational subjects in ancient Greece accepted slavery because they believed that foreigners were barbarians who deserved no better. Religions justify class structure in all civilizations. Christianity did not condemn slavery in ancient Rome, and it justified the feudal relation that Rational subjects accepted in Western civilization. But the evolution of civilization, like the evolution of the metaphysical stage of spiritual evolution, is ontologically necessary, and by explaining Western civilization as the metaphysical stage of spiritual evolution, naturalistic Reason reveals that the social contract is a test of distributive justice only in cultures that respect the moral autonomy of Rational subjects.

Contractarianism identifies what would be unjust about feudalism, if social systems were chosen, and so the Enlightenment eroded the remnants of feudalism in an aristocratic class and a government based on the divine right of kings—with a violence in the French revolution that only romantics could justify. Marx was outraged by lords benefiting at the expense of serfs, and believing that a similar relation holds between capitalists and workers, he not only founded a science that predicted its overthrow in favor of socialism but also passionately promoted a dictatorship of the proletariat. However, as ontology explains the evolution of capitalism, Marx was mistaken in condemning capitalism as a new class structure.

The motor of history is not the materialist dialectic but, rather, the reproductive mechanism. It caused the gradual evolution of capitalism within Western civilization because it had a legal system that treated associations as having rights and duties like individuals, and capitalist associations are a form of spiritual life.

Psychological-stage civilized spiritual organisms needed a class structure because it enabled the state to coordinate behavior throughout its territory. By giving different property rights to the same pieces of land to two (or more) different classes determined by kinship systems throughout its territory, it had a stable social structure rooted in the land for asserting its political authority. But the only territory-wide institution needed by capitalism is a legal system that treats capitalist associations of various sizes as autonomous beings with property rights and holds them responsible for following the law. Respect for the legal autonomy of associations eventually makes it possible for limited liability corporations to evolve, aggregating private property at whatever scale is required for capitalists to coordinate behavior in the production of commodities most efficiently. To be sure, the relation between capitalists and workers is unequal. But some such hierarchy is required to coordinate productive behavior at the scale of civilization, and since labor power is purchased on a free market, it is a voluntary relation, not a relation between classes based on kinship systems. Workers can become capitalists, capitalists can become workers, and individuals can be both.

Thus, what replaced class structures based on the kinship system was a new form of spiritual life inside spiritual organisms. Since capitalists invest in capital goods and purchase labor to produce commodities when they expect a profit, capitalist associations are double-action geometrical causes with spiritual BGSs that lead them through reproductive cycles in a region of finite resources, and so they impose natural selection on themselves. This is an embodiment of the reproductive mechanism in a spiritual world. Since the capitalist economic system is geometrical action aimed at the good within civilized spiritual organisms, it causes itself to evolve gradually in the direction of greater functional power. Thus, capitalism gives civilized spiritual organisms greater power to control conditions that promote their reproduction than a class structure. But it is also a product of the reproductive mechanism in another way. Civilized spiritual organisms are themselves a form of spiritual life in a region with a finite supply of acceleration fuel (and other material resources), and since they also impose natural selection on themselves, capitalist spiritual organisms gradually replaced feudal spiritual organisms—by war, if necessary.

What replaced the feudal class structure of Western civilization was not, therefore, another class structure. It was, rather, a form of spiritual life that can begin only during the metaphysical stage of spiritual evolution. And since the capitalist system is constituted as a product of cultural evolution by Rational selection, its moral acceptability is properly judged by what Rational subjects would agree to in a social contract. John Rawls (1921-2002) was the foremost defender of contractarianism in the 20th century, and he recognized that capitalism is not a class structure. His first principle of justice accepts the Enlightenment respect of the moral autonomy of Rational beings by requiring that everyone have the maximum liberty that is compatible with a like liberty for all. But his contribution to contractarianism was to extend this moral theory to issues of distributive justice, and for this purpose, he required that principles of justice be acceptable to self-interested Rational subjects in the *original position*, where they were under a *veil of ignorance*. That is, they would have all the scientific knowledge that is relevant in choosing which principle to accept, but they would not be biased by knowing which role they occupied in the social structure. Rawls recognized how capitalism is different from the class structure of civilization by requiring that the unequal benefits of institutions be open to everyone, where that means a fair equality of opportunity to occupy them, including education and the like. And to judge the justness of inequalities, he proposes a principle of distributive justice, called the *difference principle*, according to which inequalities in institutions are fair and just so long as the inequalities benefit the worse off as well as the better off. In that case, the better off are not better off because the worse off are worse off. Indeed, the difference principle implies that the inequality is most justified at that optimal point where any increase or decrease in the difference in the welfare of the worse off and the better off would make the worse even worse off. That is the principle that self-interested Rational subjects would accept in the original position because no one could complain about which position they occupy.[108]

Rawls' difference principle can be used to justify an expansion of the goals that governments ought to pursue beyond the Lockean ideal of protecting equal rights and serving functions that cannot be served by interactions of morally autonomous individuals in civil society. To enforce the difference principle, government would have to tinker with the rules constituting economic institutions to maximize distributive justice. Rawls proposes that, first, the inequalities be adjusted to maximize the benefits to worst off, and, then, that they be adjusted to maximize to benefit the next worse, and so on, level by level, all the way to the best off. They would be allowed to keep the benefits they still had when everyone else was as well off as possible.

This is, indeed, what would be selected in the original position when social science is crippled by physicalism. It assumes that reflective subjects understand capitalism as explained in a science based on physics. But when reflective subjects acquire naturalistic Reason, they will understand capitalism as explained in a science based on ontology, and in the original position, they will come to a different agreement about distributive justice for two reasons.

First, they will see it as a mistake to think that it is even possible to apply Rawls' difference principle in a capitalist economy. It assumes that there a quantitative measure of the benefits of unequal roles in institutions to the individuals who occupy them. That is plausible because money seems to be the relevant measure of benefits in a capitalist economic system. It is a quantity that is conserved in the economic system, and since money can be used to describe regularities quantitatively, economics seems more scientific than any other branch of social science, that is, more like physics in a science based on physics. And money is a plausible measure of benefits distributed since it is what limits the commodities that individuals can buy. It is property that Locke would recognize as the means to the pursuit of happiness. Thus, it seems that government should institute transfer payments from the best off to the worst off until that stops making the worst better off and, then, do the same for each higher income level in turn, leaving the best off with what has not

---

[108] John Rawls (1971).

been transferred to others at the end. This may well determine fair wages and salaries in a large bureaucracy, and so it appeals to collectivists who see government as an administrative state. But capitalist associations produce every kind of commodity that consumers will buy, and since they compete to do it in the most efficient way, a capitalist economic system is more like an ecology in which species change gradually in the direction of maximum functional power, that is, when as much as possible of the flow of money is used to provide commodities that consumers find useful. Administrative interventions aimed at ensuring distributive justice would destroy the usefulness of the labor market for judging how to produce commodities most efficiently, and transfer payments from successful capitalists to workers are bound to distort capitalist selection because capitalists would not make the choices about investments that cause capitalism to evolve in the direction of greater functional power. Investments that maximize net profit after such transfer payments are unlikely to lead to anything like the recent digital revolution.

Second, naturalistic Reason will lead subjects to recognize that physicalist economics is not merely misleading. It completely overlooks the main benefit of capitalism. For example, statistics about income distribution show that the income for households at the mean income in the United States has not increased for the past few decades, while the income of the top one percent has increased substantially. This complaint invites all sorts of political proposals, from justifying governmental intervention in free markets to governmental ownership of the means of production. But beings in the original position who have naturalistic Reason will see economics as blinded by physicalism and empirical lawism in economics. Without recognizing physically irreducible geometrical causes, economists, like scientists in other branches, are unable to understand the essential nature of the object they study, and so they do not recognize that capitalism is a form of spiritual life that evolves by the reproductive mechanism in civilized spiritual organisms. But naturalistic Reason reveals that capitalist associations are spiritual geometrical action aimed at the good in regions of finite resources, causing themselves to evolve gradually in the direction of greater power to produce commodities that consumers are willing to buy. It will be known in the original position that capitalist associations do this in a civilization where the gradual evolution of science and technology continues to provide more efficiently and with increasing diversity all the kinds of commodities that consumers are willing to buy. And it will be known that corporations in a capitalist spiritual organism evolve gradually in the direction of producing as efficiently as possible all the commodities that consumers are willing and able to purchase in their self-interest. Indeed, it will be known that the relevant regularity about change under capitalism is a steady improvement in the material conditions of life that will not end until spiritual organisms are as powerful as possible at controlling nature.

Beginning with the textile revolution in the middle of the 18th century, economic progress has continued through an industrial revolution powered by the steam engine, the use of electricity, indoor plumbing, and motorized transportation to the popular culture made possible by mass communication. The digital revolution is only the most recent step, while nanotechnology and biological engineering are just beginning. Indeed, all rough indications of material well-being, from advances in medicine and technology to the square footage of housing per person, show a steady increase. Economists may dismiss such observations as anecdotal and unscientific because they are not mentioned by equations that describe quantities of money. But naturalistic imagination enables those who have naturalistic Reason to predict that the worst off will steadily become better off until the capitalist form of spiritual life reaches a level of technological power over nature that frees everyone from doing work that is not a labor of love.

The issue about how to attain distributive justice is relevant because it can guide the government in serving its function. From the beginning, spiritual organisms have had an institution that serves the function of making choices about what goals to pursue in the situations that arise, including issues of war and peace with other spiritual organisms and how to punish wrongdoing. And since spiritual organisms are groups of animals, its choices had to provide the high-fueling objects and other resources that its members need for doing the thermodynamic work of going through their reproductive cycles. Production began as hunting and gathering, and after becoming agriculture, it eventually mushroomed into civilizations, with a class structure, in which government tends to stabilize as an autocratic state. But as we have seen, in a spiritual organism with a metaphysical-level of linguistic organization, cultural evolution by Rational selection pays off as the Enlightenment, instituting a liberal political order and allowing a radically new economic system to evolve, and since naturalistic Reason reveals that capitalism is a form of spiritual life that causes itself to evolve, beings in Rawls' original position will come to a different agreement about what is just. Out of respect for the moral autonomy of Rational beings, they will follow Locke and limit the power of government to doing only what cannot be done by individuals acting in their own self-interest. And in serving the function of production, they will take advantage of the nature of capitalism and give government the job of managing that derivative form of spiritual life that causes itself to evolve within civilization.

Government must provide legal institutions that protect property rights, provide markets where free exchanges can be made, and other infrastructure required for capitalism. The host spiritual organism is a region of finite resources, and since capitalist evolution depends on competition, it may have to take measures to prevent monopolies. To ensure that competition is fair, governmental institutions must be constructed so that politicians and administrators do not give advantages to certain capitalists over others in return for benefits to themselves, such as their reelection. Government also has responsibility for ensuring a fair equality of opportunity, for example, by making education available to all and prohibiting discrimination on the basis of race, ethnicity, gender, sexual orientation, and other traits for which individuals are not responsible. Since government needs revenue to serve these and other functions, it must impose taxes, and since there are winners and losers in market competition, progressive taxation of income is not unjust. But the goal of government will be to *tame* capitalism. Most obviously, it must protect the environment, that is, the commons, since damage to it is not a cost that capitalists must pay on the market. Inequalities are inevitable in capitalism, and as long as there are losers, government must provide an adequate social minimum as a safety net. Winners in the capitalist market earn their rewards by winning in a free and fair competition, and everyone will benefit from their having to compete for their rewards because it will provide all possible commodities as efficiently as possible for purchase on the market.

In short, the belief that government should seek to bring about distributive justice in capitalism by transfer payments aimed at equalizing the differences in benefits to winners and losers, echelon by echelon, is as misguided as Marx's belief that government should own the means of production. It may not be as repressive as socialism, but both are caused by the blindness of physicalism to the essential natures of the objects found in the natural world, including beings like us. The basic principle is to let the same combination of efficient causes that brought beings like us into existence in the spatio-material world also give us maximum power in control over nature for serving the function of production, limited only by the need to tame capitalism in order to attain other shared goals, such as protecting the environment, helping those who are worst off, and avoiding other unnecessary harms.

Government is the institution that serves most directly the function of the spiritual BGS in choosing goals that are good, and science based on ontology predicts that beings in Rawls' original position with naturalistic Reason will agree to principles like these for guiding governmental choices in a capitalist spiritual organism. This is not to deny that cultural evolution by Rational selection may also justify other goals of government. For example, capitalism is not a class structure since workers and capitalists are not endogamous groups. It depends only on individuals playing different roles in the market, and it is even possible for everyone to play both the role of capitalist and worker. Capitalists can (and often do) work for a living, and those who work can own stock in corporations. Government may well be justified in helping broaden the ownership of stock. Indeed, if it were necessary to limit the number of slots in the next generation, governments might be justified in guaranteeing new members a stake in the ownership of the means of production so that they can make the most of their potential role as entrepreneurs as well as their role as workers.

The requirement that inequalities benefit the worse off is not violated by some individuals being very rich, at least not as long as there is a safety net of some kind and the worse off are benefiting from the progressive capitalist evolution. There are many ways to ensure that everyone has the means to satisfy their basic needs and have health care. But if unequal outcomes of competition became so great that the inheritance of wealth threatened to establish a class structure based on kinship, there are just ways to prevent it. Parents are not doing wrong when they try to provide for the children and grandchildren. But this does not require enormous disparities in wealth, and government could require great fortunes acquired from capitalist competition by one generation to be redistributed more broadly over future generations. For example, the imposition of a progressive tax on the total wealth that individuals inherit over a lifetime would force a wider distribution to individuals. There would be little reason for the wealthy to oppose such provisions if they could be sure that a constitution would limit the unjustified growth of governmental power, that politicians would not prefer goals that are good for themselves and the groups they represent over those that are good for their spiritual organism as a whole, and that politicians and administrators no longer received rent from those to whom they gave special advantages.

The best form of capitalism and liberal political institutions results in a meritocracy. But even when the government provides freedom and a fair equality of opportunity, respect for the moral equality of everyone is still offended by differences between winners and losers that depend on the genetic lottery. Though everyone has equal rights, they do not all have equal talents, and they are not equally able to win in a capitalist system. Thus, even meritocracy seems unfair. But the answer is not visceral Marxist indignation about the inequality of outcomes. That leads to the shackling or culling out of the more talented. A better plan is to tolerate the inequalities of a spiritual organism where freedom has priority over equality of outcome until it has led to advances in genetics, biology, and neurology that make germline intervention in reproduction possible. It is not available yet, but we will have some power to control traits of offspring by the end of the century. The usual worry about this power is that winners in a meritocratic system would use it to give themselves a further advantage in the genetic lottery. But it is more difficult to discover new genes that improve the most fortunate in the genetic lottery than it is to identify the genes that make them more fortunate. There are plans to treat genetic diseases in this way, though that will be easier since only one or a few genes are responsible for them. However, once science has identified the combination of genes that are responsible for gene-based talents and has discovered how they are expressed, government could mitigate the injustice of the genetic lottery by giving parents the right to choose which traits they want for their children. Loving their children, parents would choose not only to protect them from disabilities like autism and sociopathy but also to give them talents like those that enable winners in the genetic lottery to come out better in a meritocracy. This would gradually eliminate the disadvantages caused by a low IQ, the lack of self-control caused by a genetically determined weak spiritual desire, and when more is learned about how genes affect talents, other deficiencies. Though government would ensure that individuals have all the scientific information needed to make good decisions, it would not make the decisions for them any more than it now chooses marriage mates for them. The freedom to choose whom to marry is already a form of natural selection, and the freedom to choose how biological technology will intervene in one's own germline would allow genetic evolution will keep up with cultural evolution. Meritocracy is a way of honoring excellence, and this way of eliminating the injustice of the genetic lottery would use our respect for excellence to determine the direction of evolution. Leaving the selection of traits up to those who care most about getting it right in the local situation is the best way to ensure that genetic change continues to evolve toward natural perfection.

Given the nature of spiritual organisms, this is the direction in which naturalistic Reason will lead governmental policy, and capitalism may eventually work itself out of a job. No one will have to labor for a living, and everyone will have an equal opportunity and equal talent to compete for the privilege and honor of doing what useful work still has to be done. This is the kind of heaven that has long been predicted by those who try to envision the best way for beings who can see into one another's mind to live together. Having a spiritual nature, they will treat others as they want to be treated. It will be a spiritual world without evil, and everyone will enjoy having the most perfect kind of existence possible.

It is difficult to say how long it will take for beings with naturalistic Reason to realize that possibility. But in the context of the overall course of evolution on Earth, human history is a remarkably short period, and heaven is merely a projection into the future based on the assumption that the problems that challenge us now will be solved. Life can continue to exist on Earth for millions of years—or even billions. And evolution being a creative process, it would not be surprising if the reproductive mechanism, or something like it, overcame limitations in our functional powers that are inconceivable at this stage. We can imagine something called *heaven*, but who knows what will challenge the beings who live in it?

5 Globalization and Its Obstacles

There is a more basic moral issue about who has moral rights that has been ignored in these predictions about the choices that practical Reason will make. Though morality depends on our spiritual nature, reflective subjects are members of different spiritual organisms, and the question is whether moral rules also govern their interactions with one another.

Christianity introduced the principle that everyone is morally equal, and the belief that we have a spiritual nature because we are all created in the image of God outside the natural world was an idealization of the conditions required for reflective subjects to cooperate in pursuing common goals. After its marriage with Platonic dualism in the ancient era, Christianity justified the Western feudal class structure, but Western culture held that slavery is morally wrong. This was moral progress because slavery was an internalization of the hostile relation between warring spiritual organisms. Indeed, war was the exacting group-level natural selection that was responsible for modern reflective subjects (at the psychological stage of spiritual evolution) replacing archaic humans (at the naturalistic stage), and that can be seen as the *original sin* because it gave modern humans knowledge of the difference between good and evil. Humans had evolved desires that enabled them to harm other humans, and since they had to choose between good and evil, moral rules governed their choices. Though moral rules prohibited doing evil to other members of their own spiritual organism, they permitted or even required doing evil to nonmembers. Thus, when agriculture and civilization made it possible to take prisoners from war, moral rules justified using reflective subjects as slaves, and slaves were treated like property, with no moral rights at all.

There was moral progress in the West because, after the marriage of

Christianity with Platonic metaphysics, this way of treating reflective subjects was recognized as immoral. All reflective subjects have the kind of spiritual nature on which morality is based because they can see into one another's minds. They are able to cooperate in pursuit of shared goals, and since nothing prevents it except war and doing evil to one another, practical Reason will recognize that the Christian commandment to love God and love your neighbor as yourself points to the ideal that is good for us because of our spiritual nature. Love of God represents our spiritual interest, which is independent of our self-interest, and love of one's neighbor represents a spiritual organism that includes everyone on Earth as what is good for us. This ideal is called heaven on Earth. But it is just a goal because it depends on removing the conditions, such as scarcity and past wrongdoing, that put us at war with one another. Peace was not easy for intuitionistic practical Reason to achieve because the defense of what is ideal by a metaphysical religion made theological differences, such as the Reformation, serious enough to cause religious wars. Freedom to worship as one chooses was an offspring of Enlightenment. But the cost of religious liberty was the loss of shared justification of morality, and it is evident in the rising tide of endarkenment.

But the confidence in Reason built up in the exchange of metaphysical arguments caused Western culture to evolve by Rational selection, and thus, instead of falling like other civilizations in history, the West acquired unprecedented powers. The diffusion of Enlightenment offspring to other spiritual organisms is globalization, and as we left it, predictions about where this historical development leads were divided between optimists and pessimists, and, now, we can understand the division.

Optimists like Fukuyama took their lead from the Enlightenment and projected its cultural progress into the future as *the end of history and the last man*. Though Enlightenment was followed by disillusionment about Reason, this unique heritage of Western civilization survived. Advances in science continued. Acceptance of liberal political institutions grew. And the evolution of production by capitalist selection spread wealth around the world.

But these bright offspring of the Enlightenment were only one branch of momentum from the classical Western belief in Reason. When Reason rebelled against its metaphysical family, it left intuitionism behind. Though professional philosophers continued to defend absolute idealism, most 20th-century Anglo-American philosophers became cautious under-laborers of science, and the most popular movement was the 19th-century romanticism that became 20th-century endarkenment on the Continent. After a failed attempt to use feelings and will instead of Reason as a means of attaining a transcendental goal, it gave up the belief that anything transcends Appearance and declared that the belief in the True, the Good, and the Beautiful had been shown to be false. Intuitionism gave these intuitionists a different perspective on prospects for globalization. Since they were exploring the disintegration of Western metaphysical-level culture into a psychological-level culture, they had a better insight into the obstacles facing it. Endarkenment was a return of Western culture to the psychological stage without the shared goals of traditional religion, and since its defenders were relativists about facts and values, they sensed how radically different other spiritual organisms might be from the West. Optimism about globalization seemed naïve, and endarkenment led historicists, like Huntington, to predict a clash of civilizations.

Using this account of post-Enlightenment developments in Western culture to explain the foundations for optimism and pessimism about globalization, naturalistic Reason can resolve their dispute and enable us to predict what will happen. When ontological science recognizes itself as naturalistic Reason, Reason resolves its identity crisis, and since it will restore belief in Reason, we must agree with optimists. Not only will there be certainty about the foundation from which science, political institutions, and capitalism sprang, but there will be a compelling way of resolving the disputes that arise. The main obstacle to globalization is that Western and non-Western spiritual organisms are at different stages of evolution. But bridging the difference does not require any genetic change.[109] Metaphysics is just a unique

---

[109] But if Wade (2014) is right about civilization imposing selection pressures to which their populations have adapted, populations of tribal spiritual organisms may have behavioral dispositions that impede the adoption of Western institutions. Moral autonomy and other forms of self-control, like submission to the force field of spiritual authority that helps constitute class structure, may depend on the evolution of a spiritual desire to submit to linguistic input that is more abstract than in tribal societies and whose authority is not so closely based on kinship relations. Self-conception depends on the attachment of the spiritual desire to a certain kind of ideal, and so it may be more difficult for some reflective subjects to conceive of the ideal self as submitting to general principles.

argument that any reflective subject can understand. Since that is the kind of change that can come from cultural diffusion, naturalistic Reason leads us to expect that members of all spiritual organisms will soon have naturalistic Reason. Since Western spiritual organisms are headed toward the utopia that is possible for beings who understand their own natures completely and live lives seeing into one another's minds, the destiny of humanity seems to be heaven.

However, this optimism is still about the long run, and in the short run, there is a local hurdle on Earth to be overcome. Though naturalistic Reason predicts an imminent scientific revolution, that is only the beginning of the revolution in Western culture. It culminates in a scientific explanation of philosophy, and the discovery of the theoretical identification of mind and brain will enable those who discount the illusion of intuitionism to know Reality behind Appearance. But the widespread acceptance of the naturalism of science has made the problem of mind a topic in popular culture, and its solution is subtle. What makes mind and body seem to have opposite natures is the illusion of intuitionism, and so its solution depends on discounting the illusion. But since falling for the intuitionist illusion is what is it like to be a mammal, discounting it is literally counterintuitive. Though intuitionistic metaphysics, as part of intellectual culture, has been internalized by educated Westerners, they think they know that it is childish, if not foolish, to believe that Reason can know Reality behind Appearance. That makes it hard to predict how long it will take for naturalistic Reason to catch on in the West. And Westerners have a leg up over non-Westerners.

Naturalistic Reason must overcome a much higher hurdle in non-Western spiritual organisms because culture at the psychological level does not give reflective subjects recognition of their consciousness. As naïve realists about perception, they are inside consciousness. To be sure, it is possible for reflective subjects to discover that they are conscious without having internalized a culture that has evolved by the exchange of intuitionistic metaphysical arguments. They can know that they are conscious as we did in *Chapter 1*, by reflecting on what it is like to perceive the world and recognizing the difference between the unity of consciousness and the unity of the natural world. But understanding the unity of the natural world depends on believing that what exists outside consciousness is a world with the nature described by a science committed to ontological naturalism, and since that is part of the culture that is still diffusing from the West, it could be more difficult for non-Westerners to learn to discount the intuitionist illusion than it seems at first.

In the West, the rise of science came at the expense of religion, and so endarkenment gives pessimists an insight into another obstacle to globalization. Optimists see cultures as just different ways of talking and praying. But one does not have to be religious to recognize that religion answers basic questions that reflective subjects ask about themselves and the spiritual world in which they find themselves, and pessimists doubt that culture will change as easily as fashions in dress. In civilizations at the psychological stage of spiritual evolution, religion enables members of spiritual organisms to share a world in which the difference between good and bad seems to be part of what exists independently of them, and so religion will be threatened by modernity even when it is not defended as relativism about values. Since religious institutions have anti-bodies to protect themselves, pessimists rightly expect globalization to arouse resistance. The violence of radical Islamist terrorism may be only a sample of what history has in store for the West.

Even if violence can be avoided or managed, optimism about globalization must be tempered. Since Western culture will be informed by naturalistic Reason, it might be expected to penetrate the barriers protecting non-Western religions. It explains the nature of the good by the nature of life, so it does not deny that the difference between good and bad is built into the nature of what exists. Since it explains how reflective subjects share a spiritual life, it supports values that fit comfortably in spiritual organisms. But there could still be an emotional gulf that can only be overcome by a new generation inheriting a radically different culture. Religions are able to justify a class structure in psychological-level civilizations because it gives reflective subjects a self-conception by which they organize their lives and frame the story they tell about themselves. Conceiving their ideal self as occupying an honorable role in a spiritual world, they feel shame when they do what is wrong. They know that when it is found out, they will be despised by others and lose their social status. Thus, the hurdle that naturalistic Reason must overcome is not just the intellectual challenge of understanding how it is possible for naturalists to know Reality behind Appearance. It must enable reflective subjects to conceive of their self as a BGS that knows that it is a BGS in the spatio-material world, and knowing the good, they must do the good.

As we have seen, this is possible for subjects with naturalistic Reason. Recognizing that they share a spiritual life with others, they know not only what is morally good but also why the morally good is good, and that motivates them to do what morality requires. They know that the BGS that defines forms of life means that it is possible for them to choose otherwise, and knowing free choices by reflective subjects depends on their spiritual desire, Rational subjects take responsibility for choosing goals that are good and treating others morally.

But this may be more difficult for non-Westerners than it appears to Westerners because they must do what is right even when there is no chance of wrongdoing being discovered by others. That is, their spiritual desire must make them fear guilt rather than shame. That may not seem like much of a challenge to Westerners because, even if they do not believe in a transcendent God, because they inherit a metaphysical-level culture in which reflective subjects conceive of the self as having a free will and know that they are expected to hold themselves responsible for their choices. But acquiring this kind of self-conception may require a more radical change in non-Westerners than appears at first because their spiritual desire must make them fear justified punishment whenever they do what is wrong, regardless of what others know about it. The psychological gulf between the self-conception internalized by members of a collectivist spiritual organism and the self-conception internalized by members of an individualist spiritual organism may be so great that naturalistic Reason can spread by diffusion to non-Western spiritual organisms only after the arguments accumulated as culture have changed and new a generation internalizes a radically different conception of the self. Hence, it is hard to predict how long it will take for members of non-Western civilizations to routinely do what is morally right because it is right.[110]

There is, however, one way that globalization is bound to be more problematic than expected. It is caused by the means of globalization that optimists generally prefer. They expect cultural differences to be bridged by a global labor market in which reflective subjects move freely between nations. But immigration from non-Western to Western spiritual organisms is more likely to arouse resistance to globalization. Civilization depends on members trusting one another even when they are strangers, and since optimists about globalization are members of an elite strata, they tend to underestimate how badly trust can be disrupted by immigration. Ordinary reflective subjects lead lives as one self among others in a face-to-face spiritual world, and the happiest individuals in the West seem to be members of families who live in communities where they trust one another. They share a language and culture, and knowing that they do, they take pride in doing work that contributes to the pursuit of common goals. It is easy for immigrants from other Western spiritual organisms to assimilate because they share a self-conception from a metaphysical-level culture and, at most, they must learn a new language and customs. They respect the moral autonomy of others, and though they may not share a religion, many share a sense of playing an essential role in the natural order. But when immigrants have a self-conception that was acquired in a psychological-level culture, assimilation may be more difficult. It is still possible for them to form a new identity when their numbers are small. But in larger numbers, their immigration can extinguish the sense of wellbeing that natives otherwise enjoy from living in a community with others. And when there are enough immigrants to cluster in sealed-off neighborhoods, the damage to spiritual organisms is obvious. Those who live through these disruptions of their communities have a sense of something valuable being destroyed by globalization, and the likely outcome is opposition to globalization.

Globalization by migration may be resisted in a complementary way by non-Western civilizations. Autocracy is the natural form of the state in psychological-level spiritual organisms, and though it is inherently stable, the

---

[110] For a pessimistic view of how long it will take, consider the representation of the psychological gulf between the East and the West presented in E. M. Forster (1924) *Passage to India.*

state may not only prohibit immigration but also seal off their spiritual organism from Western influences. The growing power of digital technology can be used to establish institutions that resist cultural diffusion. For example, the Chinese Communist Party is using nearly universal video surveillance, facial recognition, and artificial intelligence to keep track of everyone, and it has established a system that awards its citizens social merits and demerits based on their behavior. Since this includes what they say to others and learn from them, it can control which arguments they consider. This form of political correctness is a potentially foolproof ideological mechanism in a shame culture, where reputation is what matters most. The Chinese people may be content to live indefinitely without political freedom and accept rule by an elite class, and as growing Chinese economic and military power challenges Western hegemony, the Chinese system may become a model for establishing super-stable autocracies in other civilized spiritual organisms that have not inherited a culture that respects the autonomy and responsibility of Rational subjects. And growing opposition to the globalization of naturalistic Reason may lead to a power struggle between nations that could break out in war.

6   Short-Term Goals

Though the obstacles to globalization are serious, cultural evolution is progressive, and ontology sides with optimists in the longer term. It may be surprising that human societies are a form of life. But as naturalistic Reason explains the nature of life and the course of evolution, groups of language-using mammals that live together in a territory sharing a culture are as much geometrical action aimed at the good as prokaryotes, eukaryotes, and multicellular organisms. Though they are all forms of cellular geometrical action, their reduction to spatio-materialism reveals that animals are different from other multicellular organisms. Their cellular geometrical action includes neural geometrical action, which means that mammals are conscious. And spiritual organisms are different from other animals because they are groups of conscious animals whose neural geometrical action includes linguistic geometrical action by which their behavior is coordinated in pursuit of shared goals. They are capable of acting as a whole in their own interest, and since members of one spiritual organism can see into the minds of members of other spiritual organisms, they know that there is a way in which they are all basically equal. That is the foundation of morality among members of spiritual organisms, and naturalistic Reason will lead spiritual organisms to respect one another's moral autonomy in a similar way.

This attitude will temper the contempt for the integrity of spiritual organisms evident in the expectations of contemporary optimists about globalization, and assuming that the clash of civilizations does divert it, the direction of human history is clear. The cultural revolution in the West will spread naturalistic Reason to spiritual organisms everywhere, reforming institutions so that they respect the moral autonomy of Rational subjects, and we expect humans everywhere to be treated equally and have as much freedom as possible under that condition.

It is not possible to predict what will happen in detail because the choice depends on the situations that arise and the alternatives available. But beings with naturalistic Reason will apply their knowledge of the nature of the good to the current historical situation, and as the first step, practical Reason requires all of them to take as much time as is necessary to digest the implications of the unification of science and philosophy. No spiritual organism should use what it reveals about the natural world to determine preemptively the course of history for other spiritual organisms. Since members of different spiritual organisms have different cultures, they can have different interests, and success in solving problems depends on reaching agreement about shared goals and the means they have of attaining them. Let me suggest more tentatively some points that seem most relevant in the short term.

Beings like us are members of distinct spiritual organisms, each with its own territory, language, and culture. As a form of life, spiritual organisms have goals that are good for them, but they are not necessarily in harmony with the goals of other spiritual organisms. Since what is good for spiritual organisms is good for their members, their members have interests that do not necessarily coincide. But as a form of life, spiritual organisms are sovereigns in their own territories, and respecting their autonomy as moral agents is good for everyone. Guided by naturalistic Reason, spiritual organisms will discover a way to overcome the obstacles to globalization. The ultimate goal that they can all share is bringing about a global spiritual world where everyone has maximum freedom and an equal opportunity to enjoy the benefits of capitalist production. But the plan for the short term must rely mainly on the diffusion of culture from the West and cultural evolution by Rational selection in other spiritual organisms. The attempt to solve problems by migration between spiritual organisms will only exacerbate them. In the end, when beings like us everywhere on Earth are making plans for their progeny to live for millennia or even millions of years to come, there may be no need to control borders separating civilized spiritual organisms. But it is not easy to predict how long that will take. Nor what obstacles will turn up along the way. In the meantime, respect for the autonomy of spiritual organisms argues for granting independence to subpopulations with distinct languages and cultures, such as the Basque in Spain and France, the Kurds in Turkey and Iraq, the Uighurs in China, and the Chechens in Russia. But a global spiritual world is a single spiritual organism everywhere, and for peaceful cultural evolution by Rational selection to bring it about, some more immediate goals ought to be pursued.

Since life is a product of the reproductive mechanism, there is one short-term goal with a high priority. Population growth is the ultimate cause of the scarcity by which organisms impose natural selection on themselves, and in the case of spiritual organisms, natural selection can take the costly form of war. Though war was the form of group-level natural selection required for psychological-levels spiritual organisms to evolve from those at the naturalistic level, the outbreak of war is something that Rational subjects must control in order to bring about a peaceful global spiritual world. Since evolution is a product of the reproductive mechanism, population growth is a predicable cause of war. Scarcity can not only bring about fighting between spiritual organisms but also cause migrations. Overpopulation is not a problem in metaphysical-level spiritual organisms, but it is out of control in some spiritual organisms at the psychological level.[111] It is likely that scarcity in them will eventually cause large-scale migrations to spiritual organisms

---

[111] For example, the current population of Nigeria is about 190 million, and if it continued at its current growth rate of about 2.5% per year, it would double almost three times before the end of the century, giving Nigeria alone a population of around 1.5 billion.

where population size is under control, and this could cause conflicts that would make Huntington's warning about "bloody borders" seem optimistic.

Living at peace is a goal that is good for all spiritual organisms since their survival is at stake, and there is an obvious way to avoid war. Spiritual organisms are sovereign in their territory, and since they pursue goals that are good for themselves, they are in what Hobbes called a *state of nature*. It is potentially a war of all against all, and the solution is a social contract. But it is not necessary to set up a sovereign power over all spiritual organisms when they are guided by naturalistic Reason. Spiritual organisms can agree to principles governing their interactions that will prevent the conditions that cause war and make it possible for them to benefit from their interactions, and since they will know that it is good, they can be trusted to take responsibility for doing what is good. Spiritual organisms could control the basic cause of war by each taking responsibility for their own population growth. To be sure, such a social contract would impose a greater burden on some spiritual organisms than others, and since Western technology is largely responsible for causing overpopulation, Western spiritual organisms may be expected to provide technological assistance in order to ease the extra burden on limiting populations that are already mushrooming. But controlling population growth would be a local responsibility, and it would not have to be brought about by war.

Assuming that war can be avoided, the benefits of progressive evolution of capitalist production justify agreeing to conditions that facilitate free and fair global trade. In the near term, the evolution of production by capitalist selection will increase control over the natural world, and in the longer term, it promises to end the need for labor. The expansion of capitalism may threaten the environment, and spiritual organisms share an interest in protecting it for future generations. But there is no human threat to the natural environment that would not be mitigated, if not overcome entirely, by curtailing population growth. In the meantime, spiritual organisms can use global-level market mechanisms to pursue that shared goal. For example, a universal tax on carbon fuels could adjust prices uniformly and globally in a way that would promote technological development that is friendlier to the environment. The goodness of this goal does not depend on the threat of climate change. A sufficient reason is sharing the non-renewable resources available on Earth with the many generations of beings like us to come, instead of squandering it in just a few generations.

The long-run direction of evolution is clear. Since Rational subjects have animal bodies in the natural world, practical Reason will guide the use of advances in science and technology to control all the conditions that enable them to reproduce, including cures to genetic diseases as well as diseases caused by other forms of life, and enhancements in their neural BGSs through germ-line intervention in reproduction. With the ability to see into one another's minds, they share the natural world, and they will find a perfect way for their lives to fit with it. In that garden, Rational subjects will constitute a spiritual world in which they lead their lives. Culture will evolve by Rational selection in the direction of a global spiritual world that has long been envisioned as heaven. Beings like us will not only enjoy all the satisfactions of civil life but they will also be relieved of work that does not actualize their greatest potentials. Goals that are good for a spiritual organism are good for its members, and though language-using animals must eventually die in order to live at all, they participate in the life of a spiritual organism that may never die. There is no telling what form it will take. But the long-run outcome of evolution has been obvious to every dreamer who could envision the kinds of lives that are possible for beings who can see into one another's mind. It is treating others as you would like to be treated by them. And for Rational beings, that means respecting their moral autonomy as you would like your own moral autonomy to be respected.

How to apply practical Reason in the short run is the challenge that beings like us face now. We understand goodness, and we must choose a plan that enables us to pursue all the goals that are good for all of us in the historical situation confronting us. Cultural evolution depends on the exchange of arguments, and since Rational subjects have faculties of imagination that enable them to entertain the full range of possible arguments, cultural evolution by Rational selection is bound to identify a plan that comes close to contributing as much as possible to the natural perfection of our kind. Knowledge of the True gives us the power to do what we know we ought to do. There is only one way that it can go wrong.

It is the use of the *ideological mechanism* to control cultural evolution. There is a long history of autocratic governments, elite classes, and religious institutions using it to control reflective subjects, and it has been defended on the most righteous of grounds. It works by excluding arguments of certain kinds instead of allowing arguments from all sides to have a fair hearing. It can take many forms: censorship, punishment for blasphemy and heresy, enforcement of taboos, political correctness, and the marginalization, demonization, or extradition of those who will not be silenced. This cripples cultural evolution by Rational selection because individuals cannot judge arguments that are not proposed. Since the ideological mechanism generates consensus by rigging the reproductive mechanism responsible for cultural evolution, its use puts the utopia that can otherwise be expected in peril.

CHAPTER 12:
THE BEAUTIFUL

Since we lead our lives by making choices, beings like us are inclined to assume, even in endarkenment, that there is a real difference between good and bad. We may not know how, but it is not just whatever we happen to choose or prefer. It is paradoxical to believe that the good is just whatever we happen to prefer because, then, its goodness does not justify preferring it. We know that it matters what we choose, and we think of goodness as somehow based in Reality. Hence, the discovery that we have practical Reason will be reassuring. But to those reconciled with endarkenment, it may come as a surprise that beauty is not in the eye of the beholder. Indeed, it is avant-garde to deny that beauty has anything to do with fine art. But goals of Reason are determined by its nature as a BGS, and since Reason is a BGS that knows that it is a BGS in the spatio-material world, it knows the nature of the beautiful. A BGS has a third subfunction, and theoretical Reason enables our BGS to serve its third function as completely as possible. The Beautiful is part of the Good, and since the Good is part of the True, the Beautiful is part of the True. Since naturalistic Reason knows the nature of the beautiful, it avoids a certain kind of error in serving the BGS's output subfunction.

Practical Reason serves the basic function of a BGS, choosing goals that promote conditions that enable us to reproduce, but since it chooses not only goals but also the means to attain them, a subfunction can be distinguished. In order to distinguish it from the use of feedback to attain a single goal, a BGS was defined in *Chapter 5* as a geometrical cause with three input-output systems, serving three essential subfunctions: input, choosing, and output. When it chooses a goal that is good in a situation, it also chooses means for attaining it, and the latter choice is a distinct function since it is made in a situation for which a goal is given. In more primitive BGSs, each choice is made by a distinct tier of subsystems: an upper tier, made up of the input and choosing systems, uses input to choose a goal that is good, and a lower tier, made up the input and output systems, uses input to choose means for the goal chosen. But in subjective animals with a third level of neural organization or higher, all three subfunctions are based on a faculty of imagination, and since they use imagination to choose goals for the situation by comparing alternative plans, each of which includes means for attaining the ends it involves, the lower and upper tier functions are both served by all three subsystems (the three circuits identified in the mammalian forebrain). Nevertheless, what is good in the situation depends on determining the best means to ends, and since this latter function can be distinguished from practical Reason, the Beautiful is part of the Good.

Since the Good is part of the True, theoretical Reason knows not only the nature of the good but also the nature of the beautiful. The goal that it is good for a BGS to choose in any situation is the one that contributes most to the maximum functional power of its kind, and it is a plan that uses the best means to attain the ends involved. The best means are the most efficient means since BGSs use acceleration fuel to do thermodynamic work. The criterion is, as always, the principle of optimality, or approaching as closely as possible the ideal of the doing the most with the least (keeping in mind there are two ways of doing better: using the same means to attain more ends, and attaining the same ends with less in the way of means). Optimal means are maximally efficient because goals are good when they contribute as much as possible to maximum functional power. That is the direction of gradual evolution, and when the means do the most to attain good goals with the least cost, they are optimal because that is the most that the means used can contribute over an entire reproductive cycle to controlling conditions that make it possible to reproduce, if and when it chooses to. Thus, ontology explains the *nature of the beautiful* as maximum efficiency in the use of means to attain a given end. Rational subjects can judge the optimality of means by using their faculties of imagination to compare alternatives, and when naturalistic Reason serves this function, it is *aesthetic Reason*. Since the Beautiful is part of the True, theoretical Reason enables naturalistic Reason to avoid a certain kind of error in judging beauty.

To be sure, when theoretical Reason infers what is true as the best explanation of what is found, its inferences depend on comparing alternatives in imagination, and they are also judged by the principle of optimality. The best explanation is the one that explains the most about what is found in the world with the least in the way of causes. Since the best explanation, given what is found, is the most beautiful, aesthetic Reason might be seen as a subfunction of theoretical Reason. Indeed, theoretical physicists confess that beauty often plays a crucial role in reaching their conclusions. But the Beautiful is not part of the True in the same way that the Good is part of the True because the True is what corresponds to Reality, regardless of how it is discovered.

The Good is what contributes most to natural perfection, and the Beautiful is part of the True because the Good is part of the True and the Beautiful is part of the Good. Naturalistic Reason reveals goals are good when they contribute to maximum functional power over a reproductive cycle, and since that depends on the efficiency of the means used to attain them, means are beautiful when they do the most with the least.

1   Fine Art

Rational subjects can separate the Beautiful from the Good. That is a good explanation of the evolution of fine art in Western culture. Since meanings of sentences are constructed in imagination, verbal behavior drives imagination, so imagination can be used to judge the best means to ends of any kind. In all cultures, an appreciation of beauty is evident in the decoration of tools and precious materials and in the elaboration of vocal and bodily movements into music and dance. And it has been used to celebrate the spiritual ever since modern humans evolved. Otherwise, it is mostly just an embellishment of objects or activities that are used for other purposes, showing the exuberance of imagination. But in the West, there are works of art created to attain a transcendental goal.

Works of fine art are created for their beauty. Various mediums are used, from painting, sculpture, and architecture to music, dance, drama, and literature. These objects have an exceptional beauty that cannot be explained by any other purpose that they may also serve. Works of fine art can be identified in non-Western cultures, but there is evidence of something unique about Western art. Using the judgments of critics, historians, and others especially familiar with art to identify outstanding artistic accomplishments, statistical methods show that the number of great artists in Western culture far exceeds the number in non-Western cultures.[112]

Since metaphysics is what distinguishes Western from non-Western cultures, the likely explanation is that fine art is symptomatic of a culture evolving by Rational selection. Rational subjects know that beauty is a worthy goal since it is a transcendental goal of Reason. It is part of the Good, which is part of the True, and since the True is correspondence to Reality behind Appearance, the Beautiful must also correspond to Reality in some way. By creating objects whose primary purpose is to be beautiful, artists show the awesome power of Reason. Indeed, this motive is explicit in the motto of the romantic era: art for art's sake.

From the artist's point of view, the medium of fine art provides the means, previous accomplishments and techniques are the situation, and the goal is to create an object or performance in which the means are optimally suited to an end that they attain. Since a work of art can approximate the ideal of doing the most with the least, there are two ways that it can be optimal. It can either achieve as much as possible with the same means, or it can achieve a similar end with as few means as possible. Thus, it is possible, for example, to appreciate the beauty of both classical painting and impressionism. In the former, it comes from recognizing how much was accomplished by certain means, and in the latter, it comes from recognizing how an end was accomplished with so little in the way of means.[113] To put it negatively, classical paintings are less beautiful when they could attain more with the same cost in means, and impressionist paintings are less beautiful when they could attain the same end with even a lower cost in means. In both cases, there is plenty of room for experiments in beauty. Classical paintings may be more beautiful when they use more means to attain a greater end, and impressionist paintings may be more beautiful when they use fewer means to attain a lesser end.

---

[112] Murray (2003).

[113] Even works of modern art that seem downright ugly, like pop art, can be appreciated as beautiful, if they are seen as using the least in the way cultural means to show something profound about history, such as the degeneration of the Enlightenment into Endarkenment.

There are many fine arts, and since they all have a history, there are many ways of manifestly approaching the optimum of doing the most with the least. But since the Beautiful is part of the True, there is a fact of the matter about what is beautiful, and theoretical Reason enables us to avoid the error of judging beauty by standards other than the kind of optimality appropriate to aesthetic Reason.

The appreciation of beauty may be in the eye of the beholder, but not the nature of the beautiful. Since the Beautiful is part of the Good, it is a transcendental goal of Reason. That means that we must discount the intuitionist illusion to know the nature of the beautiful. But it does not mean that the beautiful can exist without consciousness. The nature of the good depends on the nature of life, and since the living Rational subjects who can know what is beautiful are conscious, its existence is constituted in part by its phenomenal appearance. But enjoying fine art is not the only role of aesthetic Reason. Beauty can be appreciated in the means to any end, including how we live our lives.

2 Beautiful Lives

Beauty is an appropriate criterion for judging lives of Rational subjects. They all face the same situation because they are born into the world as particular organisms, with certain talents and opportunities. And since they will all eventually die, they have the same goal: using the means available to make the most of their lives. Thus, the beauty of a life depends on how close it comes to making the most of the means available for reaching that end.

Rational subjects are members of spiritual organisms, and since a spiritual desire puts Reason in control of their behavior, they lead lives in which they treat others morally. But that is not the only way that a life is good. For one thing, as Kant held, prudence is part of the good life. Seeing Reason as a formal constraint on choices, Kant used the *categorical* imperative to explain morality. But since everyone has the goal of happiness, he used the *hypothetical* imperative to explain why Rational subjects ought to be prudent. Prudence is a means to happiness, but there is more to leading a good life. It depends on fully actualizing one's potential, or as defenders of Aristotle put it, by flourishing.

Aristotle explained virtue as the kind of excellence that actualizes the essential nature of a Rational animal. He saw virtue as a state of character in which one chooses the mean between various extremes. Courage is the mean between rashness and cowardice, temperance the mean between self-indulgence and insensibility, good temper the mean between irascibility and lack of spirit, and modesty the mean between bashfulness and shamelessness. In other words, Reason tells us that virtue is moderation. It expresses one's character, and Rational subjects are rightly held responsible for their character because the motivation and judgment required to be virtuous are acquired by practice in submitting to this spiritual input from Reason.

Aristotle held that virtue is good for Rational animals because it actualizes their nature and makes them happy. But his explanation of the nature of the good was incomplete. The good is not good because it is the end toward which *natural change* is observed to occur in substances of some natural kind. That is merely what happens necessarily in a world with final causes. In the spatio-material world, the good is good for an organism because it contributes to the natural perfection of its form of life, and since life has an essential nature, that is something that can be explained. Though moderation is one way that the life of a Rational subject can be good, there is more to leading the good life than self-control—even if that is assumed to include being moral. Excellence of many kinds in leading a life as part of a spiritual organism is necessarily good since the good is what contributes to its natural perfection.

Like all forms of life, goals are good for Rational subjects when they contribute as much as possible in a particular situation to the maximum functional power of their kind over a reproductive cycle. Since they are born into families in a spiritual world made up of subjects who can see into one another's minds, the good life begins by making the most of those relations and helping attain shared goals that are good. But Rational subjects understand the human condition, so they know that there is an enormous range of good goals that they might choose to pursue beyond those that benefit the self, family, and even their spiritual organism. They can envision goals that benefit other spiritual organisms or other forms of life, and some are far more difficult to attain. Since they are born into the world as particular individuals, with certain talents and opportunities, and know they will die, Rational subjects can make the most of their means for leading a life by taking advantage of their opportunities, developing their talents, and continuing to grow in the mastery of skills or disciplines that are required to attain more ambitious goals that are good. They might be goals of Reason itself, such as creating a work of fine art, making a discovery in science, or applying technology in a new way. But one can also be a genius at friendship, parenting, statesmanship, and even comedy.

These are beautiful lives. Judged by the principle of optimality, they are ways of making the most out of the means for leading a life. And being beautiful, they are good because the Beautiful is part of the Good.

Since life begins at birth, this understanding of how lives are beautiful is something that Rational beings acquire as they grow up. Leading a life is the construction of a work of art in real-time. It is always a work in progress. But since we can compare lives, we can judge the beauty of a morally good life. And making the most of one's life in this way is good for us, as ontology explains the nature of the good because it comes closer to natural perfection for our form of life.[114] And if one can look back on a life that is beautiful in this way, one can die happy.

3   Natural Beauty

There is a beauty about every form of life. But Rational beings are unique because the beauty of their lives comes from understanding the nature of the beautiful and how it is an essential part of what is good. All forms of life are BGSs choosing goals that are good for them as situations arise, and since they are geometrical action aimed at the good in a region of finite resources, they cause their kind to evolve in the direction of natural perfection. They are part of the beauty of nature. But only reflective subjects recognize the beauty in nature, and when naturalistic Reason enables them to understand why, their aesthetic appreciation of natural beauty is complete.

Perception may make the beauty of nature seem obvious, but the more we attend to it, the more beautiful nature seems to be. The ancient Greeks saw the beauty of fine art as the imitation of nature, and late in the Enlightenment,

---

[114] This is kind of excellence that Murray (2003, *Chapters 18-22*) calls the *Aristotelian principle* of happiness, though what he describes is probably more ambitious than what Aristotle had in mind.

when deism and natural religion replaced traditional religions, the beauty of the natural world seemed so overwhelming that it was called *sublime*, a kind of beauty that is so great it could not be measured, or even imitated by art. The term belies their inability to explain the perfection they found in nature. Its cause was a mystery recognized only in aesthetic appreciation of it. However, ontology explains not only the perfection found in the natural world but also why Rational subjects recognize it as beauty, and solving the mystery about the nature of the sublime only enhances the aesthetic enjoyment of nature's beauty.

The natural world is constituted by space and matter. But those substances are ontological causes of what is found in it in two different ways, both of which contribute to its sublimity. On the one hand, as substances enduring through time, they have powers that are expressed as interactions generating regularities about change. Those efficient causes are what enable Rational beings to know that their own existence is necessary. On the other hand, matter has a proto-phenomenal intrinsic property, and though it makes a difference in what happens only when reflective subjects recognize the difference between the unity of consciousness and the unity of the natural world outside consciousness, it is also essential to space and matter making the most out of a world constituted by substances.

As we have seen, the basic efficient causes entailed by spatiomaterial interactions include geometrical as well as physical efficient causes, and since geometrical causes can impose geometrical constraints on collective effects of physical causes, the flow of acceleration fuel through the surface of a planet like Earth can be used to do thermodynamic work. The work of molecules is geometrical action, which expresses the holistic power that matter acquires from how it interacts with the quantum structure of space in the mechanical part of the inertial system. When there are molecules that can do two basically different kinds of thermodynamic work, reproducing themselves and causing conditions that promote their reproduction, efficient causes are combined as the reproductive mechanism, and the diurnal variation in the flow of acceleration fuel on surfaces of suitable planets orbiting stars causes them to evolve. When the evolution of these double-action geometrical causes produces a cell-based BGS that can go through reproductive cycles on its own, life begins, and by choosing goals that are good for it as situations arise, its cellular geometrical action evolves gradually in the direction of maximum power to control conditions that enable it to reproduce.

Gradual evolution is one way that the reproductive mechanism produces natural perfection, but it is not the only way because evolution is progressive in two other ways. First, during each stage of gradual evolution, as BGSs of various kinds acquire every possible functional power as it becomes possible, they occupy every ecological niche that provides enough acceleration fuel for the thermodynamic work required to live in them. Thus, species of life come to exist everywhere possible, each adapting to the other, and the result is that ecologies become naturally perfect by jointly using as much of the flow of acceleration fuel from their star as possible to fuel their reproductive cycles. Second, each stage of gradual evolution gives rise to another stage whenever it is both possible and functional. After the (bi-level) reproductive mechanism breathes life into prokaryotic cells on the first floor of the edifice of life, it breathes life into eukaryotic cells on the second floor, and yet another form of cellular geometrical action comes to life on the third floor when a plan-sharing BGS enables multicellular organisms to go through cycles of reproduction on their own. Since animals on the third floor have a neural BGS to lead their bodies through reproductive cycles, neural geometrical action becomes part of the life evolving on suitable planets. And when the evolution of language brings groups of animals to life on the fourth floor, cellular geometrical action includes not only neural geometrical action but also linguistic geometrical action. There is a series of inevitable minor stages caused by levels of organization in neural BGSs on the third and fourth floors of the edifice of life that bring beings like us into existence on suitable planets everywhere.

Though our pre-Socratic first cause is just two opposite kinds of substances, their interactions constitute efficient causes that give rise to reflective subjects who live together as members of spiritual organisms at the psychological level of linguistic organization. When physics is reduced to ontology, naturalistic imagination enables reflective subjects to understand these efficient causes well enough to see how they make as much out of space and matter as possible, and thus, they can appreciate the beauty of natural perfection. But the perfection of the spatio-material world is incomparably greater because matter has proto-phenomenal intrinsic property.

Since efficient causes are responsible for every event, the phenomenal intrinsic nature of matter makes no difference in what happens. Its phenomenal intrinsic nature is nevertheless a necessary part of the evolution of the third stage of spiritual evolution, the stage during which reflective subjects discover that they are conscious. Consciousness is what it is like to be the neural geometrical action of a mammalian body because matter has a proto-phenomenal intrinsic property. The unity of consciousness in animals with a faculty of imagination makes it seem that sensory qualia in phenomenal space are the natural world in which they find their bodies, so mammals are naturally direct realists about perception. This is just an illusion inherent in being conscious, which makes no difference in how mammalian brains generate verbal behavior. But since that is what it is like to be their neural geometrical action, the assumption that the immediate presence of phenomenal properties is how they are known is implicit in the arguments that metaphysicians exchange.

Ancient metaphysicians assume that a faculty of perceptual intuition enables them to know about the natural world, and taking that to be Appearance, they assume that certain reflective phenomenal appearances are objects of a faculty of rational intuition by which they know Reality behind Appearance. When modern metaphysicians learn enough about the natural world to know that perceptual phenomenal appearances are part of the subject, they become representative realists; they notice the radical difference between the unity of consciousness and the unity of the natural world; they discover that they are conscious. This is still not an effect of consciousness on what happens. It is just what metaphysicians learn about how they exist: they are conscious, and their consciousness is just part of the world. Since there is a world external to consciousness, they discover that the natural world is the Reality that Reason knows behind Appearance, and they are confronted with an intractable ontological problem about the difference between mind and body. The problem of mind-body dualism is not solved until much later when science discovers that space is a substance that interacts with matter.

Science begins with physics using the mathematics based on rational intuition that it borrows from intuitionistic metaphysics to describe basic laws about change, and laws of physics describe quantitative regularities so completely that ontologists are eventually able to explain why mathematics seems to be known *a priori* and infer the powers by which interactions of space and matter generate all those regularities. That reveals a kind of efficient cause not recognized by physics, and since that leads to an explanation of how the language-using mammalian brain works, ontological scientists are able to infer that matter has a proto-phenomenal intrinsic property as the best explanation of how consciousness is part of the natural world. As scientific realists knowing about consciousness from outside, reflective subjects discount the illusion of intuitionism, and when they recognize that they know Reality behind Appearance, science becomes naturalistic Reason.

Discounting the intuitionist illusion does not make consciousness go away. Indeed, it is an essential part of aesthetic Reason. Beings with naturalistic Reason know that the natural world is constituted by substances in such a way that they inevitably come to exist. They appreciate the perfection that the natural world has because parts of it understand its nature so well that they know that they exist necessarily. But the universe becoming aware of its own existence and nature is only part of its perfection. Its perfection is even more complete because its perfection is mirrored in the immediate presence of its phenomenal appearance to them. Consciousness has been a mirror of nature all along, but in the end, it becomes a perfect mirror.[115]

The mirror is the phenomenal intrinsic nature of the neural geometrical action of a language-using mammal in which the linguistic geometrical action of a spiritual organism is embodied when science becomes naturalistic Reason. Though this knowledge of the perfection of the natural world depends on reflective subjects discounting the intuitionist illusion, knowledge of its perfection is mirrored in their consciousness, and since its immediate presence makes it an aesthetic appreciation of its perfection, the perfection of the natural world is at least doubled. No such Rational being would deny that consciousness makes much more out of a world constituted by space and matter than one in which matter lacks an intrinsic phenomenal nature. Thus, considering how little this mirroring costs in the way of ontological causes, it certainly seems that the spatio-material world approximates, at least, the ideal

---

[115] *Pace* Richard Rorty (1979).

of doing the most with the least in constituting a world by substances.

Since this perfection depends on linguistic geometrical action at the metaphysical level of linguistic organization being embodied in the neural geometrical action of a mammal, beings with naturalistic Reason are necessarily members of a spiritual organism who can see into one another's minds. Though their own consciousness is private, they have a spiritual nature by which they share their aesthetic appreciation of Reality with other conscious beings. Indeed, the reduction of physics to ontology shows how the evidence for Big Bang cosmology can be explained by Big Shrink cosmology in a world constituted by space and matter, and since it is infinite in both space and in time, naturalistic Reason reveals that the formation of galaxies and the evolution of life taking place on suitable planets orbiting stars leads to the existence of beings with naturalistic Reason throughout the universe. This makes the most of infinite time and infinite space. It takes a long time for naturalistic Reason to evolve on suitable planets, but since space is infinite, every inevitable step in the overall course of evolution leading to its existence can be found somewhere in the universe. Thus, the spatio-material world is perfect not only because there are always Rational beings in which the universe is aware of—and enjoy the beauty of—its nature, but also because every step of the evolutionary process that brings such beings into always exists somewhere. Since the spatio-material world had no beginning and will have no end, the labor of progressive evolution, as well as its product, exists eternally.

The Enlightenment concept of the sublime is true of the natural world. The beauty of nature is so great that it is in a category of its own. Space and matter make the most out of being, where *being* is what is constituted by substances that endure through time. What makes nature so beautiful is that it is complete in all the ways that finite Rational beings like us could expect of a perfect infinite being. The spatio-material world is omnipresent because it is infinite in space and it exists at each moment as it is present in the eternal passage of time. It is omniscient because there are always beings somewhere in space who understand the natural order completely enough to recognize the necessity of their own existence as part of it. It is omnipotent because the coordinated behavior of members of spiritual organisms can control conditions in the world as much as any form of life possibly can. It is absolutely good because members do what is good because it is good. And it is absolutely beautiful because consciousness gives Rational beings an aesthetic appreciation of its perfection that they share by seeing into the minds of other beings like themselves everywhere in the universe.

Thus, ontology solves the mystery of the sublime. Reality has the perfect nature that was traditionally attributed to a transcendent God. And solving the mystery about what makes nature uniquely beautiful does not spoil the aesthetic enjoyment of its beauty. On the contrary, solving that mystery is essential to the perfection that makes Reality beautiful.

CONCLUSION:
WHY WE EXIST

This argument has come a long way. Starting with the puzzles of physics and gaps in the scientific explanation of the natural world, the discovery that space is a substance that interacts with matter reveals that the natural world is a perfect infinite being with finite beings like us at the pinnacle of its order. The powers of space and matter are expressed by interactions that bring life and into existence, and since matter has a proto-phenomenal intrinsic property, language-using mammals are conscious. Thus, when reflective subjects acquire naturalistic Reason, conscious reflection on their aesthetic appreciation of the perfection of what exists completes its perfection.

This is a surprising discovery for physicalists. From the Copernican revolution, they learned that they were not at the center of the universe, and the four horsemen of disillusionment with Reason taught them how foolish it was to expect to understand the nature of what exists most basically. Still, the existence of animals who are able to wonder about their own existence is such a unique development that it calls for an explanation, and as it is explained in a science based on physics, the evolution of intelligent life is an accident. But even naturalists suspect that physics must leave out something basic, and physicalists now commonly explain away the impression that physics is incomplete. They argue that it is caused by the failure to consider multiverse cosmology. It holds that Big Bangs cause a huge number of universes to expand in which the laws of physics hold, but are different from one another because the laws have different physical constants. We exist in one of the very few universes in which beings like us happen to exist, so we expect the laws of physics to explain our existence. But they promise that, if we hone our physicalist intuitions, we can get over our wonder at the existence of beings like us and reconcile ourselves with the very peripheral place that we have in the natural order the physical world. And as we give up hope of ever having the kind of complete explanation of the natural world that was the original goal of science, the era of endarkenment is setting in, and all the gifts of the Enlightenment are in danger of being lost.

If, however, the argument in this trilogy is sound, the disillusionment and endarkenment that characterize the aftermath of the Enlightenment are just an adolescent phase in Reason's biography. The evolution of naturalistic Reason will give us a scientific explanation of the natural world in which the existence of beings like us who understand the nature of Reality and enjoy its perfection is the capstone of natural perfection. That is such a complete reversal of contemporary expectations that it turns wonder about our existence as part of the natural world into wonder at the existence of the natural world itself.

Our existence was once believed to be the purpose of the natural world. For example, deism, the variation on theism that was popular during the Enlightenment, held that God created the natural world for a purpose, but it denied that God acted on it afterward. God created space and time by willing the laws of physics to hold, and though he left the natural world on its own, his purpose was to bring beings like us into existence. God's reason was an unsolved theological mystery, so deism was not a complete explanation of why the natural world exists. Furthermore, if deism did explain God's purpose, it would still fall short of explaining why we exist. It would depend on the existence of a God outside space and time with that purpose, and God's existence would be unexplained.

To be sure, since God is a perfect being, his existence was supposed to be necessary. In the 11th-century, for example, Anselm held that God's perfection entailed his existence. According to his famous *ontological proof of God's existence*, God is a *being than which none greater can be conceived*, and God must exist, for if he did not, a God that does exist would be an even more perfect being. Since God's non-existence was not possible, God had to exist.

But the ontological proof of God's existence has long been dismissed as fallacious because perfection does not entail existence. *Perfection* is a property that helps define the nature of something. As a descriptive property, it distinguishes one *kind* of thing from another. But as Kant pointed out, *existence* is not descriptive of anything. Though it can be predicated of things, it does not identify their kinds. Instead, it says that they are part of the world. The world is everything that exists, and since *existence* does not describe the nature of anything, it does not describe the nature of God. Hence, all that *God's* perfection entails is that if God exists, there is a perfect being.

Since God's existence is not necessary, deism does not explain why beings like us exist, and deism is just a possible ontological explanation of what is found in the natural world. Furthermore, to be better than spatio-materialism, deism would have to explain enough more by the principle of optimality to justify the extra ontological cost of postulating a perfect being outside space and time, the most popular justification no longer holds.

Around the time of the Enlightenment, the so-called *teleological argument* was used to show the existence of a God. It held that in order to explain the purposiveness found in the natural world, there had to be a creator who designed it. Deists believed that God designed it so that the Rational beings who were part of his creation could learn the difference between good and evil from its nature. But the teleological argument lost favor in the 19th century after Darwin's discovery of natural selection, and if purposiveness is the only evidence for deism, ontologists must prefer spatio-materialism because it is a simpler explanation. Space and matter interact in a way that constitutes two kinds of efficient causes, and working together as the reproductive mechanism, they are responsible for all the purposiveness found in the natural world, including the existence of Rational beings who know Reality behind Appearance. This explains as much as deism promised with less in the way of ontological causes. Rational beings must prefer spatio-materialism to deism because it is a better ontological explanation of the natural world than deism.

If the perfection of the natural world cannot explain its existence, its existence is even more puzzling. Why is there something rather than nothing? If there were a reason why something exists, naturalistic Reason would be less incomplete because only its perfection would remain unexplained.

To give a reason for the existence of something, rather than nothing, is to show that the existence of something is necessary, and there are two ways of doing that. One is to show that it is *logically* impossible for nothing to exist, and the other is to show that it is *ontologically* impossible for nothing to exist.

Logic cannot show that something must exist because it is just the structure that language must have to represent states of affairs. Linguistic representations assert that states of affairs hold, and for an assertion to be either true or false, there must be a way of denying what is asserted. Hence, logic includes negation. Thus, when we assert that *something* exists, what we assert can be denied, and so it is logically possible that *nothing* exists.

To be sure, this explanation of how it is logically possible for nothing to exist depends on language, and since language requires users, it might seem to show that something exists. But this argument does not presuppose the existence of language or its users. The essential nature of language is what entails the possibility of denying the assertion that something exists. Logic is merely part of its nature. And since the *nature* of language tells us nothing about its *existence*, it is not logically necessary that something exists.

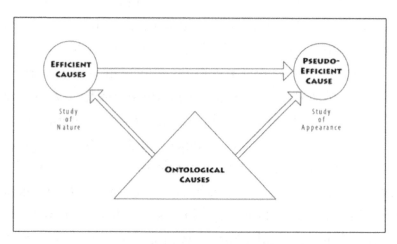

Figure 14 - The Causes that Explain Everything

By the same token, the existence of something does seem to be ontologically necessary. To ask why there is something rather than nothing is to ask for an explanation, and it would not make sense to ask for an explanation if there were no such thing as a cause. The question seems to presuppose existence because naturalistic Reason discovers that all causes are ultimately ontological. It discovers that Reality is a world constituted by space and matter, and since their natures entail everything that is necessary, all explanations are, in Reality, about what exists most basically. As we have seen, the ontological causes that explain the laws of physics entail two kinds of efficient causes, physical and geometrical, and since what happens includes the discovery of ontological science, there is also a pseudo-efficient cause. (See Figure 14, above.)

Since the world is everything that exists, everything in the world can be explained by these causes, and since that includes the nature of explanation, the nature of explanation entails that every explanation is, at bottom, ontological. To be sure, physical scientists and other intuitionists believe in other kinds of causes. But naturalistic Reason discovers that all causes are ultimately ontological, and to ask for an explanation is, therefore, to ask for an ontological cause. The question about why there is something rather than nothing presupposes—that is, entails—the existence of something. Hence, the existence of something rather than nothing is ontologically necessary. Ontological causes are substances, and since they are self-subsistent entities that endure through time and explain what is found in the world by constituting it, the one thing that ontological causes cannot explain is nothing. Hence, it is ontologically impossible that nothing exists.

This conclusion could be rejected, if it were vulnerable to refutation in the same way as the argument for the logical possibility of nothing existing. Logic depends on the nature of language, not the existence of language or its users, and so the nature language and logic entails the possibility of asserting or denying anything, including the existence of something. Ontology depends on the nature of explanation, not the existence of Rational beings who give and understand them. But naturalistic Reason implies that every explanation is necessarily about causes that are at bottom ontological, that is, about causes of existence. Thus, to ask for an explanation of why there is something rather than nothing is to assume that something exists. The answer to this question is implicit in the asking, so it is not ontologically possible that nothing exists.

But even if the existence of something is ontologically necessary, it is not ontologically necessary that what exists is perfect. Existence does not entail perfection, any more than perfection entails existence. We can conceive of a natural world constituted by substances that is not perfect, for example, a universe in which there is nothing but material bodies moving and interacting according to Newton's laws. Indeed, we can conceive of a natural world in which there are reflective subjects that are not perfect, for example, a natural world constituted by substances whose powers entail the existence of animals with the use of language who understand naturalistic and psychological explanations but do not know that all explanations are basically ontological and never discover that they exist necessarily.

But a world constituted by space and matter like ours entails the existence of beings with naturalistic Reason who know that what exists is perfect, and though they know that the existence of something is ontologically necessary, they cannot explain why what exists is perfect. The perfection of what exists is puzzling because it seems to be unique among all possible worlds in which substances are the first cause. In our natural world, beings with a cognitive power that enables them to know the nature of Reality behind Appearance necessarily come to exist, and in them, Reality knows that it is a perfect being. Furthermore, they are conscious, and though their knowledge of Reality behind Appearance depends on discounting the illusion of intuitionism, the perfection of the natural world is mirrored in their consciousness. They know what it is like to have naturalistic Reason, and they know that if they were not conscious, their enjoyment of being part of it would not be as complete. Thus, their existence as conscious reflective subjects seems to make the most out of a world constituted by substances that endure through time. The perfection of Reality is crowned by their aesthetic appreciation of its perfection.

Since we are beings like that, naturalistic Reason puts us in a position analogous to physicists before the discovery about the nature of space. Eugene Wigner (1959) described the "unreasonable effectiveness" of mathematics in discovering laws of physics as a mystery, and having discovered an ontological explanation of everything, we might, in a similar vein, describe the *unreasonable effectiveness* of space and matter in making the most out of existence as a mystery. And like Wigner, who considered mathematics a "wonderful gift which we neither understand nor deserve," we might consider the nature of space and matter a *wonderful gift which we neither understand nor deserve*. We should be grateful that the world is constituted by substances of their kinds, as he was grateful that mathematics was appropriate in physics.

But Wigner did not expect that he would ever get over his "bafflement" about the validity of mathematics, and since he was mistaken about that, perhaps it would be a mistake for us to believe that we will never get over our bafflement about the perfection of what exists. Could there be more to learn about that?

In any case, the discovery of the first cause will be a revolution in culture that changes our conception of Reality. Everything will be seen as part of an infinite perfect being.

Since scientists are naturalists reared on the humbling lessons taught by Copernicus and the four horsemen of disillusionment about Reason, they will be surprised to find themselves at the zenith of the perfection of the natural world. The anthropocentricism of the traditional view was closer to truth than physical science, though it was seeing the True as through a glass darkly.

Since philosophers have long since despaired of acquiring perfect knowledge, they will be surprised to have the wisdom to which philosophy has always aspired. Empirical science is not necessarily incomplete knowledge about the world, as metaphysicians have always assumed.

But since theists have always assumed that morality and the meaning of life depends on God's purpose in creating the natural world, they will have to give up the belief that it has an ultimate teleological explanation. What *purpose* means depends on the nature of the reflective subjects who use it to explain their behavior, and there is no basic cause in which future states help cause what happens at present. But giving up the belief that the natural world exists for a purpose is not a great loss. Theologians never found a satisfactory way to explain why God chose to create a natural world in which finite beings fashioned in his image would lead lives choosing between good and evil. And our spiritual nature as parts of the form of life that completes the perfection of the natural world does explain why the morally good is good and does, at least, give us a way of thinking about the meaning of life. Thus, even though the explanation of Western civilization as the metaphysical stage of evolution implies that the belief in a transcendent God was a phantom Reality, it also solves the ontological problem of God-nature dualism inherited from ancient metaphysics by showing empirically that God is identical to the perfect being that the natural world turns out to be. Thus, theologians may be willing to settle for finally having the proof of God's existence that they have always believed that Reason could give them.

Personal Postscript

When I was about fifteen, I told my mother that I didn't believe in God. After having sent me to Sunday school all my life, she was disappointed—and probably hurt more than I realized. But I was young, I had discovered science, and as a contrarian, I had come to believe that much of what people told me was false or misleading. I felt confident about atheism because I was sure there was nothing outside space and time. Most of the rest of my life was spent making discoveries about which I was nearly as confident, and they have led me to this defense of naturalistic Reason. As an atheist, I understand where the four horsemen of atheism are coming from when they denounce religion.[116] But I don't blame religion for causing evil in the world, and as a contrarian in this post-Christian era, I find myself sympathizing with defenders of Christianity and Judaism. I have come to conclusions about the nature of what exists that are eerily similar to those I boldly rejected as an adolescent. My mother died of a long and horrible debilitating disease at the age of 59. Though she surely had her doubts, she never lost faith in God, and my career now seems to bring me back to her. I am sad that she is not alive to know how far I have come to being the son she hoped I would be. But, perhaps, saying something about how I have crossed the bridge from atheism to God will make it easier for theists to accept naturalistic metaphysics.

As I was growing up, my mother taught Sunday school at a Presbyterian Church, and at around 14 years of age, I was preparing to become a member. After catechism class one day, I followed our pastor, Dr. Pattison, into his office. I assured him that I understood the Father and the Son, but I couldn't understand the Holy Ghost. I don't remember what he said, but it didn't satisfy me. I remember trying to picture what heaven would be like, and not much time passed before I made my declaration to my mother. At that age, I didn't know that I was a congenital contrarian, but this was an early expression of

---

[116] See Harris (2004), Dawkins (2005), Hitchens (2007), and Dennett (1995).

that disposition.

In a more constructive vein, I remember one fine spring morning, before going to high school, being apprehensive about something that might happen that day. I don't remember what it was, but it probably involved dealing with someone. I went out to the backyard to think about it, and as I looked around, it occurred to me that I was in a garden in Cheyenne, Wyoming, a small city in a continent on one of several planets orbiting the Sun. I thought about how the Sun is just one of many average stars in a galaxy, which is but one of innumerable galaxies in the universe. This is a common thought, and it wasn't the first time it had occurred to me. I had learned to appreciate science, thanks in large part to my brother, who was two years older. But this time, it struck me that everything is in space. Space really exists. There is nothing outside it. And space seemed so big that my worry vanished into insignificance. Thinking of myself in that context felt comforting, even joyful.

As a child, I would probably have been diagnosed as suffering attention deficit hyperactive disorder, if ADHD had been recognized in the 1940s. But adolescence brought relief in the form of an ability to concentrate on abstractions. Mathematics was easy for me, and as an artist, my mother's advice for dealing with a problem was to put things in perspective. So I had a conception of coherence, and I wanted to see the Big Picture, a system in which everything had a place. More than anything, I wanted to know what is true, and with a contrarian nature, it was easy to believe that what most people believed was false. As it happened, I lived within two or three blocks of the Carnegie Library and the State Library. Both were organized on the Dewey Decimal System, and since its first substantive field is philosophy, I discovered books that talked about attempts to know the Big Picture and the problems encountered. I didn't understand much of what I read. But I knew there were others who wanted to get to the bottom of everything. To know the True, I would have to study what philosophers were saying. Around that time, I overheard my mother saying to a friend on the phone, "Oh, Phillip? He's discovered books."

Born two weeks before World War II began, I was a few years ahead of the baby boom. From the beginning, a smooth path was laid out for me to become a philosophy professor. I went to the University of Colorado in

Boulder on scholarship. I began with a major in mathematics because I was good at it. But I didn't understand what mathematics was about, and since physics is about what happens in space, it was easy to believe that I understood what natural science is about. What puzzled me most were the social sciences, history, and fine art. Everyone else seemed to find them easy to understand, but I had no simple necessary truth to organize my thinking about them. A four-year honors program that covered the whole history of Western culture from ancient Greece to the 20th century reinforced my love and respect for philosophy. In my junior year, I switched my major to philosophy. I had found a teacher, David Hawkins, a philosopher of science who defended unorthodox views in science rather than focusing on epistemological issues. As graduation approached, the director of the honors program, Wally Weir, another philosopher, told me about the expansion of graduate schools in anticipation of the baby boom and suggested that I apply to study philosophy at the graduate level. I was emboldened to think of myself as a teacher of philosophy, earning a living doing what I loved doing most.

I was accepted at Johns Hopkins University when ordinary language philosophy was most fashionable. I was wary of analytic philosophy since most of my philosophy teachers had been American pragmatists who complained about it taking over the discipline. Studying it, I learned how important it is to be careful and rigorous in constructing arguments. But I was after bigger game than the analysis of language. I wanted to know what is true, not the limits on what can be known, and I held open the possibility of discovering it by refusing to let myself pretend to believe anything that I did not really believe, even if everyone around me took it for granted. And in the back of my mind was the notion that space is so basic to our thinking about everything that it is somehow overlooked.

Fortunately, the chairman appointed to build up the department at Johns Hopkins in anticipation of the baby boom was Maurice Mandelbaum, a philosopher of history who knew the history of philosophy. From him, I learned how to think about great ideas as evolving with a necessity that does not depend on who defends them. I wrote my dissertation under him, defending methodological individualism against his thesis that societal facts are irreducible to physical facts. I now see that he was closer to the truth than

I was at the time. But working on this issue turned out to be a great gift because I discovered a simple truth about the social that would enable me to understand how social science is related to natural science. It is what I would later call the essential nature of spiritual organisms.

I am profoundly grateful to these three men, Walter Weir, David Hawkins, and Maurice Mandelbaum, for launching me on my career as a philosopher, and I wish they had lived to see what they did for me. But I was diverted from philosophical work during the tumult of the anti-war movement and hippie rebellion in the late 1960s and early '70s.

When I took up writing again, I was still a naturalist who looked down on religion. I still had space in the back of my mind. And as a contrarian, I was willing to believe that overlooking it was somehow causing problems in science. What I had learned by writing my dissertation was that beings like us could see into one another's minds, and so I started at the top of the natural order looking for ways that space could solve problems. A long manuscript I wrote during my first sabbatical leave distinguished two sciences of the human, one based on a cognitive faculty built into our brains that enables us to move around and interact with other objects in space, which I now call *naturalistic imagination*, and another based on the use of language that enables us to see into other minds, now called *psychological imagination*. One science studied what seemed transparent to me, and the other studied what once puzzled me. With that understanding of how natural science is more basic than the social sciences (and psychology), I took up the study of neural anatomy in an attempt to find how the faculty of naturalistic imagination is embodied in the human brain.

As a teacher of philosophy during this period, I had an insight that led me to organize all my courses around the history of philosophy. Recognizing the difference between the phenomenal appearance of the natural world and the faculty built into the brain that enables us to perceive and understand the natural world, I accepted epiphenomenalism and assumed that consciousness could somehow be explained as what it is like to be a human brain. From the beginning, I knew the difference between consciousness and reflection, or the cognitive power to reflect on our psychological states and see into the minds of others that I saw as based on the use of language. The difference between phenomenal space and the space in which material bodies exist led me to recognize how much traditional philosophy depends on the mistaken assumption that perception and reflection are forms of intuition. Thus, instead of dismissing metaphysics as a naïve willingness to believe in absolute truth and using skeptical arguments about it to teach philosophy as lessons in critical thinking, I looked for ways to explain its history as an evolution of ideas in a direction that came ever closer to the truth. I knew that it was bound to fail because of what I now call *intuitionism*. But I learned how to explain the history of metaphysics as the evolution of culture by Rational selection toward a better explanation of Reality behind Appearance, one that forced Intuitionistic Rationalists to struggle with ontological problems posed by its inherent dualism, as described in *Part Two* of *Volume III*. Thus, I taught students a double-sightedness about the history of philosophy, seeing it not only from the point of view of the subject, taken by the illusion of intuitionism, but also from the outside, as part of the natural world. And I learned to sympathize with Christians trying to solve theological puzzles.

From these discoveries about forty years ago until I retired from teaching in 2000, I tried to fit everything together as parts of a Big Picture based on evolution. As a naturalist, I took evolution by natural selection for granted. But starting at the top of the natural order, I could not believe that the existence of beings like us is an accident, and more convinced than ever that the problems of science were caused by somehow overlooking a role that space plays, I followed my contrarian instinct and looked for ways of taking space into account that would solve them. By teaching the history of philosophy, from the pre-Socratics through all the great metaphysicians to the rise of science, I learned that the basic causes of existence are substances, and so I believed that space must be a substance in the same sense as matter. I believed that ontology can solve what physicalists now call the *hard problem of mind* because what it is like to be a brain could be explained by intrinsic phenomenal properties of substances helping constitute it. And looking for a way that space could make evolution progressive, I came to believe that space is somehow responsible for what I now call *geometrical causes*. That enabled me to explain evolution more completely than Darwinism since I could see molecules evolving because they were driven through reproductive cycles by the cycle of night and day and see stages of evolution following one another because of successive levels of geometrical organization. This enabled me to use what I had learned from my study of neural anatomy to explain the evolution of the mammalian brain from the vertebrate brain (as presented in *Volume II*), and I could see how a yet higher level of neural organization could explain the use of language and reflection. But in order to pull it all together, I had to take up the study of biology from scratch (having foolishly skipped it in high school) and figure out how the overall course of evolution could be explained by a series of stages of evolution, beginning with the origin of prokaryotic life, as depicted in Figure 3 of *Volume III*.

The big picture was taking shape. But at the bottom of the natural order, there was physics, closest to space, where everything comes down to powers of space and matter. From the beginning, I realized that to defend my belief that space is a substance, I had to show that spacetime is just an incomplete description of what exists. It was not hard to find a way to show that Einstein's special theory of relativity could be true in a world constituted by space and matter since Lorentz had already explored that possibility. I was excited by the many discoveries in particle physics at the time since they helped me think about how interactions of space could help matter constitute basic particles. But I didn't understand the equations of quantum mechanics well enough to show how it causes what I now call the *Lorentz deformations*. And since I assumed that quantum mechanics explains composite bodies, I did not understand how space is responsible for geometrical causes. Thus, what I had at the time of my retirement in the year 2000 was a picture of evolution as progressive. It was a series of stages caused by levels of geometrical organization that explained how reflective subjects come to exist, how the brain works, and why reflective subjects are conscious. And believing that it was an inevitable change in the direction of greater functional power, I saw it as explaining the nature of the good.

While I was teaching, I tried many times to publish my discoveries in books and articles. But for one reason or another, I almost always failed. In part, the problem was that my argument was not yet complete. I had only parts of a Big Picture. I was confused about how space and matter explain geometrical causes and how evolution explains goodness. I saw Western philosophy as the beginning of a stage of evolution, and though I knew that consciousness is reducible to phenomenal intrinsic properties of substances helping constitute the brain, it was not yet part of a rigorous explanation of all the stages of evolution. I tried to publish parts that were complete, and the comments of readers revealed that the main obstacle to publishing them was that my views are heretical. In physics, I was defending absolute space and time against spacetime. In science, I was defending an explanation of evolution as progressive against Darwinian accidentalism. In philosophy, I was defending a solution to the hard problem of mind instead of showing why it is so hard. In the history of philosophy, I was explaining metaphysics as progress in discovering the True against the view that it was a foolish mistake. And in the academic world generally, I was defending the possibility of science explaining the natural order completely against the growing consensus about the inability of arguments to solve basic problems and other forms of endarkenment, such as multiculturalism, postmodernism, and relativism. Of course, it didn't help when I tried to compensate for the missing pieces by presenting my argument as a defense of a new way of doing metaphysics. Everyone knew that metaphysics was barking up the wrong tree. And, finally, when my manuscripts were rejected, I did not usually send them to other publishers because I had always found solutions to new problems, and I was off working on a better version of my argument.

When I was teaching at American University, I had help from students. And over the years, there were periods when I had useful feedback from discussions with a few colleagues. At first, nearly a half-century ago, Jeff Reiman encouraged me, and at times after that, he was particularly helpful in pointing out places where my argument needed work. Charley Hardwick was a philosopher whose original interest was religion, and he helped me see how there could be truth in it. Along with Jeff and Charley, Jon Wisman, a philosopher who defected to economics, was a member of a study group that read many books over many years, and repeatedly, they generously read and responded to my writings. But my way of writing had become a method of research and development that caused arguments to evolve in my brain in a way that did not depend on arguing with others. It was easy to abandon beliefs when I encountered problems along the way because mistaken beliefs had not been published. Tough problems often forced me to worry that I might be on the wrong track. But I never gave up because I always eventually found solutions that thrilled me with new insights. My hunch about the unrecognized role of space was confirmed repeatedly. The Big Picture evolving in my mind was always becoming simpler while explaining more and more details.

When I retired, I continued to use writing to make my arguments evolve. But I also had the time to take up the puzzles of modern physics. As a reductionist, I knew that if I was on the right track, there must be a way of founding my argument on an ontological explanation of physics. But I did not understand the equations of physics well enough to know what it is. I was not afraid of mathematics since I had enjoyed it when I was young. I had figured out how the spacetime of special relativity could be explained by absolute space and time (Scribner 1989). But I was certainly not a master of mathematics and far too old to become one. What I could do with my level of understanding of mathematics, however, was figure out how the equations used in modern physics correspond to interactions of space and matter that I could understand in naturalistic imagination. Beginning with my ideas about how space and matter constitute the particles included in the Standard Model, I looked for ontological mechanisms that explained the laws of classical physics, which gave me an early form of what I now call the *inertial system*. Knowing that the Lorentz transformation equations that Einstein derived in his special theory of relativity could be explained by Lorentz deformations, I was able to figure out what corresponds to the complicated tensor equations of Einstein's general theory of relativity. And by solving Lorentz's problem with the velocity dependence of mass, I figured out how the inertial system explains the laws of quantum mechanics, including ontological mechanisms for the Lorentz deformations. It solved the puzzles of quantum mechanics, and the solution revealed that geometrical causes are as basic as physical causes. Putting it all together, therefore, I had an ontological bridge between laws of quantum and gravitational physics that solves the problem in physics about their mathematical disparity.

The path to this discovery is just opposite to its explanation. I had a hunch that space plays an unrecognized role in determining what happens in the natural world, and starting at the top of the natural order, I worked my way down to the bottom, where I discovered how space does it. Thus, using spatio-materialism to show that ontology is a more basic branch of science than physics, I had a foundation for demonstrating consequences that I had already worked out. That is the unique argument presented here. It unifies not only physics but also science, and since consciousness is an essential part of the cause of a third stage of spiritual evolution, it is a naturalistic metaphysics in which Reason knows Reality behind Appearance. This unites science and philosophy and gives beings like us naturalistic Reason. I always wanted to find the Big Picture, and I was lucky in believing that it depended somehow on space. But now, in the end, it turns out to be the picture of a perfect being. It is as perfect as being can be if what exists is constituted by something as simple as substances, and as we have seen, it is doubly perfect because its recognition of its own perfection is mirrored in the consciousness of beings like us.

I find myself, therefore, recognizing that my mother's belief in God was not mistaken. She was merely seeing God through a glass darkly. I am still an atheist because it is not reasonable to believe in the existence of anything outside space and time, much less a creator of the natural world out there. But I find myself believing in God. Since what exists is a perfect being, God exists. Like other theists, the mistake that my mother made was to read the perfection suggested by the purposiveness of life in the natural world as the intention of a creator who transcended it. Pantheism turns out to be true, as many naturalists would be happy to believe, if they thought it could be justified. Intuitionistic metaphysics made Christian theology possible, and it is so uncanny how completely it identified the nature of God that I would call myself a *Christian pantheist*. All the perfections traditionally attributed to God can be found in the natural world, and it has them in a way that solves all the problems of traditional theology. So, let me say what I would tell my mother, if she were still alive. It may be of interest to theists who are trying to reconcile themselves with naturalistic metaphysics.

Theists hold that God is *infinite*. And God is infinite, if God is the world described by a science based on ontology. Space has no end, and since the natural world has neither a beginning nor an end in time, it is also eternal.

Theists hold that God is *omnipresent* in the natural world. And God is ubiquitous, if God is constituted by space and matter. The mystery about how God can be omnipresent in a natural world to which he gives existence is solved by pantheism. God "creates" it by constituting it.

Theists believe that God is a Rational being who acts with a purpose, and their main objection to pantheism is that it does not explain the *personal nature* of God. They believe that God is omniscient, omnipotent, and absolutely good, and substances are just self-subsistent entities existing in definite ways as they endure through time. But as we have seen, a natural world constituted by space and matter can have all the perfections attributed to God as a person. Its ontological causes entail a kind of change that brings all the personal perfections attributed to God into existence. Furthermore, this solves the problems caused by holding that these perfections characterize a being outside space and time.

God has a personal nature because there are *omniscient* Rational beings in the natural world. Indeed, they exist on suitable planets throughout the universe because the substances constituting the world generate change in the direction of natural perfection, and inevitable stages of evolution bring them into existence. When reflective subjects acquire naturalistic Reason, they know the essential natures of everything in the natural world, and they understand what really exists deeply enough to know the necessity of their own existence and the nature of the good. This is not omniscience about all the details of events over time, as theists can expect of a God outside space and time. But it is the kind of omniscience that naturalists can expect of an infinite being in space that endures through time.

There will be an *omnipotent* Rational being in the natural world when Rational beings are all parts of a global spiritual organism that coordinates their behavior in pursuit of common goals that are good. This spiritual organism can do anything that can be done by life as we know it in the natural world, and that is the sense of omnipotence appropriate for an omniscient being that can act only in the natural world.

And *absolutely good* Rational beings come to exist in the natural world. When reflective subjects acquire naturalistic Reason, they know the nature of the good, and since they know not only what is good but also why it is good, they choose the good and hold themselves responsible for doing what is good.

To be sure, they will not be absolutely good until they agree about how best to solve the problems of sharing their planet and constitute a global spiritual world for one another. But as we have seen, evolution at the metaphysical stage of gradual evolution is change in the direction of an omniscient, omnipotent, absolutely good Rational being.

Nor can this pantheistic explanation of the perfections of God be dismissed as settling for second best. Though God exists only at present, God is conscious, and since omniscience is immediately present, what it is like to be God is absolutely beautiful. On the other hand, the attribution of these perfections to a transcendent being who created the world is problematic.

For example, the omniscience of a transcendent creator of the natural world is incompatible with our free will. If God knew what happened at every moment in the entire history of the natural world when he created it, beings like us would not have free will because he would have already made all our choices for us. This has puzzled theists ever since Augustine. But the problem does not arise for pantheism because there is no being who knows all the details about what happens. Notice, however, that this is not to defend free will by denying the possibility, in principle, of predicting all our choices. In the spatio-material world, every event is completely determined. Pantheism is compatible with free will because, as we have seen, choices are effects of geometrical causes that serve the function of guiding behavior by constraining physical causes. They are life, that is, geometrical action aimed at the good. In Rational beings, the geometrical cause of free will is reasoning about what to do, and they need a spiritual desire to follow reason because choosing to satisfy that desire is how they take responsibility for what they do.

Another problem is posed by the assumption that the creator of the natural world is supposed to be a perfect being. But how could a God who is both omnipotent and absolutely good create a world in which there is evil? I'm sure my mother wondered how God could have created a world in which she would suffer rheumatoid aches and pains for decades only to slowly suffocate to death at the end. She did an abstract painting not long before she died, called *Shiva*, which unmistakably depicted a destructive force. Theists have long struggled to explain how a God who does not hate us could inflict such evil on us. It could not be attributed to an evil power because that would mean that

God is not all-powerful. Their best explanation of the ways of God was to insist that evil was somehow justified as part of God's mysterious purpose in creating the natural world and promise that, in an afterlife in his presence, we would understand his purpose in creating evil. But if God is the natural world, the existence of evil does not pose a theological problem. It is a necessary part of the natural world as a perfect being.

It helps to distinguish two kinds of evil: natural evil and moral evil. Natural evil is the harm inflicted on us by nature, such as disease, accidents, genetic defects, natural disasters, and death, while moral evil is the harm that beings like us inflict on one another, such as murder and war.

Though a transcendent God can be blamed for creating a world with natural evil, an immanent God cannot, because natural evil is an essential part of the perfection of the natural world. Life cannot evolve by the reproductive mechanism without evil. The ultimate cause of natural selection is scarcity caused by reproduction and population growth in regions of finite resources, and thus, without the evil of scarcity, beings like us could not evolve. Nor can conscious reflective subjects exist without dying since death is the price of sexually reproducing animal life. Other bad things, like plagues and asteroids impacting a planet, just happen in a world where quantitative regularities are generated by interactions of space and matter. Though natural evil cannot be eliminated from the natural world, it can be mitigated by our action, and with the increasing power of technology, it can become negligible. Beings like us will eventually be able to protect ourselves from natural harm. That is another way that the natural world is perfect. Knowing that the natural evil we still suffer at this stage is a necessary part of such progress would have made it easier for my mother to endure it. At least, she would not have had to suspect that the creator of the natural world does not love us or intends for us to suffer.

Moral evil is the harm that we inflict on one another, and since it comes into existence at an inevitable stage of evolution, it is also a necessary part of the perfection of the natural world. There was no moral evil before the evolution of psychological sentences. Animals with the use of naturalistic sentences still acted on the strongest desire at the moment, and though it included the desire to submit to a leader, subjects could not reflect on what they were doing. The use of psychological sentences enabled subjects to think about the goals at which their behavior was directed, think about the choices they made, including whether to submit to spiritual input or not, and, thus, choose between good and evil. Theists attributed moral evil to original sin, and that can be seen as close to the truth in the spatio-material world.

The original sin was the choice that Adam and Eve made in the Garden of Eden to eat fruit from the tree of the knowledge of good and evil, and God punished them and their progeny for disobeying his command by forcing them to suffer the harm that they could inflict by choosing evil, including death. Original sin can be interpreted as war, the form of group-level natural selection that replaced archaic humans (at the naturalistic level) with modern humans (at the psychological level). War gave modern humans desires that enabled them to act on other language-using animals in ways that they knew would harm them, and it gave reflective subjects the power to choose to harm them intentionally. The naturalistic stage may not have been a Garden of Eden, but language-using animals still had the innocence of dumb animals. By imposing natural selection on themselves in the form of war, they lost their innocence because the use of psychological sentences enabled them to know what they were doing. They were tempted to sin, and they saw themselves as choosing between good and evil.

Furthermore, Christians believed that original sin can be overcome because it was forgiven when God sacrificed his Son and, with the grace of God, they could resist the temptation to sin. Ontology also promises that original sin will be overcome. But it will happen only when Reason matures, beings like us are able to understand the cause of war, and they control the conditions that cause it. More generally, moral evil will not be overcome entirely until we solve our social, economic, and political problems. When no one is forced to inflict harm on others, knowledge of the nature of moral goodness will cause everyone to choose to do what is morally right. The fact that they must suffer moral evil in the meantime is not a mystery about God's purpose in creating the natural world, but simply the way that life evolves in the direction of natural perfection. Thus, ontology also predicts the evolution of heaven on Earth, like the global spiritual world described earlier.

Given how all the perfections traditionally attributed to God hold of the natural world, pantheism has a naturalistic solution to the problem with the doctrine of the Trinity. How can there be a single God with three persons: the Father, the Son, and the Holy Spirit? The *Father* is what really exists. He is our natural world constituted by space and matter as substances enduring through time. That is, instead of using mathematics as a language to will laws of nature to hold in the natural world, the Father is the ontological cause, and interactions of space and matter generate all the regularities that lead inevitably to the existence of reflective subjects. The *Son* represents the conscious reflective subjects who acquire naturalistic Reason when science and philosophy are unified during the metaphysical stage. Since they know the True, the Good, and the Beautiful, they embody the perfections traditionally attributed to God as a person. And since they are members of spiritual organisms, the spiritual input that guides their behavior is the *Holy Spirit*. When the evolution of naturalistic Reason is complete, right makes might. (This is what Pastor Pattison could not explain to me.)

Thus, pantheism solves the ontological problems with the doctrine of the trinity that the Bishops of the Church at the Council of Nicaea tried to paper over. They were monotheists, but their interpretation of the Bible portrayed God as three persons, and as we have seen, they failed to explain how all three could be constituted by one and the same substance. But as ontology explains the natural world, the Father, Son, and Holy Spirit are all just space and matter and the change generated by their interaction. Indeed, the three faces of the Christian God are explained in a way that may even be acceptable to Jews, since pantheism implies that original sin is overcome, not by the sacrifice of a single divine individual, but, rather, by the sacrifices that all reflective subjects make in respecting one another's moral autonomy. Jews are the *chosen people* because they are the people that God chose to teach that lesson.

Pantheism also solves the ontological problem that the Council of Chalcedon papered over: How could the Son be both divine and mortal? If the Son is the part of the trinity that represents reflective subjects who are informed by naturalistic Reason, his dual nature is explained by the immanence of the perfect being. But the Son turns out to be mortal. Death is the dues that must be paid to lead the life of an animal.

Having to give up belief in personal immortality may be the most unpalatable consequence of pantheism. It was easy for theists to believe that the self somehow transcended space and time because one can sense the difference between the unity of consciousness and the unity of the natural world, and the belief that one has a permanent personal relationship with God is basic to the self-conception of theists. It seems natural to think of a holy Father watching over every choice, and his judgments matter because they have eternal significance. But this is also how pantheists lead their lives. They make choices as if a transcendent God were watching over them.[117] As reflective subjects, pantheists see their choices in the same way a transcendent God would because they know that there is a real difference between good and evil. They know that they can choose to do evil. But they also know that they can choose to do what is good, and there are goals beyond self-interest worth aspiring to. Life still has meaning, as theists believed, because it matters what we choose. Its meaning does not come from God having a special purpose for our lives. That was of little use to theists in any case because, as Augustine lamented, God did not announce his purpose for one's life plainly. And it is also good for pantheists to pray for guidance because that is to pause long enough to look deep into the self that one has become, to recognize the entire situation in which one chooses, and to take responsibility for what one does. And as conscious beings with naturalistic Reason recognize, the human condition is participating in the life of a spiritual organism, and since spiritual organisms do not have to die, pantheists, at least, share in an immortal life that is always embodied in conscious reflective subjects. Indeed, if evolution is in the direction of heaven on Earth, the life of their spiritual organism will last not only for billions of years but may even survive the Sun turning into a red giant by using acceleration fuel from a white dwarf to live on. The goodness that accumulates in the natural world is conserved.[118] In any case, their spiritual world is part of the natural world, and though it is a world in time, they have a spiritual nature that they know they share with other beings like them throughout the universe.

As a Christian, my mother was fascinated by the Book of Revelation, and as she suffered, what she wanted to believe was that life has a meaning. What I would explain to her is how I believe life has meaning. I would tell her how

---

[117] This is how the wisdom of Judeo-Christian theism is embraced by Jordan Peterson (2018).

[118] I owe this way of putting it and much else to my colleague, Charley Hardwick.

the natural world is a perfect being and how evolution is change in the direction of natural perfection. The wisdom of practical Reason comes largely from the Christian commandment to love God and to love our neighbor as we love ourselves, and I would tell her about how it can be seen as an expression of our spiritual nature, how we are parts of a form of life on the highest level of geometrical organization, and how the sacrifice of Christ to forgive our sins was a vivid way of promising that it leads to heaven on Earth. I believe that my mother would have been comforted by knowing that I had become a Christian pantheist. She might even have agreed with me about the nature of God, accepted her personal mortality even in the awful way it ended, and taken comfort in sharing in the immortal life of our spiritual organism.

SELECTED REFERENCES

Baggott, Jim (2013) *Farewell to Reality: How Modern Physics Has Betrayed the Search for Scientific Truth*. New York: Pegasus Books.

Carrol, Sean (2016) *The Big Picture: On the Origin of Life, Meaning, and the Universe Itself*. New York: Dutton.

Chalmers, David (1996) *The Conscious Mind: In Search of a Fundamental Theory*. New York: Oxford University Press.

Churchland, P. M. (1988) *Matter and Consciousness*, Revised Edition. Cambridge, MA: MIT Press.

Churchland, P. S. (1994) 'Can Neurobiology Teach us Anything about Consciousness?', *Proceedings and Addresses of the American Philosophical Association*, 67(4): pp. 23-40.

Crick, F. H. C. and C. Koch (1990) 'Towards a neurobiological theory of consciousness', *Seminars in the Neurosciences*, 2: pp. 263-75.

Dawkins, Richard (2006) *The God Delusion*. Boston, MA: Houghton Mifflin.

Damasio, Antonio (1994) *Descartes' Error: Emotion, Reason and the Human Brain*. New York: Putnam Books.

Damasio, Antonio (2010) *Self Comes to Mind: Constructing the Conscious Brain*. New York: Vintage Books.

Dennett, D. C. (1978) 'Why You Can't Make a Computer that Feels Pain?', *Brainstorms*, pp 190-229. Cambridge, MA:MIT Press: Cambridge, MA.

Dennett, D. C. (1988) 'Quining Qualia', *Consciousness in Contemporary Science*, pp. 42–77. New York: Oxford University Press. Edited by Marcel, A and Bisiach, E.

Dennett, D. C. (1995) *Darwin's Dangerous Idea: Evolution and the Meanings of Life*. New York: Simon and Schuster.

Dennett, Daniel C. (2013) *Intuition Pumps and Other Tools for Thinking*. London: Penguin.

Dennett, Daniel C. (2017) *From Bacteria to Bach and Back: The Evolution of Minds*. New York: W. W. Norton & Company.

Descartes, René (1985) *The Philosophical Writing of Descartes: Vol.I*. Translated by Cottingham, John, Robert Stoothoff, Dugald Murdoch. Cambridge, MA: Cambridge University Press.

Dewey, John (1910) *How We Think*. Boston, MA: D. C. Heath and Co., Publishers.

Drake, Stillman (1957) *Discoveries and Opinions of Galileo*. New York: Anchor.

Feigl, H. (1958) 'The "Mental" and the "Physical": Concepts, Theories and the Mind-Body Problem', *Minneapolis, Minnesota Studies in the Philosophy of Science, Vol. 2*. Edited by Feigl, H., Scriven, M. and Maxwell, G.

Ferguson, Niall (2011) *Civilization: The West and the Rest*. London: Penguin Books.

Forster, E. M. (1924) *Passage to India,*. New York: Harcourt Brace.

Freud, Sigmund (1994) *Civilization and its Discontents*. New York: Dover Publications, Inc. (Originally published (1930) London: Hogarth Press, London.)

Fukuyama, Francis (1992) *The End of History and the Last Man*. New York: The Free Press.

Fukuyama, Francis (2011) *The Origins of Political Order: From Prehuman Times to the French Revolution*. New York: Farrar, Straus and Giroux.

Goldberg, Jonah (2018) *Suicide of the West: How the Rebirth of Tribalism, Populism, Nationalism, and Identity Politics is Destroying American Democracy*. New York: Crown Forum.

Hardwick, Charley (1996) *Events of Grace: Naturalism, Existentialism, and Ttheology*. Cambridge, UK: Cambridge University Press.

Harris, Sam (2004) *The End of Faith*. New York: W.W. Norton & Company.

Hawkins, David (1967) *The Language of Nature: An Essay in the Philosophy of Science*. San Francisco, CA: W. H. Freeman and Company

Hitchens, Christopher (2007) *God is Not Great*. New York: Twelve Books.

Holland, Tom (2016) 'Tom Holland: Why I was wrong about Christianity', *New Statesman*, 14 (September 2016).

Holland, Tom (2019) *Dominion: The Making of the Western Mind* (U.S. edition subtitled 'How the Christian Revolution Remade the World'), London: Little, Brown.

Horkheimer, Max and Theodor Adorno (1947) *Dialectic of Enlightenment*. Republished (2007). Standford, CA: Stanford University Press.

Huff, Toby E. (2003) *The Rise of Early Modern Science: Islam, China, and the West*, Second Edition. Cambridge: Cambridge University Press.

Huff, Toby E. (2011) *Intellectual Curiosity and the Scientific Revolution: A Global Perspective, Part I*. Cambridge: Cambridge University Press.

Hume, David (1779) *Dialogues Concerning Natural Religion*. London: Penguin Books.

Humphrey, Nicholas (1992) *A History of the Mind*. New York: Simon & Schuster.

Humphrey, Nicholas (2011) *Soul Dust: The Magic of Consciousness*. Princeton, NJ: Princeton University Press.

Huntington, Samuel P. (1997) *The Clash of Civilizations and the Remaking of World Order*. New York: Simon & Schuster.

Huxley, T. H. (1874) 'On the Hypothesis that Animals are Automata, and its History', *The Fortnightly Review* 16 (New Series): pp. 555–580. Reprinted (1898) in *Method and Results: Essays by Thomas H. Huxley*. New York, D. Appleton and Company, New York.

Kant, Immanuel (1784) 'An Answer to the Question: "What is Enlightenment?". Available at https://web.cn.edu/kwheeler/documents/what_is_enlightenment.pdf. (Accessed 24 March 2022.)

Koch, Christof (2012) *Consciousness: Confessions of a Romantic Reductionist*. Cambridge, MA: The MIT Press.

Koch, Christof (2019) *The Feeling of Life Itself - Why Consciousness is Widespread but Can't be Computed*. Cambridge, MA: The MIT Press.

Kripke, Saul (1980) *Naming and Necessity*. Cambridge, MA: Cambridge University Press.

Mandelbaum, Maurice (1955) 'Societal Facts', *British Journal of Sociology*, 6: pp. 305-17.

Mandelbaum, Maurice (1971) *History, Man & Reason: A Study in Nineteenth Century Thought*. Baltimore, MD: The Johns Hopkins Press.

Marx, Karl (1867) *Das Kapital: A Critque of Politcal Economy*. Seattle, WA: Pacific Publishing. Translated by Samuel Moore.

McGinn, Colin (2004) *Consciousness and Its Objects*. Oxford, UK: Oxford University Press.

Moore, G. E. (1903) *Principia Ethica*, Republished (1993). Cambridge, MA: Cambridge University Press.

Moore, G. E. (1939) 'Proof of an External World', *Proceedings of the British Academy* 25, pp. 273-300.

Murray, Charles (2003). *Human Accomplishment: The Pursuit of Excellence in the Arts and Sciences, 800 B. C. to 1950*. New York: HarperCollins Publishers.

Nagel, Thomas (1974) 'What is it Like to be a Bat?', *The Philosophical Review*, Vol. 83(4), pp. 435-450.

Nagel, Thomas (1979) *Mortal Questions*. Cambridge, MA: Cambridge University Press.

Nagel, Thomas (2012) *Mind and Cosmos: Why the Materialist Neo-Darwinian Conception of Nature is Almost Certainly False*. Oxford, UK: Oxford University Press.

Nagel, Thomas (2012) 'Types of Intuition: Thomas Nagel on human rights and moral knowledge', *New York Review of Books*, Vol. 43(11), pp. 3-8.

Newton, Isaac (1999) *Mathematical Principles of Natural Philosophy*. Berkeley, CA: University of California Press, Berkeley. Originally published (1687). Translated by I. B. Cohen and A. M. Whitman.

Peterson, Jordan B. (2018) *12 Rules for Life: An Antidote to Chaos*. Toronto, Canada: Random House.

Pinker, Steven (2018) *Enlightenment Now: The Case for Reason, Science, Humanism, and Progress*. London: Allen Lane Penguin Random House.

Place, U.T. (1956) 'Is Consciousness a Brain Process?', *British Journal of Psychology*, 47, pp. 44-50.

Preston, Aaron (2004) 'Prolegomena to any Future History of Analytic Philosophy', *Metaphilosophy* Vol. 35(4).

Popper, Karl R. (1971) *The Open Society and its Enemies, Vol. 1: The Spell of Plato*. Revised Edition. Princeton, NJ: Princeton University Press.

Putnam, Hilary (1967) 'The Nature of Mental States', reprinted (1975/1985b), *Putnam*, pp. 429–440.

Putnam, Hilary (1973) 'Meaning and Reference', *Journal of Philosophy* **70**, pp. 699–711.

Putnam, Hilary (1975/1985A) 'The Meaning of "Meaning', *Mind, Language and Reality: Philosophical Papers, Volume 2,* pp. 215-271. Cambridge, MA: Cambridge University Press.

Putnam, Hilary (1975/1985B) 'Philosophy and Our Mental Life', *Mind, Language and Reality: Philosophical Papers, Volume 2*, pp. 291-303. Cambridge, MA: Cambridge University Press.

Putnam, H. (1981) 'Brains in a vat', Chapter 1, *Reason, Truth, and History,* pp. 1–21. Cambridge, MA: Cambridge University Press.

Putnam, Hilary (1990) *Realism with a Human Face,* Cambridge, MA: Harvard University Press. Edited by James Conant.

Quine, W. V. O. (1960) *Word and Object.* Cambridge, MA: MIT Press.

Quine, W. V. O. (1969) 'Epistemology Naturalized', *Ontological Relativity and Other Essays*, pp. 69-60. New York: Columbia University Press.

Quine, W. V. O. (1992) *The Pursuit of Truth,* Revised edition. Cambridge, MA: Harvard University Press.

Rawls, John (1971) *A Theory of Justice,* Cambridge, MA: Belknap Press of Harvard University Press.

Reiman, Jeffrey (1990) *Justice and Modern Moral Philosophy.* New Haven, CN: Yale University Press.

Rorty, Richard (1979) *Philosophy and the Mirror of Nature.* Princeton, NJ: Princeton University Press.

Rosenberg, Alexander (2015) *Philosophy of Social Science,* Fifth edtion. Oxford, UK: Clarendon Press, Oxford and Westview Press.

Scribner, Phillip (1972) 'Escape from Freedom and Dignity', *Ethics* Vol. 83(1).

Scribner, Phillip (1989) 'Relativity and Absolute Space', *Physics Essays* Vol. 2(1) pp. 18-30.

Searle, John (1980) 'Minds, Brains, and Programs'. *Behavioral and Brain Sciences* 3, pp: 417-424.

Searle, John (1992) *The Rediscovery of the Mind.* Cambridge, MA: Bradford Books, MIT Press.

Shapiro, Ben (2019) *The Right Side of History: How Reason and Moral Purpose Made the West Great.* New York: Broadside Books, HarperCollins Publishers.

Smart, J. J. C. (1959) 'Sensations and Brain Processes', *Philosophical Review,*68, pp. 141-156.

Strawson, G. (2006) 'Realistic Monism: Why Physicalism Entails Panpsychism', *Journal of Consciousness Studies* Volume 13(10–11), pp. 3-31. London: Exeter, Imprint Academic

Tononi, Giulio (2004) 'An Information Integration Theory of Consciousness', *BMC Neuroscience.* Available at: https://doi.org/10.1186/1471-2202-5-42. (Accessed 24 March 2022.)

Wade, Nicholas (2014) A Troublesome Inheritance: Genes, Race and Human History, Penguin Press, New York.

Whitehead, Alfred North (1979) *Process and Reality.* New York: Free Press.

Wigner, E. P. (1960) 'The unreasonable effectiveness of mathematics in the natural sciences', *Communications on Pure and Applied Mathematics*, 13: pp. 1–14. (Richard Courant lecture in mathematical sciences delivered at New York University, May 11, 1959.)

INDEX

A

B

C

D

E

F

G

H

I

J

K

L

N

O

P

T

U

V

W

Z

ABOUT THE AUTHOR

Phillip Scribner was born in Denver, Colorado and reared mostly in Cheyenne, Wyoming. He graduated *magna cum laude* from the University of Colorado in Boulder in 1961 with a major in philosophy, and he received his Ph.D. in philosophy from Johns Hopkins University (Baltimore, Maryland) in 1966. After teaching at the University of Nebraska in Lincoln for four years, he taught philosophy at the American University in Washington, D.C. for thirty years. He started writing the argument that has become this trilogy around 1975, continued working on it after retiring from teaching in 2000, and completed it in 2022 at the age of 82.

Made in the USA
Middletown, DE
28 July 2022

70152486R00250